RHODODENDRON
HANDBOOK
1963

PART ONE

Rhododendron Species
in General Cultivation

RHODODENDRON GROUP
THE ROYAL HORTICULTURAL SOCIETY
VINCENT SQUARE, LONDON, S.W. 1

NEW EDITION 1963

PUBLISHED NOVEMBER 1963

© The Royal Horticultural Society

Editor

P. M. SYNGE, F.L.S.

Editorial Committee

SIR ERIC SAVILL, K.C.V.O., C.B.E., M.C., V.M.H. (Chairman)

COL. THE LORD DIGBY, K.G., D.S.O., M.C., T.D., V.M.H.

T. H. FINDLAY, M.V.O., V.M.H.

DR. H. R. FLETCHER, F.R.S.E., V.M.H.

MRS. R. HARRISON

H. G. HILLIER, F.L.S., V.M.H.

SIR GILES LODER, BART.

G. H. PINCKNEY

J. L. RUSSELL

1156

Printed in Great Britain by

SPOTTISWOODE, BALLANTYNE AND CO. LTD

LONDON AND COLCHESTER

CONTENTS

Part One

Foreword

This edition of that part of the *Rhododendron Handbook* which
relates to species in general cultivation is largely a new work.

The genus *Rhododendron* in its many species covers an
enormously wide range. In addition, almost without exception,
each species of *Rhododendron* can vary greatly from one plant
to another in colour, in shape and size of bloom, in foliage, in
habit, and in other characteristics. This is well illustrated,
especially as to blooms, at the Rhododendron Show. Such
variations have recently been recognized to be almost as pronounced within most of the species as they are in the case of
hybrids. This variability is one of the great charms of rhododendrons, but it does complicate the task of identifying the
different species and of appraising and acknowledging their
qualities.

The novelty of this edition lies largely in the fact that it does
for the first time fully recognize and give effective expression
to this variability. It achieves this by a new system of rating,
the description of which follows the lists of species in their
Series. The system is simple (much easier in practice than may
appear at first sight) and logical, and above all flexible. Not only
does it indicate the general merits of each species in terms of
hardiness, habit, foliage and quality of flower, but it can indicate
what degree of variability in each of these characteristics is
shown by each species.

For a fuller appreciation of what underlies this new system I
commend the article in the *Rhododendron and Camellia Year
Book* of 1962 by Dr. Harold Fletcher entitled, "The Rating of
Merit of Rhododendron Species".

The new system in fact owes its genesis to Dr. Fletcher, and
to him also are due the thanks of rhododendron lovers for the
immense care and time which he has devoted to re-writing and
expanding the descriptions of the species for this book, and to
applying the new merit rating to them. In this he has been
helped by the constructive comments and experience of various
members of the Rhododendron and Camellia Committee of
the R.H.S.; in particular Sir Eric Savill and Mr. T. H. Findlay
spent several days closeted with Dr. Fletcher in the final
revision of the work.

The present edition not only includes the seed numbers of
recent collections, but also most valuably repeats all the old
collector's numbers, some of which, rather frustratingly, had
been omitted from recent editions of the Handbook.

I therefore warmly commend this book to all growers or lovers of rhododendrons, as the most useful reference book on the species ever published. I know that all who use it will join me in gratitude to those whose zeal, energy, and skill have contributed to it so much that is new.

ABERCONWAY

President,

The Royal Horticultural Society

BIBLIOGRAPHICAL NOTE

The present Handbook is the successor of the Year Book of the Rhododendron Association published annually from 1929 to 1939 by the Association, which has now become the Rhododendron Group of The Royal Horticultural Society, and thus makes available to the general public the lists of species etc. formerly published in the Association's Year Book. It is proposed to revise and publish this Handbook about every five years. The first revised edition of this Handbook was published in 1947, the second in 1952 and the third in 1956.

Articles of general nature, on the cultivation, classification etc. of Rhododendrons are published in the Royal Horticultural Society's annual Rhododendron and Camellia Year Book of which the first number, as the Rhododendron Year Book, appeared in December 1946.

A List of Rhododendrons in their Series

l = lepidote; e = elepidote; Q = rhododendrons which are not at present in cultivation as far as is known

No. 1. Albiflorum Series (e)

albiflorum, *Hook.*   Q

No. 2. Anthopogon Series (l)

anthopogon, *D. Don*
anthopogonoides, *Maxim.*   Q
cephalanthum, *Franch.*
collettianum, *Aitch. et Hemsl.*
hypenanthum, *Balf. f.*
kongboense, *Hutch.*
laudandum, *Cowan*
platyphyllum, *Balf. f. et W. W. Sm.*   Q
pogonophyllum, *Cowan et Davidian*   Q
primulaeflorum, *Bur. et Franch.*
radendum, *Fang*   Q
rufescens, *Franch.*   Q
sargentianum, *Rehd. et Wils.*
trichostomum, *Franch.*

KEY TO THE SPECIES

A. Leaves bristly.
   B. Leaf-bud scales deciduous; corolla densely scaly outside; calyx 1–2 mm. long, ovate; stamens 5. (Flowers purplish-white) . . . . . . *radendum*
   B. Leaf-bud scales persistent; corolla not scaly outside; calyx 5–6 mm. long, pointed; stamens 6. (Flowers white to pink) . . . . *pogonophyllum*
A. Leaves not bristly.
   B. Stamens 6–10.
      C. Stamens 10. (Flowers white tinged with rose) . *collettianum*
      C. Stamens 6–8.
         D. Leaf-bud scales deciduous. (Flowers pink, white or yellow) . . . . . *anthopogon* (part)
         D. Leaf-bud scales persistent.
            E. Flowers yellow.
               Under surface of leaves usually dark reddish-brown . . . . . *hypenanthum* (part)
            E. Flowers pink or white.
               Under surface of leaves usually pale brown to fawn . . . . . . *cephalanthum* (part)

B. Stamens 5.
  C. Ovary hairy, scaly.
    D. Corolla tube hairy outside; under surface of leaves chocolate brown; calyx scaly outside, flower stalk scaly. (Flowers palest pink, almost white) . . . . . *laudandum*
    D. Corolla tube not hairy outside; under surface of leaves yellowish-green or fawn; calyx not scaly outside; flower stalk not scaly. (Flowers white, yellow, greenish-yellow, whitish-pink) . *anthopogonoides* (part)
  C. Ovary not hairy, scaly.
    D. Leaves linear or linear-lanceolate, 4–5 times as long as broad; calyx minute, 1–2 mm. long. (Flowers pink or white) . . . . *trichostomum* (part)
    D. Leaves wide, elliptic to oblong, obovate or rounded; calyx large, 4–8 mm. long (except *R. rufescens* 2–3 mm.)
      E. Corolla densely scaly outside.
        F. Corolla tube and lobes scaly outside; leaf-bud scales persistent. (Flowers lemon-yellow) . . . . *sargentianum*
        F. Corolla lobes scaly outside; tube not scaly; leaf-bud scales deciduous. (Flowers white) . . . . *primulaeflorum* var. *lepidanthum*
      E. Corolla not scaly or sometimes lobes slightly scaly outside.
        F. Corolla tube markedly puberulous outside.
          G. Under surface of leaves chocolate-brown; leaf-bud scales persistent. (Flowers white) . . . . *laudandum* var. *temoense*
          G. Under surface of leaves pale brown or fawn; leaf-bud scales deciduous.
            H. Corolla short, 8–10 mm long. Flowers rose. . . . *kongboense*
            H. Corolla long, 12–14 mm. long. Flowers white with yellow tube, or white or yellow. . . *primulaeflorum* var. *cephalanthoides*
        F. Corolla tube not puberulous or sometimes very slightly puberulous outside.
          G. Leaf-bud scales persistent.
            H. Leaves about 5 cm. long, nearly 2·6 cm. broad; leaf-bud scales broadly ovate or rounded. (Flowers white, occasionally faintly flushed rose) . . *platyphyllum*
            H. Leaves 1·3–4·2 cm. long, 0·8–2 cm. broad; leaf-bud scales narrow, linear or lanceolate.
              I. Under surface of leaves usually dark reddish-brown. Corolla not scaly outside. Flowers yellow. . . *hypenanthum* (part)
              I. Under surface of leaves usually fawn.

J. Corolla not scaly outside.
Flowers white or rose . *cephalanthum*
(part)

J. Corolla lobes sparsely
scaly outside. Flowers
yellow . . . *cephalanthum*
var. *nmaiense*

G. Leaf-bud scales deciduous.
H. Under surface of leaves dark
reddish-brown.
I. Leaves 1–1·9 cm. long.
(Flowers white or pink) . *rufescens* (part)
I. Leaves 2·6–3·8 cm. long.
J. Calyx 2–3 mm. long.
(Flowers white or pink) *rufescens* (part)
J. Calyx 4–5 mm. long.
(Flowers pink, white or
yellow) . . . *anthopogon*
(part)

H. Under surface of leaves pale
brown, olive-green or fawn
I. Calyx large, 4–5 mm., sometimes 3 mm. long.
J. Flower stalk scaly; calyx
scaly outside; leaves narrowly elliptic, 5–8 mm.
broad, rarely more, nar-
rowed at base or narrow-
ly rounded. (Flowers
white with yellow tube,
white, yellow, purplish
or pale rose) . . *primulaeflorum*
J. Flower stalk not scaly;
calyx not scaly outside;
leaves broadly elliptic,
1·3–1·9 cm. broad or
rounded, base broadly
rounded. (Flowers
white, yellow, greenish-
yellow, whitish-pink) . *anthopogonoides*
(part)

I. Calyx small, 1–2 mm. long.
(Flowers pink or white) . *trichostomum*
(part)

No. 3. Arboreum Series (e)

Subseries Arboreum

arboreum, *Smith*
Subspecies :
campbelliae, *Hook. f.*
cinnamomeum, *Wall.*
nilagiricum, *Zenker*
windsori, *Nutt.* Q
delavayi, *Franch.*
lanigerum, *Tagg*
niveum, *Hook. f.*
peramoenum, *Balf. f. et Forrest*
wattii, *Cowan* Q
zeylanicum, *Hort. ex Loud.*

3

Subseries Argyrophyllum (e)

argyrophyllum, *Franch.*
chienianum, *Fang* Q
coryanum, *Tagg et Forrest*
denudatum, *Lévl.* Q
farinosum, *Lévl.*
floribundum, *Franch.*
fokienense, *Franch.* Q
formosanum, *Hemsl.* Q
hunnewellianum, *Rehd. et Wils.*
hypoglaucum, *Hemsl.*
insigne, *Hemsl. et Wils.*
longipes, *Rehd. et Wils.* Q
pingianum, *Fang* Q
ririei, *Hemsl. et Wils.*
rockii, *Wils.* Q
simiarum, *Hance*
thayerianum, *Rehd. et Wils.*
youngae, *Fang* Q

No. 4. Auriculatum Series (e)

auriculatum, *Hemsl.*

No. 5. Azalea Series (e)

Subseries Canadense

albrechtii, *Maxim.*
canadense, *(L.) Torrey*
pentaphyllum, *Maxim.*
vaseyi, *A. Gray*

Subseries Luteum

alabamense, *Rehd.*
arborescens, *(Pursh) Torrey*
atlanticum, *(Ashe) Rehd.*
austrinum, *Rehd.*
bakeri, *Lemmon et McKay*
calendulaceum, *(Michx.) Torrey*
canescens, *(Michx.) Sweet*
luteum, *Sweet*
molle, *(Blume) G. Don*
nudiflorum, *(L.) Torrey*
oblongifolium, *(Small) Millais*
occidentale, *A. Gray*
prunifolium, *(Small) Millais*
roseum, *(Loisel.) Rehd.*
serrulatum, *(Small) Millais*
speciosum, *(Willd.) Sweet*
viscosum, *(L.) Torrey*

Subseries Nipponicum

nipponicum, *Matsumura*

4

annamense, *Rehd.* Q
atrovirens, *Franch.* Q
boninense, *Nakai* Q
breviperulatum, *Hayata* Q
chunii, *Fang* Q
hainanense, *Merrill* Q
indicum, (*L.*) *Sweet*
kaempferi, *Planch.*
kanehirai, *Wils.* Q
kiusianum, *Makino*
kwangtungense, *Merr. et Chun*
lasiostylum, *Hayata* Q
linearifolium, *Sieb. et Zucc.*
longiperulatum, *Hayata* Q
macrogemmum, *Nakai* Q
mariae, *Hance*
microphyton, *Franch.*
minutiflorum, *Hu* Q
miyazawae, *Nakai et Hara*
mucronatum, *G. Don* (ledifolium, *G. Don*)
naamkwanense, *Merr.*
nakaharai, *Hayata*
obtusum, (*Lindl.*) *Planch.*
oldhamii, *Maxim.*
ovatosepalum, *Yamam.*
pulchrum, *Sweet*
rivulare, *Hand.-Mazz.*
rubropilosum, *Hayata*
rufohirtum, *Hand.-Mazz* Q
saisiuense, *Nakai* Q
sasakii, *Wils.* Q
scabrum, *G. Don*
seniavinii, *Maxim.* Q
serpyllifolium, *Miquel*
simsii, *Planch.*
subsessile, *Rendle* Q
tamurai, *Masamune* Q
tosaense, *Makino*
tschonoskii, *Maxim.*
tsoi, *Merrill* Q
yedoense, *Maxim.*

Subseries Schlippenbachii

amagianum, *Makino*
farrerae, *Tate*
mariesii, *Hemsl. et Wils.*
quinquefolium, *Bisset et Moore*
reticulatum, *D. Don ex G. Don*
sanctum, *Nakai* Q
schlippenbachii, *Maxim.*
weyrichii, *Maxim.*

Subseries Tashiroi

tashiroi, *Maxim.* Q

No. 6. Barbatum Series (e)

Subseries Barbatum

argipeplum, *Balf. f. et Cooper* Q
barbatum, *Wall.*
imberbe, *Hutch.*
smithii, *Nutt. ex Hook.*

Subseries Crinigerum

bainbridgeanum, *Tagg et Forrest*
crinigerum, *Franch.*

Subseries Glischrum

diphrocalyx, *Balf. f.*
erosum, *Cowan*
exasperatum, *Tagg*
glischroides, *Tagg et Forrest*
glischrum, *Balf. f. et W. W. Sm.*
habrotrichum, *Balf. f. et W. W. Sm.*
hirtipes, *Tagg*
rude, *Tagg et Forrest*
spilotum, *Balf. f. et Farrer*
vesiculiferum, *Tagg*

Subseries Maculiferum

anwheiense, *Wils.*
longesquamatum, *C. K. Schneid.*
maculiferum, *Franch.*
monosematum, *Hutch.*
morii, *Hayata*
nankotaisanense, *Hayata* Q
ochraceum, *Rehd. et Wils.* Q
pachytrichum, *Franch.*
pseudochrysanthum, *Hayata*
strigillosum, *Franch.*

No. 7. Boothii Series (1)

Subseries Boothii

boothii, *Nutt.*
chrysodoron, *Tagg ex Hutch.*
dekatanum, *Cowan* Q
mishmiense, *Hutch. et Ward*
sulfureum, *Franch.*

Subseries Megeratum

leucaspis, *Tagg*
megeratum, *Balf. f. et Forrest*

Subseries Tephropeplum

auritum, *Tagg*
chrysolepis, *Hutch. et Ward*
tephropeplum, *Balf. f. et Farrer*
xanthostephanum, *Merr.*

KEY TO THE SPECIES

A. Style short, stout and sharply bent; corolla rotate or campanulate.
  B. Inflorescence 1–2-(rarely 3-) flowered; scales on the under surface of the leaves with very narrow rim, almost bladder-like; dwarf shrubs 30–60 cm. high (rarely shorter or taller).
    C. Flower stalk densely bristly, not scaly or sometimes with one or two scales; under surface of leaves markedly glaucous; flowers yellow; corolla campanulate or rotate-campanulate . . . *megeratum*
    C. Flower stalk not bristly (sometimes sparsely puberulous), densely scaly; under surface of leaves faintly glaucous; flowers white; corolla rotate . *leucaspis*
  B. Inflorescence 3–10-flowered; scales on the under surface of leaves with broad rim, entire; shrubs often epiphytic, 30 cm.–3 m. high.
    C. Calyx a mere rim; ovary 6-celled. (Flowers canary yellow, unspotted). . . . . . *chrysodoron*
    C. Calyx with large leafy lobes, 3–13 mm. long; ovary 5-celled.
      D. Leaves acuminate or acute at the apex; flower stalks usually bristly; leaf surface and/or margin bristly; young branchlets and leaf stalks densely bristly.
        E. Flowers bright lemon-yellow, unspotted; inflorescence 7–10-flowered; flower stalks sparsely to densely bristly . . . *boothii*
        E. Flowers bright lemon-yellow, upper lobe of corolla heavily spotted reddish-brown; inflorescence 3–4-flowered; flower stalks densely woolly . . . . . *mishmiense*
      D. Leaves rounded or obtuse at the apex; flower stalks, leaf surface and margin not bristly; young branchlets and leaf stalks not bristly or more or less bristly.
        E. Calyx 3–6 mm. long; corolla 1·5–1·9 cm. long; scales on the under surface of leaves usually uniform. (Flowers yellow) . *sulfureum*
        E. Calyx 8 mm. long; corolla 2·5 cm. long; scales on the under surface of leaves markedly different in size. (Flowers yellow) . *dekatanum*
A. Style long, slender and straight; corolla tubular-campanulate.
  B. Calyx a mere rim; scales on the under surface of leaves 3–4 times their own diameter apart; corolla tube and lobes with bands of scales outside. (Flowers bright canary yellow) . . . . *chrysolepis*
  B. Calyx with large leafy lobes, 3–8 mm. long; scales on the under surface of leaves one-half to their own diameter apart; scales on corolla tube and lobes scattered or absent.
    C. Calyx lobes reflexed. (Flowers creamy-white with a slight tinge of pink on the lobes, or sulphur-yellow) . . . . *auritum*
    C. Calyx lobes erect or spreading.

D. Flowers yellow; corolla rather densely scaly outside; calyx lobes erect or sometimes spreading . . . . *xantho-stephanum*

D. Flowers pink or rose, rarely white; corolla not scaly outside, rarely scaly; calyx lobes spreading. . . . . *tephropeplum*

No. 8. Camelliaeflorum Series (l)

camelliaeflorum, *Hook f.*
lucidum, *Nutt.* Q

No. 9. Campanulatum Series (e)

campanulatum, *D. Don*
fulgens, *Hook. f.*
lanatum, *Hook. f.*
miniatum, *Cowan* Q
sherriffii, *Cowan*
tsariense, *Cowan*
wallichii, *Hook. f.*

KEY TO THE SPECIES

A. Leaves rounded, widest at the middle, obtuse at the base; capsule broad and stout, or elongate-cylindric, slightly or moderately curved . . . . . . *Campanulatum* series

A. Leaves oblanceolate to obovate, widest above the middle, usually narrowed to the base; capsule narrowly elongate-cylindric, slightly or moderately curved (sickle-shaped) . . . . *Fulvum* series

B. Ovary glabrous; branchlets, petiole and pedicel glabrous (sometimes more or less hairy).

C. Flowers lilac or pale lilac to rosy-purple.

D. Indumentum on lower surface of leaf usually continuous, suède-like or smooth, rarely patchy or absent, composed of branched (ramiform) hairs . . . . . *R. campanulatum*

D. Indumentum on lower surface of leaf discontinuous, of scattered tufts, composed of sheaf-like (fasciculate) hairs . . . *R. wallichii*

C. Flowers deep blood red.

D. Inflorescence compact, 8–14-flowered, indumentum (continuous, woolly, rarely sparse or absent) composed of sheaf-like (fasciculate) hairs . . . . *R. fulgens*

D. Inflorescence lax, 2–6-flowered, indumentum not composed of fasciculate hairs.

E. Branchlets eglandular, calyx often up to 1·4 cm. long, corolla 2·8–3 cm. long, branches of hairs long and narrow . . . *R. miniatum*

E. Branchlets glandular, calyx 3–5 mm. long, corolla 3·5–4 cm. long, branches of hairs short and broad . . . . . *R. sherriffii*

B. Ovary densely tomentose; branchlets, petiole and pedicel densely tomentose.

C. Flowers sulphur-yellow, leaves 6–12 cm. long . *R. lanatum*
C. Flowers white or pink, leaves 2·2–6·2 long . *R. tsariense*

No. 10. Campylogynum Series (l)

campylogynum, *Franch.*

No. 11. Camtschaticum Series (e)

camtschaticum, *Pallas*
glandulosum, *Standley ex Small*   Q
redowskianum, *Maxim.*   Q

No. 12. Carolinianum Series (l)

carolinianum, *Rehd.*
chapmanii, *A. Gray*
minus, *Michaux* (punctatum, *Andrews*)

No. 13. Cinnabarinum Series (l)

cinnabarinum, *Hook. f.*
concatenans, *Hutch.*
igneum, *Cowan*   Q
keysii, *Nutt.*
xanthocodon, *Hutch.*

No. 14. Dauricum Series (l)

dauricum, *Linn.*
mucronulatum, *Turcz.*

No. 15. Edgeworthii Series (l)

bullatum, *Franch.*
edgeworthii, *Hook. f.*
pendulum, *Hook. f.*
seinghkuense, *Ward*

No. 16. Falconeri Series (e)

arizelum, *Balf. f. et Forrest*
basilicum, *Balf. f. et W. W. Sm.*
coriaceum, *Franch.*
decipiens, *Lacaita*
eximium, *Nutt.*
falconeri, *Hook. f.*
fictolacteum, *Balf. f.*
galactinum, *Balf. f.*
hodgsonii, *Hook. f.*
lanigerum, *Tagg*
preptum, *Balf. f. et Forrest*
rex, *Lévl.*
sino-falconeri, *Balf. f.*   Q

No. 17. Ferrugineum Series (l)

ferrugineum, *Linn.*
hirsutum, *Linn.*
kotschyi, *Simonk.*

9

No. 18. Fortunei Series (e)

Subseries Calophytum

calophytum, *Franch.*
openshawianum, *Rehd. et Wils.*   Q

Subseries Davidii

davidii, *Franch.*
huianum, *Fang*   Q
planetum, *Balf. f.*
praevernum, *Hutch.*
sutchuenense, *Franch.*

Subseries Fortunei

chengianum, *Fang*   Q
chlorops, *Cowan*
decorum, *Franch.*
diaprepes, *Balf. f. et W. W. Sm.*
discolor, *Franch.*
faithae, *Chun.*   Q
fortunei, *Lindl.*
glanduliferum, *Franch.*   Q
hemsleyanum, *Wils.*
houlstonii, *Hemsl. et Wils.*
platypodum, *Diels*   Q
serotinum, *Hutch.*
vernicosum, *Franch.*
  geographical forms of vernicosum:
    araliaeforme, *Balf. f. et Forrest*
    euanthum, *Balf. f. et W. W. Sm.*
    rhantum, *Balf. f. et W. W. Sm.*
    sheltonae, *Hemsl. et Wils.*

Subseries Griffithianum

griffithianum, *Wight*

Subseries Orbiculare

cardiobasis, *Sleumer*   Q
orbiculare, *Decaisne*

Subseries Oreodoxa

erubescens, *Hutch.*
fargesii, *Franch.*
oreodoxa, *Franch.*
  geographical forms of oreodoxa :
    haematocheilum, *Craib*
    limprichtii, *Diels*
    reginaldii, *Balf. f.*
praeteritum, *Hutch.*

No. 19. Fulvum Series (e)

fulvum, *Balf. f. et W. W. Sm.*
uvarifolium, *Diels*

A. Leaves rounded, widest at the middle, obtuse at the base; capsule broad and stout, or elongate-cylindric, slightly or moderately curved . . . . . *Campanulatum series*

A. Leaves oblanceolate to obovate, widest above the middle, usually narrowed to the base; capsule narrowly elongate-cylindric, slightly or moderately curved (sickle-shaped). . . . . . . *Fulvum* series

    B. Indumentum on the lower surface of the leaves brown or tawny, more or less granular, composed of mop-like (capitellate) hairs . . . . . *R. fulvum*

    B. Indumentum on the lower surface of the leaves whitish or fawn, not granular, smooth, more or less woolly, composed of tree-like (dendroid) hairs . . . *R. uvarifolium*

No. 20. Glaucophyllum Series (I)

Subseries Genestierianum

genestierianum, *Forrest*
micromeres, *Tagg*

Subseries Glaucophyllum

brachyanthum, *Franch.*
charitopes, *Balf. f. et Farrer*
glaucophyllum, *Rehder*
shweliense, *Balf. f. et Forrest*
tsangpoense, *Hutch. et Ward*

KEY TO THE SERIES

A. Scales on the under surface of leaves of two kinds, smaller pale yellow, and larger brown.
    B. Flowers yellow . . . . . . *brachyanthum*
    B. Flowers pink or purple
        C. Leaves lanceolate to oblanceolate, often pointed at the apex; calyx markedly pointed; style short, stout and sharply bent or deflexed, or long, slender and straight. (Flowers pink or pinkish-purple). *glaucophyllum*
        C. Leaves obovate, obovate-elliptic or oblong-elliptic, rounded at the apex or sometimes obtuse; calyx rounded (in *R. charitopes* sometimes pointed); style short, stout and sharply bent or deflexed.
            D. Corolla densely scaly outside; style hairy or not hairy. (Flowers pale pink, tinged yellow, upper three lobes spotted pink) . . . *shweliense*
            D. Corolla not scaly or sometimes sparsely scaly outside; style not hairy.
                E. Calyx 6–10 mm. long; leaves broadly obovate. (Flowers apple-blossom pink speckled with crimson, or rose-crimson not spotted) . . . . . *charitopes*
                E. Calyx 4–6 mm. long; leaves narrowly obovate, obovate-elliptic or oblong-elliptic. (Flowers pink, deep cerise or violet) . *tsangpoense*
A. Scales on the under surface of leaves of one kind, brown or pale brown.
    B. Scales on the under surface of leaves minute, widely separated, 4–10 times their own diameter apart; leaves acutely acuminate at the apex; corolla not scaly but glaucous outside, plum-purple . . . *genestierianum*

B. Scales on the under surface of leaves varying much in
size, dense, $\frac{1}{2}$–$1\frac{1}{2}$ times their own diameter apart;
leaves obtuse at the apex; corolla tube and lobes
densely scaly but not glaucous outside, creamy-
yellow, rarely white . . . . *micromeres*

No. 21. Grande Series (e)

coryphaeum, *Balf. f. et Forrest*
giganteum, *Forrest ex Tagg*
grande, *Wight*
macabeanum, *Watt ex Balf. f.*
magnificum, *Ward*
mollyanum, *Cowan et Davidian*
peregrinum, *Tagg*
praestans, *Balf. f. et W. W. Sm.*
protistum, *Balf. f. et Forrest*
pudorosum, *Cowan*
semnoides, *Tagg et Forrest*
sidereum, *Balf. f.*
sinogrande, *Balf. f. et W. W. Sm.*
watsonii, *Hemsl. et Wils.*

No. 22. Griersonianum Series (e)

griersonianum, *Balf. f. et Forrest*

No. 23. Heliolepis Series (l)

bracteatum, *Rehd. et Wils.*
brevistylum, *Franch.*
desquamatum, *Balf. f. et Forrest*
fumidum, *Balf. f. et W. W. Sm.*
heliolepis, *Franch.*
invictum, *Balf. f. et Farrer* Q
leclerei, *Lévl.* Q
oporinum, *Balf. f. et Ward*
pholidotum, *Balf. f. et W. W. Sm.*
rubiginosum, *Franch.*

No. 24. Irroratum Series (e)

Subseries Irroratum

aberconwayi, *Cowan*
agastum, *Balf. f. et W. W. Sm*
annae, *Franch.*
anthosphaerum, *Diels*
   Subspecies :
     hylothreptum, *Balf. f. et W. W. Sm.*
araiophyllum, *Balf. f. et W. W. Sm.*
cerochitum, *Balf. f. et Forrest* Q
dimitrum, *Balf. f. et Forrest*
epapillatum, *Balf. f. et Cooper* Q
eritimum, *Balf. f. et W. W. Sm.*
   Subspecies :
     chawchiense, *Balf. f. et Farrer* Q
     gymnogynum, *Balf. f. et Forrest*
     heptamerum, *Balf. f.*
     persicinum, *Hand.-Mazz.* Q

hardingii, *Forrest*
irroratum, *Franch.*
kendrickii, *Nutt.*
laxiflorum, *Balf. f. et Forrest*
leptopeplum, *Balf. f. et Forrest*   Q
lukiangense, *Franch.*
   Subspecies :
      admirabile, *Balf. f. et Forrest*   Q
      adroserum, *Balf. f. et Forrest*
      ceraceum, *Balf. f. et W. W. Sm.*
      gymnanthum, *Diels*
mengtszense, *Balf. f. et W. W. Sm.*   Q
ningyuenense, *Hand.-Mazz.*
ombrochares, *Balf. f. et Ward*   Q
pankimense, *Cowan et Ward*
papillatum, *Balf. f. et Cooper*   Q
pennivenium, *Balf. f. et Forrest*
pogonostylum, *Balf. f. et W. W. Sm.*
ramsdenianum, *Cowan*
shepherdii, *Nutt.*
spanotrichum, *Balf. f. et W. W. Sm.*
tanastylum, *Balf. f. et Ward*

Subseries Parishii

agapetum, *Balf. f. et Ward*
cookeianum, *Davidian*
elliottii, *Watt ex W. W. Sm.*
eriogynum, *Balf. f. et W. W. Sm.*
facetum, *Balf. f. et Ward*
kyawi, *Lace et W. W. Sm.*
parishii, *C. B. Clarke*
schistocalyx, *Balf. f. et Forrest*
venator, *Tagg*

No. 25. Lacteum Series (e)

aberrans, *Tagg et Forrest*   Q
agglutinatum, *Balf. f. et Forrest*
beesianum, *Diels*
dictyotum, *Balf. f. ex Tagg*
dignabile, *Cowan*   Q
dryophyllum, *Balf. f. et Forrest*
dumosulum, *Balf. f. et Forrest*
lacteum, *Franch.*
nakotiltum, *Balf. f. et Forrest*   Q
phaeochrysum, *Balf. f. et W. W. Sm.*
pomense, *Cowan et Davidian*   Q
przewalskii, *Maxim.*
traillianum, *Forrest et W. W. Sm.*
wightii, *Hook. f.*

KEY TO THE SPECIES

A. Indumentum on the under surfaces of the leaves forming a
   continuous covering.

B. Corolla *yellow*; ovary 9-10-celled; hairs on the under
surfaces of the leaves ramiform or radiate.
 C. Leaves usually oval, ovate-elliptic or broadly elliptic; inflorescence somewhat compact; corolla
 unspotted; *hairs radiate*; Chinese species . . *lacteum*
 C. Leaves usually oblong-elliptic, oblong or oblanceolate; inflorescence usually lax; corolla spotted;
 hairs ramiform; Himalayan species . . . *wightii*
B. Corolla *white, pink or rose*; ovary 5-11-celled; hairs on
the under surfaces of the leaves long-rayed or radiate.
 C. Calyx minute, 1-2 mm. long; inflorescence 8-25-
 flowered.
 D. Ovary densely tomentose.
 E. Indumentum on the under surfaces of the
 leaves suède-like or felty; hairs radiate with
 oblong or ovoid arms or *long-rayed*.
 F. Leaves 9-30 cm. long; inflorescence 10-
 25-flowered; *hairs radiate* . . . *beesianum*
 F. Leaves 5-13·5 cm. long; inflorescence
 8-15-flowered; *hairs long-rayed*.
 G. Indumentum bistrate, grey or fawn,
 arms of hairs long . . . *nakotiltum*
 G. Indumentum unistrate, brown, rust
 or cinnamon-coloured, arms of
 hairs shorter . . . . *dictyotum*
 (part)
 E. Indumentum on the under surfaces of the
 leaves usually powdery; hairs radiate with
 somewhat pear-shaped arms . . . *traillianum*
 (part)
 D. Ovary glabrous or sometimes sparsely floccose.
 E. Indumentum on the under surfaces of the
 leaves usually powdery; *hairs radiate with
 somewhat pear-shaped arms*.
 F. Leaves usually 7·5-17 cm. long, 2·8-
 6·8 cm. broad; ovary eglandular . *traillianum*
 (part)
 F. Leaves usually 3·5-7·2 cm. long, 1·6-
 2·5 cm. broad; ovary glandular or
 eglandular . . . . . *aberrans*
 E. Indumentum on the under surfaces of the
 leaves suède-like, felty or agglutinate; *hairs
 long-rayed*.
 F. Indumentum on the under surfaces of
 the leaves suède-like or felty; branchlets and petioles eglandular; ovary
 sparsely floccose or glabrous.
 G. Branchlets and petioles usually densely or moderately tomentose; pedicels usually floccose; ovary sparsely
 floccose or glabrous; leaves lanceolate, oblong-lanceolate, oblong,
 elliptic or oblong-ovate.
 H. Leaves large, usually 7·5-14 cm.
 long.
 I. Corolla 3·2-5 cm. long; hairs
 of the indumentum with
 broad ribbon-like oblongoid
 arms . . . . *dictyotum*
 (part)
 I. Corolla 2-4 cm. long; hairs of
 the indumentum with nar-
 row arms . . . *dryophyllum*
 H. Leaves small, usually 3·8-7 cm.
 long . . . . . *dumosulum*

G. Branchlets, petioles, pedicels and ovary usually glabrous; leaves ovate, elliptic to oblong . . . *przewalskii* (part)

    F. Indumentum on the under surfaces of the leaves usually agglutinate; branchlets and petioles glandular or eglandular; ovary glabrous

      G. Leaves large, usually 7·5–14 cm, long; corolla 3–5 cm. long . *phaeochrysum*

      G. Leaves small, usually 4–7·2 cm. long; corolla 2–3·5 cm. long . *agglutinatum*

C. Calyx large, lobes unequal, the longest 1·2 cm. long, the shortest 5 mm. long; inflorescence about 5-flowered . . . . *pomense*

A. Indumentum on the under surfaces of the leaves discontinuous, consisting of scattered hairs or a thin veil of hairs.

  B. Branchlets, petioles and pedicels floccose, glandular or eglandular; ovary densely floccose to glabrous, glandular or eglandular; leaves up to 18 cm. long; hairs of the indumentum somewhat *radiate* . . . *dignabile*

  B. Branchlets, petioles, pedicels and ovary usually glabrous, eglandular; leaves up to 11 cm. long; hairs of the indumentum *long-rayed* . . . . . *przewalskii* (part)

No. 26. Lapponicum Series (I)

achroanthum, *Balf. f. et W. W. Sm.*
alpicola, *Rehd. et Wils.*
amundsenianum, *Hand.-Mazz.* Q
blepharocalyx, *Franch.*
bulu, *Hutch.* Q
capitatum, *Maxim.*
chamaezelum, *Balf. f. et Forrest*
chryseum, *Balf. f. et Ward*
compactum, *Hutch.*
complexum, *Balf. f. et W. W. Sm.*
cuneatum, *W. W. Sm.*
dasypetalum, *Balf. f. et Forrest*
diacritum, *Balf. f. et W. W. Sm.*
drumonium, *Balf. f. et Ward*
edgarianum, *Rehd. et Wils.*
fastigiatum, *Franch.*
fimbriatum, *Hutch.*
flavidum, *Franch.*
glomerulatum, *Hutch.*
hippophaeoides, *Balf. f. et W. W. Sm.*
idoneum, *Balf. f. et W. W. Sm.*
impeditum, *Balf. f. et W. W. Sm.*
intricatum, *Franch.*
lapponicum, *Wahl.*
litangense, *Balf. f. et Forrest et Hutch.*
lysolepis, *Hutch.*
microleucum, *Hutch.*
nigropunctatum, *Bur. et Franch.*
nitidulum, *Rehd. et Wils.*
nivale, *Hook. f.*

orthocladum, *Balf. f. et Forrest*
paludosum, *Hutch. et Ward*
parvifolium, *Adams*
peramabile, *Hutch.*
polifolium, *Franch.*
polycladum, *Franch.*   Q
ramosissimum, *Franch.*
ravum, *Balf. f. et W. W. Sm.*
rupicola, *W. W. Sm.*
russatum, *Balf. f. et Forrest*
scintillans, *Balf. f. et W. W. Sm.*
setosum, *D. Don*
spilanthum, *Hutch.*
stictophyllum, *Balf. f.*
tapetiforme, *Balf. f. et Ward*
telmateium, *Balf. f. et W. W. Sm.*
thymifolium, *Maxim.*
tsaii, *Fang*   Q
verruculosum, *Rehd. et Wils.*
violaceum, *Rehd. et Wils.*
websterianum, *Rehd. et Wils.*
yungningense, *Balf. f. ex Hutch.*

No. 27. Lepidotum Series (l)
Subseries Baileyi

baileyi, *Balf. f*

Subseries Lepidotum

lepidotum, *Wall.*
lowndesii, *Davidian*

KEY TO THE SPECIES

A. Inflorescence 1–3-(rarely 4-)flowered, umbellate; under surfaces of leaves greenish, scales entire; leaves small 0·4–2·6 cm. long, rarely more.
  B. Usually evergreen shrub up to 1·50 m. high; leaves and pedicels not bristly; scales on the under surfaces of leaves overlapping to one-half their own diameter apart; flowers pink, purple, rose, crimson, yellow or white . . . . *lepidotum*
  B. Deciduous shrub up to 12 cm. high; margins of leaves bristly, pedicels bristly; scales on the under surfaces of leaves 2–5 times their own diameter apart; flowers pale yellow with greenish-yellow spots at the base of the upper three lobes . . . . *lowndesii*
A. Inflorescence 5–18-flowered, often distinctly racemose; under surfaces of leaves cinnamon or rust coloured, rarely greenish-brown, scales crenulate; leaves large, usually 3–7 cm. long. (Flowers reddish-purple or deep purple, with or without darker spots) . . . . . *baileyi*

No. 28. Maddenii Series (l)
Subseries Ciliicalyx

amandum, *Cowan*   Q
burmanicum, *Hutch.*
carneum, *Hutch.*
ciliatum, *Hook. f.*

ciliicalyx, *Franch.*
ciliipes, *Hutch.*   Q
cubittii, *Hutch.*
cuffeanum, *Craib*
dendricola, *Hutch.*
fletcherianum, *Davidian*
formosum, *Wall.*
inaequale, *Hutch.*
iteophyllum, *Hutch.*
johnstoneanum, *Watt*
lasiopodum, *Hutch.*
ludwigianum, *Hosseus*   Q
lyi, *Lévl.*
missionarum, *Lévl.*   Q
notatum, *Hutch.*   Q
pachypodum, *Balf. f. et W. W. Sm.*
parryae, *Hutch.*
pilicalyx, *Hutch.*   Q
pseudociliicalyx, *Hutch.*   Q
roseatum, *Hutch.*   Q
rufosquamosum, *Hutch.*   Q
scopulorum, *Hutch.*
scottianum, *Hutch.*
smilesii, *Hutch.*   Q
supranubium, *Hutch.*
surasianum, *Balf. f. et Craib*
taronense, *Hutch.*
valentinianum, *Forrest*
veitchianum, *Hook.*
walongense, *Ward*

Subseries Maddenii

brachysiphon, *Balf. f.*
calophyllum, *Nutt.*   Q
crassum, *Franch.*
excellens, *Hemsl. et Wils.*   Q
maddenii, *Hook. f.*
manipurense, *Balf. f. et Watt*
odoriferum, *Hutch.*
polyandrum, *Hutch.*

Subseries Megacalyx

dalhousiae, *Hook. f.*
headfortianum, *Hutch.*
levinei, *Merrill*   Q
liliiflorum, *Lévl.*   Q
lindleyi, *Moore*
megacalyx, *Balf. f. et Ward*
nuttallii, *Booth*
rhabdotum, *Balf. f. et Cooper*
sinonuttallii, *Balf. f. et Forrest*
taggianum, *Hutch.*

No. 29. Micranthum Series (l)

micranthum, *Turcz.*

No. 30. Moupinense Series (l)

dendrocharis, *Franch.*   Q
moupinense, *Franch.*
petrocharis, *Diels*   Q

No. 31. Neriiflorum Series (e)

Subseries Forrestii

chamae-thomsonii, *(Tagg et Forrest) Cowan et Davidian*
erastum, *Balf. f. et Forrest*   Q
forrestii, *Balf. f. ex Diels*
porphyrophyllum, *Balf. f. et Forrest*   Q
serpens, *Balf. f. et Forrest*   Q
trilectorum, *Cowan*   Q

Subseries Haematodes

beanianum, *Cowan*
catacosmum, *Balf. f. ex Tagg*
chaetomallum, *Balf. f. et Forrest*
chionanthum, *Tagg et Forrest*
coelicum, *Balf. f. et Farrer*
haematodes, *Franch.*
hemidartum, *Balf. f. ex Tagg*
mallotum, *Balf. f. et Ward*
pocophorum, *Balf. f. ex Tagg*

Subseries Neriiflorum

albertsenianum, *Forrest*
euchroum, *Balf. f. et Ward*   Q
floccigerum, *Franch.*
neriiflorum, *Franch.*
  Subspecies :
    agetum, *Balf. f. et Forrest*   Q
    euchaites, *Balf. f. et Forrest*
    phaedropum, *Balf. f. et Farrer*
    phoenicodum, *Balf. f. et Farrer*
sperabile, *Balf. f. et Farrer*
sperabiloides, *Tagg et Forrest*

Subseries Sanguineum

aperantum, *Balf. f. et Ward*
citriniflorum, *Balf. f. et Forrest*
  Subspecies :
    aureolum, *Cowan*   Q
    citriniflorum, (typical)
    horaeum, *Balf. f. et Forrest*
    rubens, *Cowan*   Q
dichroanthum, *Diels*
  Subspecies :
    apodectum, *Balf. f. et W. W. Sm.*

  dichroanthum, (typical)
  herpesticum, *Balf. f. et Ward*
  scyphocalyx, *Balf. f. et Forrest*
  septentrionale, *Cowan*
eudoxum, *Balf. f. et Forrest*
 Subspecies :
  brunneifolium, *Balf. f. et Forrest*
  eudoxum, (typical)
fulvastrum, *Balf. f. et Forrest*
 Subspecies :
  epipastum, *Balf. f. et Forrest* Q
  fulvastrum, (typical)
  mesopolium, *Balf. f. et Forrest*
  trichomiscum, *Balf. f. et Forrest* Q
  trichophlebium, *Balf. f. et Forrest* Q
parmulatum, *Cowan*
sanguineum, *Franch.*
 Subspecies :
  aizoides, *Cowan* Q
  atrorubrum, *Cowan* Q
  cloiophorum, *Balf. f. et Forrest*
  consanguineum, *Cowan*
  didymoides, *Tagg et Forrest* Q
  didymum, *Balf. f. et Forrest*
  haemaleum, *Balf. f. et Forrest*
  himertum, *Balf. f. et Forrest*
  leucopetalum, *Balf. f. et Forrest*
  melleum, *Cowan* Q
  mesaeum, *Cowan*
  roseotinctum, *Balf. f. et Forrest*
  sanguineoides, *Cowan*
  sanguineum, (typical)
temenium, *Balf. f. et Forrest*
 Subspecies :
  albipetalum, *Cowan*
  chrysanthemum, *Cowan*
  dealbatum, *Cowan* Q
  gilvum, *Cowan*
  glaphyrum, *Balf. f. et Forrest*
  pothinum, *Balf. f. et Forrest*
  rhodanthum, *Cowan* Q
  temenium, (typical)

No. 32. Ovatum Series (e)

bachii, *Lévl.* Q
hongkongense, *Hutch.* Q
leptothrium, *Balf. f. et Forrest*
ovatum, *Planchon*
vialii, *Delavay et Franch.* Q

No. 33. Ponticum Series (e)

Subseries Caucasicum

adenopodum, *Franch*.
brachycarpum, *D. Don et G. Don*
caucasicum, *Pallas*
chrysanthum, *Pallas*
degronianum, *Carriere*
fauriei, *Franch*.
hyperythrum, *Hayata*
makinoi, *Tagg*
metternichii, *Sieb. et Zucc*.
smirnowi, *Trautv*.
ungernii, *Trautv*.
yakusimanum, *Nakai*

Subseries Ponticum

catawbiense, *Michaux*
macrophyllum, *D. Don ex G. Don*
maximum, *Linn*.
ponticum, *Linn*.

No. 34. Saluenense Series (l)

calostrotum, *Balf. f. et Ward*
chameunum, *Balf. f. et Forrest*
fragariflorum, *Ward*
keleticum, *Balf. f. et Forrest*
nitens, *Hutch*.
prostratum, *W. W. Sm*.
radicans, *Balf. f. et Forrest*
saluenense, *Franch*.

KEY TO THE SPECIES

A. Scales on the under surface of the leaves *overlapping, crenulate*; pedicels 0·8–3·2 cm. long; corolla 1·5–3 cm. long, puberulous outside.
  B. Branchlets and petioles moderately to densely bristly.
    C. *Erect* shrubs up to 1·20 m. high; leaves up to 3·6 cm. long; upper surface of leaves densely scaly or not scaly.
      D. Shrub usually 60 cm.–1·20 m. high; leaves large usually 2–3·6 cm. long; upper surface of leaves moderately or rather densely scaly . *saluenense*
      D. Shrub, 12–60 cm. high; leaves small, usually 0·5–2 cm. long; upper surface of the leaves often not scaly or with a few scales . . *chameunum*
    C. *Prostrate spreading* shrub, up to 45 cm. high; leaves 0·4–1·5 cm. long (rarely longer); upper surface of leaves not scaly . . . . *prostratum*
  B. Branchlets and petioles not bristly.
    C. Upper surface of the leaves *mat*, densely scaly, the scales *overlapping* (rarely up to three-fourths their own diameter apart) . . . *calostrotum*
    C. Upper surface of the leaves shining, not scaly or if scaly the scales 2–6 *times their own diameter apart.*

D. Erect shrub, 30–45 cm. high or more; flowers
appearing late, in June–July . . . *nitens*
D. Semi-prostrate or completely prostrate matted,
spreading shrubs, flowers appearing early, in
May–June.
   E. Semi-prostrate spreading shrub; leaves up
to twice as long as broad, oblong, elliptic,
or ovate-elliptic (rarely lanceolate) . . *keleticum*
   E. Completely prostrate matted shrub; leaves
3–5 times as long as broad, linear, lanceolate, or narrowly oblanceolate . . *radicans*
A. Scales on the under surface of the leaves *widely spaced*,
1½–6 times their own diameter apart, *entire*; pedicels 5–7
mm. long; corolla 1·1–1·5 cm. long, glabrous outside . *fragariflorum*

No. 35. Scabrifolium Series (l)

hemitrichotum, *Balf. f. et Forrest*
mollicomum, *Balf. f. et W. W. Sm.*
pubescens, *Balf. f. et Forrest*
racemosum, *Franch.*
scabrifolium, *Franch.*
spiciferum, *Franch.*
spinuliferum, *Franch.*

No. 36. Semibarbatum Series (e)

semibarbatum, *Maxim.*

No. 37. Stamineum Series (e)

cavaleriei, *Lévl.* Q
championae, *Hook.*
esquirolii, *Lévl.* Q
feddei, *Lévl.* Q
hancockii, *Hemsl.* Q
henryi, *Hance* Q
latoucheae, *Franch.* Q
leiopodum, *Hayata* Q
leucobotrys, *Ridley* Q
moulmainense, *Hook.*
oxyphyllum, *Franch.*
pectinatum, *Hutch.*
stamineum, *Franch.*
stenaulum, *Balf. f. et W. W. Sm.*
taiense, *Hutch.* Q
tutcherae, *Hemsl. et Wils.* Q
westlandii, *Hemsl.* Q
wilsonae, *Hemsl. et Wils.*

No. 38. Taliense Series (e)
Subseries Adenogynum

adenogynum, *Diels*
adenophorum, *Balf. f. et W. W. Sm.*
alutaceum, *Balf. f. et W. W. Sm.*
balfourianum, *Diels*
bureavii, *Franch.*
bureavioides, *Balf. f.*

circinnatum, *Cowan et Ward*   Q
codonanthum, *Balf. f. et Forrest*   Q
cruentum, *Lévl.*   Q
detersile, *Franch.*
detonsum, *Balf. f. et Forrest*
dumicola, *Tagg et Forrest*
elegantulum, *Tagg et Forrest*   Q
faberi, *Hemsl.*
faberioides, *Balf. f.*   Q
mimetes, *Tagg et Forrest*
prattii, *Franch.*
wuense, *Balf. f.*

Subseries Roxieanum

bathyphyllum, *Balf. f. et Forrest*
comisteum, *Balf. f. et Forrest*   Q
globigerum, *Balf. f. et Forrest*
gymnocarpum, *Balf. f. ex Tagg*
iodes, *Balf. f. et Forrest*
lampropeplum, *Balf. f. et Forrest*   Q
microgynum, *Balf. f. et Forrest*
perulatum, *Balf. f. et Forrest*   Q
pronum, *Tagg et Forrest*
proteoides, *Balf. f. et W. W. Sm.*
recurvoides, *Tagg et Ward*
roxieanum, *Forrest*
russotinctum, *Balf. f. et Forrest*
triplonaevium, *Balf. f. et Forrest*
tritifolium, *Balf. f. et Forrest*

Subseries Taliense

aganniphum, *Balf. f. et Ward*
clementinae, *Forrest*
doshongense, *Tagg*
flavorufum, *Balf. f. et Forrest*
glaucopeplum, *Balf. f. et Forrest*
principis, *Bur. et Franch.*   Q
purdomii, *Rehd. et Wils.*   Q
schizopeplum, *Balf. f. et Forrest*
sphaeroblastum, *Balf. f. et Forrest*
taliense, *Franch.*
vellereum, *Hutch. ex Tagg*

Subseries Wasonii

coeloneurum, *Diels*   Q
inopinum, *Balf. f.*
paradoxum, *Balf. f.*
rufum, *Batal.*
wasonii, *Hemsl. et Wils.*
weldianum, *Rehd. et Wils.*
wiltonii, *Hemsl. et Wils.*

No. 39. Thomsonii Series (e)

KEY TO SUBSERIES

A. Style glandular to the tip.

  B. Corolla bowl- or saucer-shaped, yellow, white or pink; calyx usually 0·4–1·2 cm. long .   .   .   .   *Souliei subseries*

  B. Corolla campanulate, pink or rose; calyx 1–5 mm. long or a mere rim.

    C. Leaves orbicular or ovate; low spreading shrub; branchlets setose-glandular; inflorescence 2–3- (rarely up to 5-)flowered .   .   .   *Williamsianum subseries*

    C. Leaves oblong or oblong-elliptic; erect shrubs; branchlets not setose-glandular; inflorescence 5–7-flowered .   .   .   .   *Cerasinum subseries*

A. Style eglandular or glandular at the base (rarely to three-fourths its length but never to the tip).

  B. Corolla usually *funnel-shaped*; branchlets setose-glandular or not setose-glandular; capsule slender, curved (sickle-shaped); leaves oblong, elliptic or oblong-oval .   .   .   .   .   *Selense subseries*

  B. Corolla *campanulate*; branchlets not setose-glandular; capsule short, stout or oblong or slender, straight or curved; leaves orbicular, broadly elliptic, obovate or oblong.

    C. Ovary eglandular .   .   .   .   .   .   *Thomsonii subseries*

    C. Ovary glandular.

      D. Leaves orbicular, elliptic or oblong; calyx large, 0·4–2 cm. long; flowers *crimson*, pink or white (sometimes yellow); style eglandular; capsule short, stout or broadly oblong, straight .   *Thomsonii subseries*

      D. Leaves orbicular or elliptic (in *R. panteumorphum* oblong); calyx small, usually 1–3 mm. (sometimes up to 5 mm.) long; flowers yellow, pink or white; style glandular at the base or up to one-half its length or eglandular; capsule slender, often curved .   .   .   *Campylocarpum subseries*

Subseries Campylocarpum

callimorphum, *Balf. f. et W. W. Sm.*
caloxanthum, *Balf. f. et Farrer*
campylocarpum, *Hook. f.*
myiagrum, *Balf. f. et Forrest*
panteumorphum, *Balf. f. et W. W. Sm.*
telopeum, *Balf. f. et Forrest*

KEY TO THE SPECIES

A. Flowers yellow.

  B. Leaves elliptic or ovate or oblong.

    C. Leaves elliptic or ovate, Himalayan species. .   *R. campylocarpum*

    C. Leaves usually oblong (sometimes elliptic) predominantly Chinese species .   .   .   *R. panteumorphum*

  B. Leaves more or less orbicular.

    C. Average leaf length to breadth 5–4 cm. .   .   *R. caloxanthum*

    C. Average leaf length to breadth 4–3 cm. .   .   *R. telopeum*

A. Flowers rose or pink or white.

  B. Flowers rose or pink .   .   .   .   .   .   *R. callimorphum*

  B. Flowers white .   .   .   .   .   .   *R. myiagrum*

Subseries Cerasinum

bonvalotii, *Bur. et Franch.*   Q
cerasinum, *Tagg*

KEY TO THE SPECIES

A. Corolla large, 3·5–4·5 cm. long; leaves 5–10 cm. long .   *R. cerasinum*
A. Corolla small, 2·3 cm. long; leaves 4–5 cm. long .   .   *R. bonvalotii*

Subseries Selense

calvescens, *Balf. f. et Forrest*   Q
dasycladoides, *Hand.-Mazz.*   Q
dasycladum, *Balf. f. et W. W. Sm.*
erythrocalyx, *Balf. f. et Forrest*
esetulosum, *Balf. f. et Forrest*
eurysiphon, *Tagg et Forrest*
jucundum, *Balf. f. et W. W. Sm.*
martinianum, *Balf. f. et Forrest*
selense, *Franch.*
setiferum, *Balf. f. et Forrest*
vestitum, *Tagg et Forrest*

KEY TO THE SPECIES

A. Indumentum on the under surface of the leaves absent or
   a thin veil of hairs.
  B. Branchlets and, usually, petioles setose-glandular.
    C. Ovary tomentose (glandular); under surface of the
      leaves often with long stalked glands.
      D. Leaves oblong, 3–7·6 cm. long, under surface
        with long stalked glands (rarely eglandular) .   *R. dasycladoides*
      D. Leaves oblong-lanceolate, 7–10 cm. long, under   *R. selense* var.
        surface eglandular .   .   .   .   .   *duseimatum*
    C. Ovary not tomentose (glandular); under surface of
      leaves without long stalked glands.
      D. Corolla unspotted or with a few spots, funnel-
        shaped or funnel-campanulate.
        E. Leaves usually 2–4 cm. long; inflorescence
          usually 1–3-flowered, rarely more .   .   *R. martinianum*
        E. Leaves usually 5–12 cm. long; inflorescence
          5–12-flowered.
          F. Under surface of the leaves markedly
            glaucous .   .   .   .   .   *R. jucundum*
          F. Under surface of the leaves pale green.
            G. Leaves thin, chartaceous in texture,
              oval, elliptic or oblong; calyx
              usually 1–2 mm. (sometimes 3–6
              mm.) long. .   .   .   .   *R. dasycladum*
            G. Leaves thick, coriaceous in texture,
              oblong; calyx 3 mm.–1 cm. long .   *R. setiferum*
      D. Corolla copiously spotted with crimson, cam-
        panulate .   .   .   .   *R. eurysiphon*
  B. Branchlets and petioles not setose-glandular.
    C. Leaves usually more than 7·5 cm. long and 4 cm.
      broad; leaf base usually cordate, sometimes
      rounded or obtuse; calyx 1 mm.–1 cm. long;
      corolla usually 3·5–4·5 cm. long (rarely less).
      D. Under surface of the leaves glabrous; leaves
        thin, chartaceous in texture .   .   .   *R. erythrocalyx*
      D. Under surface of the leaves with a thin veil of
        hairs; leaves coriaceous in texture .   .   *R. esetulosum*

24

B. Flowers pale or deep yellow or greenish-yellow . *Triflorum subseries*

B. Flowers white, pink, purple, lavender to intense violet.
  C. Midrib on the under surfaces of the leaves hairy . *Augustinii subseries*

  C. Midrib on the under surfaces of the leaves not hairy . . . . *Yunnanense subseries*

Subseries Augustinii

augustinii, *Hemsl.*
bivelatum, *Balf. f.* Q
hirsuticostatum, *Hand.-Mazz.* Q
trichanthum, *Rehd.*

KEY TO SPECIES

A. Branchlets, petioles, upper surfaces of the leaves, pedicels, calyx, corolla tube and ovary pubescent or glabrous, not bristly (petiole rarely bristly-floccose in *R. augustinii*).
  B. Leaves evergreen.
    C. Corolla 2·2–4·3 cm. long; leaves usually lanceolate or oblong-lanceolate, apex acuminate or acute, lamina 3·3–12 cm. long; flowers pink, white, lilac-purple, pale or deep lavender-rose to intense violet; stamens hairy towards the base . *R. augustinii*
    C. Corolla 2 cm. long; leaves obovate or elliptic, apex obtuse, lamina 3·1–3·8 cm. long; flowers rose; stamens glabrous . . . . . . *R. bivelatum*
  B. Leaves semi-deciduous (flowers whitish-rose) . . *R. hirsuticostatum*

A. Branchlets, petioles, upper surfaces of the leaves bristly and often pubescent, pedicels, calyx, corolla tube and ovary bristly . . . . *R. trichanthum*

Subseries Hanceanum

afghanicum, *Aitch. et Hemsl.* Q
hanceanum, *Hemsl.*

KEY TO THE SPECIES

A. Style short, bent, shorter than the corolla; corolla 0·8–1·3 cm. long, campanulate; scales on the under surfaces of the leaves contiguous to their own diameter apart; leaves lanceolate or oblong-lanceolate; rachis 2–5 cm. long . . . . *R. afghanicum*

A. Style long, straight, longer than the corolla; corolla 1·3–2·1 cm. long, funnel-campanulate; scales on the under surfaces of the leaves 1½–5 times their own diameter apart; leaves ovate, obovate or ovate-lanceolate; rachis 0·8–2 cm. long . . . . *R. hanceanum*

Subseries Triflorum

ambiguum, *Hemsl.*
bauhiniiflorum, *Watt ex Hutch.*
flavantherum, *Hutch. et Ward*
kasoense, *Hutch. et Ward*
keiskei, *Miq.*
lutescens, *French.*
triflorum, *Hook. f.*
wongii, *Hemsl. et Wils.* Q

KEY TO THE SPECIES

A. Inflorescence axillary in the uppermost few leaves and terminal; corolla pubescent outside; leaves markedly acutely acuminate at the apex . . . . . *R. lutescens*

A. Inflorescence terminal (rarely axillary and terminal); corolla not pubescent outside (except sometimes in *R. triflorum* and *R. bauhiniiflorum*); leaves obtuse, acute or acuminate at the apex.

  B. Corolla not scaly outside; leaves broadly obtuse at the apex, lamina up to 3 cm. long, and up to 1·5 cm. broad . . . . *R. wongii*

  B. Corolla usually moderately or densely scaly outside; leaves acuminate or acute or obtuse at the apex, lamina up to 8 cm. long, and up to 3·2 cm. broad.

    C. Scales on the under surfaces of the leaves contiguous to their own diameter apart.

      D. Corolla flat, saucer-shaped, usually 3·8–4·3 cm. across . . . . . *R. bauhinii-florum*

      D. Corolla widely funnel-shaped, usually 1·5–3·6 cm. across.

        E. Under surfaces of the leaves usually glaucous; petiole not bristly; large shrub up to 5·80 m. high; (Himalayan and Chinese species).

          F. Scales on the under surfaces of the leaves minute, more or less equal in size, similar in colour, dark or pale brown; midrib on the upper surfaces of the leaves not hairy; bark of the stem and branchlets smooth, flaky . *R. triflorum*

          F. Scales on the under surfaces of the leaves large, of different sizes, dissimilar in colour, yellowish-brown and blackish, or yellowish-brown and dark brown; midrib on the upper surfaces of the leaves hairy; bark of the stem and branches rough . . . *R. ambiguum*

        E. Under surfaces of the leaves usually pale green, not glaucous; petiole bristly or not bristly; small shrub usually up to 60 cm. high, rarely more; (Japanese species) . *R. keiskei* (part)

    C. Scales on the under surfaces of the leaves widely spaced, 2–5 times their own diameter apart .

      D. Corolla widely funnel-shaped; under surfaces of the leaves usually pale green; midrib on the upper surfaces of the leaves puberulous; petiole bristly or not bristly; inflorescence 3–6-flowered; small shrub usually up to 60 cm. high, rarely more; (Japanese species) . *R. keiskei* (part)

      D. Corolla tubular-campanulate or tubular; under surfaces of the leaves pale glaucous green; midrib on the upper surfaces of the leaves not puberulous; petiole not bristly; inflorescence 2–3-flowered; large shrub 90 cm.–3 m. high; (Assam and Tibet species).

        E. Calyx a mere rim or 5-lobed, 0·5 mm. long; corolla tubular-campanulate . . . *R. kasoense*

        E. Calyx distinctly 5-lobed, 4 mm. long; corolla broadly tubular or tubular-campanulate . . . . *R. flavantherum*

28

amesiae, *Rehd. et Wils.*
bodinieri, *Franch.*
concinnoides, *Hutch. et Ward*
concinnum, *Hemsl.*
davidsonianum, *Rehd. et Wils.*
hormophorum, *Balf. f. et Forrest*
hypophaeum, *Balf. f. et Forrest*
longistylum, *Rehd. et Wils.*
oreotrephes, *W. W. Sm.*
polylepis, *Franch.*
rigidum, *Franch.*
searsiae, *Rehd. et Wils.*
siderophyllum, *Franch.*
tatsienense, *Franch.*
vilmorinianum, *Balf. f.*
yunnanense, *Franch.*
zaleucum, *Balf. f. et W. W. Sm.*

KEY TO THE SPECIES

A. Under surfaces of the leaves markedly glaucous.
  B. Scales on the under surfaces of the leaves widely spaced, 1½–4 times their own diameter apart; corolla moderately scaly outside; under surfaces of the leaves intensely glaucous . . . . *zaleucum*
  B. Scales on the under surfaces of the leaves closely spaced, one-half or rarely their own diameter apart; corolla not scaly or sometimes tube sparsely scaly outside; under surfaces of the leaves bluish-glaucous *searsiae*
A. Under surfaces of the leaves pale green or brown or pale glaucous green.
  B. Flowers purple, dark purple, reddish-purple or purplish-violet; corolla moderately or rather densely scaly outside (except in *R. apiculatum*).
    C. Leaves lanceolate, oblong-lanceolate or oblanceolate, 3–4 times as long as broad; scales on the under surfaces of the leaves usually overlapping or contiguous; scales on the branchlets and usually on the under surfaces of the leaves flaky . . *polylepis*
    C. Leaves oval, ovate, elliptic, ovate-lanceolate or sometimes oblong-lanceolate, usually as long as broad or up to twice as long as broad; scales on the under surfaces of the leaves one-half to their own diameter apart or contiguous; scales on the branchlets and on the under surfaces of the leaves not flaky.
      D. Petioles bristly; branchlets, pedicels and calyx bristly or not bristly . . . . . *amesiae*
      D. Petioles, branchlets, pedicels and calyx not bristly.
        E. Corolla widely funnel-shaped, 1·5–3·5 cm. long; (Szechuan and Yunnan species).
          F. Upper surfaces of the leaves scaly; the scales on the under surfaces of the leaves contiguous to their own diameter apart; branchlets, petioles and pedicels rather densely or moderately scaly . . . . . . *concinnum* (part)

F. Upper surfaces of the leaves not scaly; the scales on the under surfaces of the leaves 1½–2 times their own diameter apart; branchlets not scaly or sparsely scaly, petioles and pedicels sparsely scaly . . . . . *apiculatum*

E. Corolla tubular-campanulate, 1·6–2·6 cm. long; (Assam species) . . . *concinnoides*

B. Flowers white, pink, rose or pale lavender; corolla not scaly or sparsely or moderately scaly outside.

 C. Upper surfaces of the leaves and/or margins and/or petiole bristly.

  D. Leaves completely deciduous . . . *hormophorum* (part)

  D. Leaves evergreen or semi-deciduous.

   E. Scales on the under surfaces of the leaves widely spaced, usually 2–6 times their own diameter apart; leaves evergreen or semi-deciduous; corolla not scaly or sparsely or sometimes moderately scaly outside; pedicels not pubescent . . . *yunnanense* (part)

   E. Scales on the under surfaces of the leaves closely spaced, usually ½–1½ times their own diameter apart; leaves evergreen; corolla moderately scaly outside; pedicels often pubescent . . . . *vilmorinianum* (part)

 C. Upper surfaces of the leaves and margins, and petioles not bristly.

  D. Scales on the under surfaces of the leaves closely set, usually contiguous to their own diameter apart.

   E. Leaves lanceolate, oblong-lanceolate or narrowly oblong.

    F. Corolla small, usually 1·2–1·5 cm. long *hypophaeum*

    F. Corolla large, usually 1·8–3·5 cm. long.

     G. Inflorescence terminal and axillary; flowers usually in several clusters towards the apex of the branchlets; pedicels usually densely scaly . *siderophyllum* (part)

     G. Inflorescence terminal, or terminal and axillary; flowers often in only one or two clusters towards the apex of the branchlets; pedicels usually moderately scaly.

      H. Lamina of leaf V-shaped or flat; pedicels not pubescent; calyx margin often eciliate; ovary not bristly . . . *davidsonianum*

      H. Lamina of leaf flat; pedicels often pubescent; calyx margin often ciliate or bristly; ovary bristly at the apex or not bristly *vilmorinianum* (part)

   E. Leaves orbicular, oval, ovate, elliptic, obovate or ovate-lanceolate.

    F. Corolla scaly all over the tube and lobes outside . . . . . . *concinnum* (part)

    F. Corolla usually not scaly or sparsely scaly or sometimes only the lobes moderately scaly outside.

30

G. Inflorescence terminal and axillary; flowers usually in several clusters towards the apex of the branchlets; leaf apex often acuminate or acute   *siderophyllum* (part)

G. Inflorescence terminal, or terminal and axillary; flowers often in only one or two clusters towards the apex of the branchlets; leaf apex usually rounded or obtuse.

    H. Leaves not rigid; branchlets green or deep pink, often not scaly or sparsely scaly; upper surfaces of the leaves often not scaly or sparsely scaly; under surfaces of the leaves often pale glaucous green; corolla 1·8–4 cm. long .   .   .   .   *oreotrephes* (part)

    H. Leaves rigid, branchlets deep crimson, moderately or rather densely scaly; upper surfaces of the leaves moderately or rather densely scaly; under surfaces of the leaves usually pale green; corolla usually 1·4–2·3 cm. long .   .   .   *tatsienense*

D. Scales on the under surfaces of the leaves widely spaced, 2–8 times their own diameter apart.

  E. Leaves completely deciduous .   .   .   *hormophorum* (part)

  E. Leaves evergreen or semi-deciduous.

    F. Leaves lanceolate, oblong-lanceolate or narrowly-oblanceolate.

      G. Leaf apex markedly long acuminate   *bodinieri*

      G. Leaf apex acute, shortly acuminate or obtuse.

        H. Corolla large, usually 1·8–3·4 cm. long; leaves 1–3 cm. broad; calyx a mere rim or 5-lobed, 0·5–1 mm. long.

          I. Upper surfaces of the leaves usually green; leaves evergreen or semi-deciduous; branchlets, petioles and midrib on the upper surfaces of the leaves usually puberulous; branchlets moderately or sparsely scaly; pedicels moderately or sparsely scaly or not scaly; under surfaces of the leaves pale green or pale glaucous green .   .   .   .   *yunnanense* (part)

          I. Upper surfaces of the leaves pale bluish-green; leaves evergreen; branchlets, petioles and midrib on the upper surfaces of the leaves usually not puberulous; branchlets usually not scaly or sparsely scaly; pedicels

31

not scaly or rarely sparsely
scaly; under surfaces of the
leaves pale glaucous green .　*rigidum* (part)

H. Corolla small, usually 1–3–1·6
cm. long; leaves 0·6–1·5 cm.
broad; calyx 5-lobed, 1–3 mm.
long　.　.　.　.　*longistylum*

F. Leaves orbicular, oval, ovate, elliptic or
oblong.

G. Leaves green above; scales on the
under surfaces of the leaves usually
2–3 times their own diameter apart　*oreotrephes*
(part)

G. Leaves pale bluish-green above;
scales on the under surfaces of the
leaves usually 4–8 times their own
diameter apart .　.　.　.　*rigidum* (part)

No. 42. Uniflorum Series (1)

imperator, *Hutch. et Ward*
ludlowii, *Cowan*
monanthum, *Balf. f. et W. W. Sm.*　Q
patulum, *Ward*
pemakoense, *Ward*
pumilum, *Hook. f.*
uniflorum, *Hutch. et Ward*

KEY TO THE SPECIES

A. Leaf margin undulate, faintly but distinctly notched;
calyx large, 5–7 mm. long. (Flowers yellow, spotted
reddish-brown inside tube) .　.　.　.　.　*ludlowii*

A. Leaf margin entire; calyx minute, 1–2 mm. long, rarely
3–4 mm.

B. Flowers bright yellow; corolla not hairy outside; scales
on the under surface of leaves markedly different in
size, mostly large; small to medium sized shrub, up
to 1·20 m. high; leaves large, usually 2·6–5 cm. long
and 1·3–2·5 cm. broad .　.　.　.　.　*monanthum*

B. Flowers pink, rose or purple; corolla densely hairy
outside; scales on the under surface of leaves small,
uniform (in *R. pemakoense* varying); dwarf, erect or
prostrate shrubs, 15–60 cm. high; leaves small, less
than 2·6 cm. long, rarely longer, less than 1·3 cm.
broad (*R. pemakoense* rarely broader).

C. Leaves elliptic or obovate-elliptic; corolla campanulate, 1·3–1·9 cm. long, rarely longer; style
usually about half as long as corolla. (Flowers
pink or rose) .　.　.　.　.　*pumilum*

C. Leaves lanceolate, oblanceolate, oblong-obovate
or obovate; corolla funnel-shaped, 2·2–3·5 cm.
long; style equal to or longer than corolla (except
in *R. uniflorum*).

D. Leaves obovate or oblong-obovate, apex
rounded or obtuse; erect or semi-erect shrubs.

E. Scales on the under surface of leaves 3–6
times their own diameter apart; style not
hairy. (Flowers purple) .　.　.　*uniflorum*

E. Scales on the under surface of leaves ½–1½
times their own diameter apart; style hairy
or not hairy. (Flowers purple or pinkish-
purple) .　.　.　.　.　.　*pemakoense*

D. Leaves lanceolate or oblanceolate, apex usually
   acute; prostrate shrubs with spreading
   branches.
   E. Scales on the under surface of leaves 2–6
      times their own diameter apart. (Flowers
      bright purple or pinkish-purple, not
      marked) . . . . . . *imperator*
   E. Scales on the under surface of leaves 1–1½
      times their own diameter apart. (Flowers
      purple, the upper lobe spotted crimson-
      purple; or pinkish-purple) . . . *patulum*

No. 43. Vaccinioides Series (1)

asperulum, *Hutch. et Ward*   Q
emarginatum, *Hemsl. et Wils.*   Q
euonymifolium, *Lévl.*   Q
insculptum, *Hutch. et Ward*   Q
kawakamii, *Hayata*   Q
quadrasianum, *Vidal*   Q
rosmarinifolium, *Vidal*   Q
vaccinioides, *Hook. f.*
vidalii, *Rolfe*   Q

No. 44. Virgatum Series (1)

oleifolium, *Franch.*
virgatum, *Hook. f.*

Species Unplaced in above Series

asterochnoum, *Diels*   Q
beyerinckianum, *Koorders*
brookeanum, *Low ex Lindl.*
dimidiatum, *Balf. f.*
jasminiflorum, *Hook.*
lochae, *F. Muell.*
magorianum, *Balf. f.*   Q
malayanum, *Jack*
potanini, *Batalin*   Q
pyrrhoanthum, *Balf. f.*
retusum, *Benn.*
yakuinsulare, *Masam*—Azalea S.

RHODODENDRON SPECIES

IN THIS Handbook, the descriptions of the 1956 edition of the former Handbook have been revised and amplified. In addition a new system of merit rating has been devised in an endeavour to give the grower a truer picture of the species he cultivates or desires to cultivate.

To express the varying merit of the numerous species, a series of symbols has been used, as follows:

H   Hardiness and constitution
F   Flower qualities
L   Leaf qualities
P   Plant size and habit

Obviously not all species are of equal hardiness and constitution, and to express the variability of H, four categories—1, 2, 3, 4—have been used, instead of the six categories—A, B, C, D, E, F—of the former Handbook. Thus

H^4 represents a species hardy anywhere in the British Isles and corresponds to A and B of the former Handbook.

H^3 represents a species hardy in the South and West, and along the seaboard, and in sheltered gardens inland, and corresponds to C and D of the former Handbook.

H^2 represents a species which requires protection in the most sheltered gardens, and corresponds to E in the former Handbook.

H^1 represents a species which usually can be grown only as a greenhouse plant and corresponds to F in the former Handbook.

Experience has shown that some forms of certain species clearly are hardier than others; that some *forms* are adequately represented by H^3, for instance, and others by H^4. Such species therefore can be satisfactorily rated for hardiness only by the symbol H^{3-4}.

Flower (F) and foliage (L) characters have also been graded each into four categories which roughly correspond to the number of stars used in the former Handbook. Thus

$$F^4 \text{ and } L^4 \;=\; \text{excellent}$$
$$F^3 \text{ and } L^3 \;=\; \text{good}$$
$$F^2 \text{ and } L^2 \;=\; \text{fair}$$
$$F^1 \text{ and } L^1 \;=\; \text{of little merit}$$

Increased experience of species in cultivation has shown that, as with hardiness, all species vary considerably in the degree of merit of their flower and flower trusses, and of their leaves. For instance some forms of a certain species may have such fine flowers and foliage, as to merit, in this system, the use of the rating F^4L^4, whilst other forms of the same species may deserve only the rating F^2L^2. Such a variable species therefore, in the present system, is rated $F^{2-4} L^{2-4}$.

Likewise to express the great variability in size and habit (P) of certain species, a series of categories has been used, as follows:

P^d.	=	dwarf	P^c.	=	compact
P^m.	=	medium	P^s.	=	straggling
P^t.	=	tall	P^p.	=	prostrate

In some species two categories may be appropriate. Thus a species, dwarf and compact in habit, is represented by the symbol P$^{d.c.}$

As this Handbook deals, with only a very few exceptions, with species in general cultivation, those species which in the former Handbook fell into the category Q—species not in general cultivation—have been omitted from this section of the book. They are included, however, in the Series list at the beginning and are also listed on p. 234.

In the descriptions of the species, the heights given, are, for the most part, those which have been attained by plants in the British Isles. Sometimes, in the case of *R. giganteum* for instance, the height is that to which the species attains in the wild; it will be a guide as to what those who are fortunate in being able to cultivate such a species may reasonably anticipate.

The times of flowering are those appropriate to the British Isles.

Apart from details of awards given to individual species by The Royal Horticultural Society, the descriptions of the species also give details of the hybrids of any particular species which have also received R.H.S. awards. Such awards are abbreviated thus:

F.C.C.	=	First Class Certificate
A.M.	=	Award of Merit .
A.G.M.	=	Award of Garden Merit
P.C.	=	Certificate of Preliminary Commendation
B.C.	=	Botanical Certificate.

The symbols H.C.C. which sometimes occur in the descriptions refer to the Horticultural Colour Chart.

Any assistance in correcting mistakes, both in the merit ratings and in the descriptions, will be welcomed for consideration when revising future editions.

Glossary of Some Botanic Terms used

ADPRESSED: lying close and flat against.

AGGLUTINATE: glued or joined together.

APPRESSED: *see* ADPRESSED.

AURICLE: with an ear like appendage.

AXILLARY: growing in the angle formed by junction of leaf and stem.

BULLATE: blistered or puckered, usually applied to foliage.

CAPITATE: collected in a dense head-like cluster.

CLONE: the vegetatively produced progeny of a single individual whether a species or hybrid.

EPIPHYTIC: growing on another plant but deriving no nourishment from it.

FLOCCOSE: covered with close woolly hairs which fall away in little tufts.

GLABROUS: smooth and without hairs.

GLAUCOUS: covered with waxy bloom which may be grey or bluish.

IMPRESSED: sunken as veins may be.

INDUMENTUM: a hairy covering, particularly of the underside of leaves.

MUCRONATE: abruptly terminated by a hard, sharp point.

NECTARY: a gland consisting of a group of cells through the outer walls of which a solution of sugar is excreted.

PILOSE: covered with soft long hairs.

RETICULATE: netted.

REVOLUTE: rolled back, often applied to the leaf margin when rolled towards the lower side.

SETOSE: covered with stiff hairs.

STOLONIFEROUS: bearing a branch arising from near the base of the parent stem, often below the surface of the soil.

STYLE: the usually attenuated part of a pistil or carpel between the ovary and stigma.

ZYGOMORPHIC: term for a flower of irregular shape, capable of division into equal halves along one vertical line only.

RHODODENDRON FLOWER SHAPES

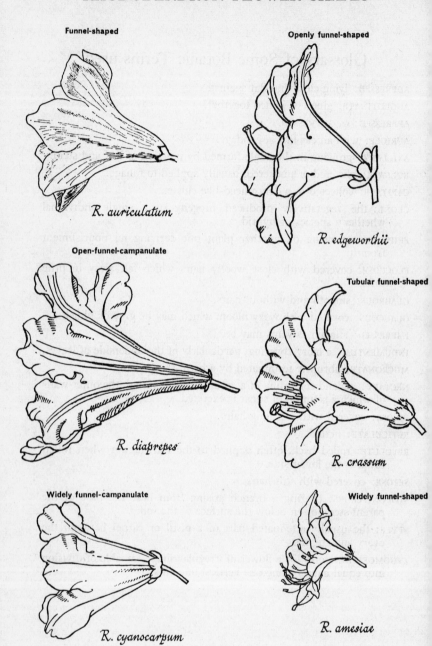

Funnel-shaped

R. auriculatum

Openly funnel-shaped

R. edgeworthii

Open-funnel-campanulate

R. diaprepes

Tubular funnel-shaped

R. crassum

Widely funnel-campanulate

R. cyanocarpum

Widely funnel-shaped

R. amesiae

RHODODENDRON FLOWER SHAPES

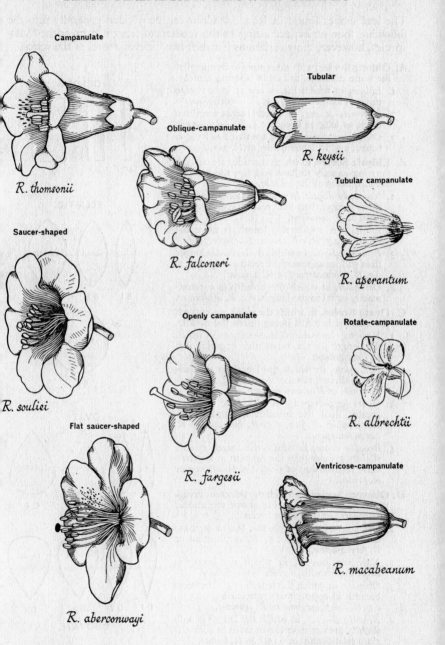

Campanulate

R. thomsonii

Oblique-campanulate

R. falconeri

Tubular

R. keysii

Tubular campanulate

R. aperantum

Saucer-shaped

R. souliei

Openly campanulate

R. fargesii

Rotate-campanulate

R. albrechtii

Flat saucer-shaped

R. aberconwayi

Ventricose-campanulate

R. macabeanum

RHODODENDRON LEAF SHAPES

The leaf shapes found in Rhododendron can be divided generally into the following four series, according to the relation of length to breadth. Many species, however, show variations between two, or even more, of the series.

A. **Oblong Series**, with sides more or less parallel for some distance, the ends tapering rapidly.
   1. *Linear*, in which leaves are at least twelve times as long as wide, e.g. *R. linearifolium*.
   2. *Narrowly oblong*, in which leaves are three times as long as broad, e.g. *R. calophytum*.
   3. *Oblong*, in which leaves are twice as long as broad, e.g. *R. aganniphum* or *R. paradoxum*.

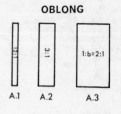

OBLONG

A.1 A.2 A.3

B. **Elliptic Series,** in which the sides are curved, tapering equally to base and tip, the greatest breadth being at the middle.
   1. *Narrowly elliptic*, in which the length is three times greater than the breadth, e.g. *R. coriaceum* or *R. oreodoxa*.
   2. *Elliptic*, in which the length is twice the breadth, e.g. *R. ciliatum* or *R. oreotrephes*.
   3. *Broadly elliptic*, in which the leaves are longer than wide in approximate relationship of 3 : 2, e.g. *R. cyanocarpum* or *R. parishii*.
   4. *Orbicular*, in which the breadth is approximately equal to the length, e.g. *R. orbiculare*.

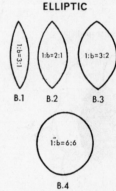

ELLIPTIC

B.1 B.2 B.3

B.4

C. **Ovate Series**, in which the sides are curved, the greatest breadth being below the middle.
   1. *Narrowly lanceolate* (lance-shaped), in which the length is six times the breadth, e.g. *R. iteophyllum*.
   2. *Lanceolate*, in which the length is approximately three times the breadth, e.g. *R. davidsonianum* or *R. griersonianum*.
   3. *Ovate* (egg-shaped), in which the length is greater than the breadth in approximate relationship of 3 : 2, e.g. *R. bureavii* or *R. campylocarpum*.
   4. *Broadly ovate*, in which the length is only slightly greater than the breadth in approximate relationship of 6 : 5, e.g. *R. ovatum* or *R. prattii*.

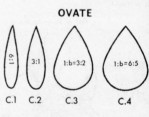

OVATE

C.1 C.2 C.3 C.4

D. **Obovate Series,** in which the sides are curved, the greatest breadth being above the middle (the reverse of the Ovate Series).
   1. *Oblanceolate*, in which the length is three times the breadth, e.g. *R. corphyaeum* or *R. ferrugineum*.
   2. *Narrowly obovate*, in which the length is twice the breadth, e.g. *R. dichroanthum*.
   3. *Obovate*, in which the length is greater than breadth in approximate relationship of 3 : 2, e.g. *R. campylogynum* or *R. crassum*.
   4. *Broadly obovate*, in which the length is only slightly greater than the breadth in approximate relationship of 6 : 5, e.g. *R. lochae*.

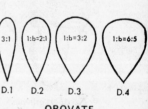

D.1 D.2 D.3 D.4

OBOVATE

A fuller account of the terms used for description of leaf shapes may be found in the Supplement to the *R.H.S. Dictionary of Gardening*, pp. 318–322.

List of Rhododendron Species

(*s. = series, s.s. = subseries.*)

R. aberconwayi
(After the late Lord Aberconway
President of the R.H.S. 1931
to 1953)
H⁴ F²⁻⁴ L¹⁻² Pm.

May–June

s. and s.s. Irroratum.

Shrub up to 8 ft. rather loose-growing. Lvs. 2–4 in. long, hard, thick, oblong-elliptic to elliptic. Fls. 6–12 per truss, 2–3 in. diam., flat saucer-shaped, white or white tinged pink almost un-spotted or with many crimson spots. Rather variable from seeds even of hand-pollinated plants. Yunnan.

'His Lordship' is an A.M. clone (Commissioners of Crown Lands, Windsor, 1945).

R. achroanthum
(*ill-coloured*)
H⁴ F² L¹ Pd.c.

April–May

s. Lapponicum.

Shrub up to 3 ft. Lvs. ⅔ in. long, oblong-elliptic, densely scaly. Fls. in clusters of 3–5, ½ in. long, widely funnel-shaped, deep magenta-red, purple, plum-purple to deep violet-purple. Yunnan, N.E. Upper Burma, 12–13,000 ft.

R. adenogynum
(*with glandular ovary*)
H⁴ F² L² Pm.

April

s. Taliense. *s.s.* Adenogynum.

Slow growing shrub up to 9 ft. Lvs. 4–5 in. long, oblong-obovate to lance shaped, tawny below. Fls. about 12 to the truss, up to 2 in. long, funnel-shaped, deep rose in bud opening to white shaded rose at base or with a magenta tint and many crimson spots. Yunnan, Szechwan, S.E. Tibet, 11–12,000 ft. B.M. 9253.

R. adenophorum
(*gland-bearing*)
H⁴ F¹⁻² L²⁻³ Pm.

April

s. Taliense. *s.s.* Adenogynum.

Shrub up to 8 ft. Lvs. up to 4 in. long, lance-olate or oblong-lanceolate, thick cinnamon or fulvous indumentum below. Fls. about 10 to the truss, 1½ in. long, funnel-shaped, rose with a few crimson markings. Similar to *R. adenogynum* but more glandular. Yunnan, 12,000 ft.

R. adenopodum
(*with glandular pedicel*)
H⁴ F²⁻³ L²⁻³ Pm.

April–May

s. Ponticum. *s.s.* Caucasicum.

Shrub up to 10 ft. Lvs. 4–7 in. long, narrow, densely covered below with grey or pale fawn felty indumentum. Fls. in elongate trusses of 6–10, about 1½ in. long, funnel-campanulate, pale rose, more or less spotted. Variable from seeds of hand self-pollinated plants. Not very closely allied to any Chinese Rhododendron; nearest of

41

R. adenopodum
(*continued*)

kin in Caucasus and Japan. Szechwan, Hupeh, 5–7,000 ft.
A.M. 1926 (G. W. E. Loder, Ardingly).

R. adroserum
(*glandular*)

see *R. lukiangense* subsp. *adroserum*.

R. aganniphum
(*snowy, alluding to whitish indumentum*)
H4 F1–2 L1–2 Pm.

May–June

s. *and s.s.* Taliense.
Shrub up to 15 ft. Lvs. up to 4 in. long, 2 in. broad, oblong, covered below with smooth white or yellowish-white indumentum. Fls. in trusses of 8–12, 1½ in. long, funnel-campanulate, white to deep rose with few or many crimson spots. Allied to *R. flavorufum*; also suggests a small version of *R. clementinae*. S.E. Tibet, N.W. Yunnan, 14–15,000 ft.

R. agapetum
(*delightful*)
H1–2 F3–4 L2–3 Pt.s.

June

s. Irroratum. *s.s.* Parishii.
Shrub or scraggy tree up to 20 ft. Lvs. 4–6 in. long, oblong. Fls. in trusses of 8–10, 2 in. long, tubular-campanulate, crimson-scarlet. Akin to *R. kyawi*. Upper Burma, 6–7,000 ft.

R. agastum
(*charming*)
H3 F2 L2 Pt.

Feb.–March

s. *and s.s.* Irroratum.
Shrub or tree up to 20 ft. Lvs. 3–5 in. long, oblong to obovate, apex rounded, lower surface with thin pale olive to fawn indumentum. Fls. in trusses of 10–20, 2 in. long, tubular-campanulate pale or deep rose, or white tinged pink, blotched or spotted. Somewhat anomalous in the Irroratum series by reason of the round leaf apex and the thin indumentum. It links the Irroratum and Arboreum series. Yunnan, 6–9,000 ft. B.M. 9577.

R. agglutinatum
(*stuck together, referring to the hairs on the lower surface of the leaf*)
H3–4 F1–2 L1–2 Pt.

April

s. Lacteum.
Shrub or tree up to 20 ft. Lvs. 1½–3 in. long, oval covered below with a tawny agglutinate indumentum. Fls. in trusses of 10–15, 1½ in. long, funnel-campanulate, white, creamy-white or pink, with or without crimson spots. Closely allied to *R. phaeochrysum*. Szechwan, Yunnan, Tibet, Bhutan, 11–16,000 ft.

R. alabamense
(*native of Alabama*)
H4 F2–3 L1 Pd.m.

Late April–May

s. Azalea. *s.s.* Luteum.
Shrub up to 5 ft., often low growing and stoloniferous. Lvs. deciduous, glaucous or pale green beneath, up to 2½ in. long, 1¼ in. broad, elliptic to obovate to oblong. Fls., 6–10 per truss, about 1 in. long and 1½ in. across, tubular-funnel shaped, white, with or without yellow blotch, with lemon fragrance. The best forms are quite beautiful. Alabama, Georgia, Eastern Mississippi and Tennessee.

42

R. albertsenianum
(After M. O. Albertson,
Chinese Maritime Customs)
H⁴ F¹⁻² L¹⁻² Pm.

April

s. *and* s.s Neriiflorum.
Shrub up to 7 ft. Lvs. 2½–4 in. long, narrow oblong, with brown woolly indumentum beneath. Fls. in trusses of 5–6, 1–1½ in. long, bell-shaped, bright rose-crimson without markings. It recalls in general appearance such members of the Taliense series as *R. russotinctum*. Yunnan, 10,000 ft.

R. albiflorum
(*with white flowers*)
H²⁻³ F¹ L¹ Pm.

June–July

s. Albiflorum.
Shrub up to 6 ft. Lvs. deciduous, scattered, or clustered at ends of short branchlets, 1–3 in. long, elliptic to oblong. Fls. single or in pairs from axillary buds along branchlets of previous year, appearing after the leaves, pendent, about 1 in. long, white to pale lemon. Difficult to grow well. High mountains of Oregon and Washington. B.M. 3670.

R. albrechtii
(After Dr. M. Albrecht,
Russian Naval Surgeon)
H⁴ F³⁻⁴ L¹⁻² Pm.–c.

April–May

s. Azalea. s.s. Canadense.
Deciduous shrub up to 10 ft. or more. Lvs. in clusters of 5 at ends of branchlets, up to 4½ in. long and 2½ in. broad, obovate to oblong-obovate. Fls. opening before or with the leaves, in cluster of 3–4, 2 in. diam., rotate-campanulate, deep rose, or, less desirable, bright purplish-rose, with olive-green spots. A very beautiful azalea. C. and N. Japan. B.M. 9207.
'Michael McLaren' is an F.C.C. clone (Lord Aberconway and the National Trust, Bodnant Gardens, 1962).

R. alpicola
(*a dweller in high mountains*)
H⁴ F¹⁻² L¹ Pd.

April–May

s. Lapponicum.
Shrub up to 3 ft. Lvs. ¼ in. long, elliptic. Fls., solitary, about ½ in. long, funnel-shaped, lavender-purple or rose. Szechwan, S.E. Tibet, 12–15,000 ft.

R. alutaceum
(*like soft leather, referring to the leaves*)
H⁴ F¹⁻² L² Pm.

April

s. Taliense. s.s. Adenogynum.
Shrub up to 14 ft. Lvs. 3–6 in. long, oblong, leathery with thick buff woolly indumentum on under surface. Fls. up to 12 per truss, 1½ in. long, funnel-campanulate, rose, spotted and blotched with crimson. Similar to *R. adenogynum* and *R. adenophorum* but lacking the large calyx. Yunnan, 12,000 ft.

R. amagianum
(*from Mount Amagi, Japan*)
H⁴ F³ L²⁻³ Pm.–t.

June–July

s. Azalea. s.s. Schlippenbachii.
Deciduous shrub up to 12 ft. Lvs. 2½ in. long, rhomboid to broadly ovate, in threes at the ends of the branchlets. Fls. 3–4 per truss, up to 1½ in. long, funnel-shaped, orange-red. A splendid late flowering shrub. Related to *R. weyrichii*. Japan. B.M. n.s. 379.
A.M. 1948 (Lord Aberconway, Bodnant).

43

R. ambiguum
(*doubtful*)
H4 F2–3 L1 Pm.–t.

April–May

s. *and* s.s. Triflorum.
    Shrub up to 18 ft. Lvs. 2–3 in. long, ovate-lanceolate. Fls. in clusters of 2–7, about 1½ in. long, zygomorphic, greenish-yellow or pale yellow, with greenish spots. Related to *R. triflorum* and *R. bauhiniiflorum*. Szechwan, 7,500–14,700 ft. B.M. 8400.
    A parent of the A.M. clones 'Biskra' and 'Mosaique'.

R. amesiae
(After Mary S. Ames, of Long Eaton, Mass.)
H4 F1–2 L1 Pm.

Late May

s. Triflorum. s.s. Yunnanense.
    Shrub up to 12 ft. Lvs. 1¼–3 in. long, ovate, ovate-elliptic to elliptic, densely scaly below. Fls. in clusters of 2–5, widely funnel-shaped, zygomorphic, purple or dark reddish-purple, with or without darker spots. Closely allied to *R. concinnum*. Szechwan, 7,500–9,800 ft. B.M. 9221.

R. annae
(After a French lady)
H3–4 F1–2 L1–2 Pm.

June–July

s. *and* s.s. Irroratum.
    Shrub up to 8 ft. Lvs. up to 5 in. long, 1 in. broad, narrow lanceolate. Fls. in trusses of 8–12, c. 1 in. long, cup or openly bell-shaped, creamy-white flushed rose, purple spotted. Kweichow.

R. anthopogon
(*with bearded flowers—referring to hairs in floret tube*)
H4 F2–3 L1 Pd.

April

s. Anthopogon.
    Small shrub up to 2 ft. Lvs. 1–1½ in. long, up to 1 in. broad, obovate-elliptic, densely scaly below. Fls. in small tight truss, ¾ in. long, narrowly tubular, cream-pink, deciduous leaf-bud scales. Nepal, Sikkim, Assam, 9–16,000 ft. B.M. 3947.
    Var. *haemonium* has narrower leaves and yellow flowers. Bhutan.

R. anthosphaerum
(*round-flowered*)
H3 F1–2 L1 Pt.

Feb.–March

s. *and* s.s. Irroratum.
    Tree up to 30 ft. Lvs. 3–5 in. long, oblanceolate. Fls. in trusses of 10–15, up to 2 in. long, tubular campanulate, rose-magenta to mauve with deep black-crimson blotch. Yunnan, S.E. Tibet, 10–11,000 ft. B.M. 9083.

    A form growing to a height of 10 ft. with smaller and narrower leaves and with fls. deep magenta-rose, crimson-rose, pale yellow or white, with or without crimson spots, is known as sub-species *hylothreptum* (H3 F1 L1 Pm.), *March–April*.

R. anwheiense
(*from Anwhei, China*)
H4 F1–2 L1–2 Pm.

April–May

s. Barbatum. s.s. Maculiferum.
    Spreading shrub up to 12 ft. Lvs. up to 3 in. long, ovate-lanceolate. Fls. in trusses of 6–10, 1 in. long, campanulate, white or white flushed pink, with or without purplish-red spots. Anwhei Province, China, 5–6,000 ft.

R. aperantum
(*limitless*)
H4 F2–3 L1–2 Pd.

April–May

s. Neriiflorum. *s.s.* Sanguineum.

A very slow growing dwarf spreading shrub up to 2 ft. Lvs. aggregated towards the apices of branchlets, about 1½ in. long, ovate to obovate to oblanceolate. Fls. in trusses of 1–4, up to 2 in. long, tubular-campanulate, varying in colour from white, yellow, orange-red to pink, rose, or dark crimson. Very shy to flower in cultivation. N.E. Upper Burma, Yunnan, 12,000 ft. Farrer described it in Burma as forming an indescribable riot of colour covering the high alpine slopes for miles in company with *R. caloxanthum, chaetomallum* and *charitopes.* B.M. 9507.

A.M. 1931 (Marquess of Headfort, Kells) to form with crimson fls.

R. apodectum
(*acceptable*)

see *R. dichroanthum* subsp. *apodectum.*

R. araiophyllum
(*narrow-leaved*)
H3 F1–2 L2–3 Pm.–t.

April

s. and s.s. Irroratum.

Slender branched shrub up to 16 ft. Lvs. red when young, revolute, floccose, mature 2–5 in. long, lanceolate. Fls. in clusters of about 6, up to 1½ in. long, cup-shaped, white or white suffused with rose with a crimson blotch and a few or many crimson spots. Notable for the young growth. Yunnan, N.E. Upper Burma, 9–10,000 ft.

R. arborescens
(*becoming tree-like*)
H4 F2–3 L1–2 Pm.–t.

June–July

s. Azalea. *s.s.* Luteum.

Shrub up to 15 ft. with smooth and hairless branchlets. Lvs. deciduous, 1½–3½ in. long, obovate or elliptic to oblong-lanceolate, glaucous or green beneath. Fls. in clusters of 3–6, up to 2 in. long and broad, tubular-funnel shaped, white with red style, sometimes with yellow blotch, sometimes with pink or reddish flush, strong heliotrope fragrance, always appearing after the leaves and sometimes rather hidden by the leaves. The good forms with glossy foliage and large flowers can provide a display in white unequalled among late azaleas. E. North America.

In its native habit *R. arborescens* occasionally hybridizes with *R. viscosum* and *R. bakeri* to yield forms with pink or yellowish flowers. A low growing form has been described as var. *richardsonii.*

'Ailsa' is an A.M. clone with up to 10 white yellow-blotched flowers to the truss (Murray Adams Acton, London, 1952).

45

R. arboreum
(*tree-like*)
H$^{2-4}$ F$^{3-4}$ L$^{3-4}$ P^t.

Jan.–April

s. *and* s.s. Arboreum.

Tree up to 40 ft. Lvs. up to 8 in. long, 2½ in. broad, oblong-lanceolate to oblong-oblanceolate, rich green and glossy above, white to fawn to cinnamon or rusty-brown below. Fls. in round compact trusses of 15–20, 2 in. long, tubular-campanulate, blood-red, pink or white, sometimes spotted. Blood-red forms are the most tender. Forms with rich pink flowers with deeper coloured spots are known as forma *roseum* (B.M. 4381) and those with white purple-spotted flowers as forma *album* (B.M. 3290). Temperate Himalaya, Kashmir to Bhutan, Khasia Hills, Ceylon, 5–10,000 ft.

Other forms of *R. arboreum* now regarded as subsp. have been named as follows:

R. campbelliae (after the wife of Dr. Campbell, co-traveller with Hooker in Himalaya); H$^{2-3}$ F$^{2-3}$ L$^{2-3}$ P^t.; *April*; lvs. rusty tomentose below; fls. purplish-rose. Sikkim.

R. cinnamomeum (cinnamon-coloured); H^3 F$^{2-3}$ L$^{3-4}$ P^t.; *May*; lvs. with rusty brown indumentum below; fls. white or pale rose with purple or yellow spots. Sikkim, Nepal (B.M. 3825).

R. nilagiricum (from the Nilgiris, Madras, India); H^3 F$^{2-3}$ L$^{2-3}$ P$^{m.-t.}$; lvs. rusty tomentose below; fls. varying from rose to deep crimson. Nilgiris, Madras (B.M. 9323).

'Sir Charles Lemon' with white flowers and leaves very rusty below is usually regarded as an *R. arboreum* hybrid, raised from seeds introduced by Sir J. Hooker.

R. arboreum is a parent of the A.M. clones 'Duke of Cornwall' (1907), 'John Holms' (1959), 'Trelawney' (1936), 'Androcles' (1948), 'Ernest Gill' (1918), 'Fulgarb' (1937), 'Hermione' (1941), 'Gill's Triumph' (1906), 'Glory of Penjerrick' (1904), 'Eureka' (1939), 'Euphrosyne' (1923), 'Bibiani' (1934), 'Cornubia' (1912), 'Dame Nellie Melba' (1926), 'Leonardslee Primrose' (1933), 'Eurydice' (1939), 'Springtime' (1945).

The following are F.C.C. clones: 'Cardinal' (1937), 'Altaclarense' (1865), 'Beauty of Tremough' (1902), 'Choremia' (1948). 'Nobleanum' is an A.G.M. plant.

R. argyrophyllum
(*with silver leaves*)
H^4 F$^{3-4}$ L$^{2-3}$ P$^{m.-t.}$

May

s. Arboreum. s.s. Argyrophyllum.

Large shrub up to 20 ft. Lvs. up to 6 in. long, 1½ in. broad, oblong-lanceolate or oblong, with a thin silvery or white, felty or plastered indumentum beneath. Fls. 6–12 in a lax truss, 1½ in. long,

46

R. argyrophyllum
(*continued*)

campanulate, white or white flushed rose or pink with deeper pink spots, sometimes blotched. Szechwan, 6–9,000 ft.

A.M. 1934 (G. W. E. Loder, Wakehurst Place, Sussex); a form with flowers white flushed rose and spotted a deeper rose.

Several forms of this variable species have been named as follows:

Var. *cupulare* with smaller more cup-shaped flowers; Szechwan.

Var. *omeiense* with smaller leaves with a more deeply coloured indumentum; Szechwan.

Var. *leiandrum* with glabrous filaments; Szechwan. (B.M. 8767)

Var. *nankingense*, a district geographical form readily distinguishable by the broader and longer leaves shining above and large flowers of a stronger colour.

'Chinese Silver' is an A.M. clone of var. *nankingense* with a truss of 16 flowers, Persian Rose (H.C.C. 620/3) shaded with deeper flushes on the lobes (Crown Estate Commissioners, Windsor, 1957).

R. arizelum
(*notable*)
H$^{3-4}$ F$^{2-3}$ L$^{3-4}$ Pm.-t.
April

s. *Falconeri*.

Shrub or small tree up to 20 ft. with young growths covered with cinnamon or greyish tomentum. Lvs. up to 10 in. long, 4 in. broad, thick, oval, obovate or oblanceolate, dark green and rugulose above, with thick persistent cinnamon or brown indumentum below. Fls. in a truss of 15–25, up to 2 in. long, obliquely campanulate, white, creamy-yellow, deep yellow, sometimes shaded with rose, with dark crimson blotch. Yunnan, Upper Burma, 9–12,000 ft.

A form with crimson flowers from S.E. Tibet has been named var. *rubicosum* and was given an A.M. in 1963 (Earl of Stair, Lochinch Castle).

'Brodick' is an A.M. clone with flowers of Solferino Purple H.C.C. 26/3–26/2 with a small blotch of crimson black (Brodick Castle Gardens, 1963).

R. artosquameum
(*with compressed scales*)

see *R. oreotrephes*.

R. atlanticum
(*from the Atlantic seaboard*)
H^4 F$^{2-3}$ L$^{1-2}$ Pd.-m.
Early to late May

s. Azalea. s.s. Luteum.

Stoloniferous shrub up to 3 ft., occasionally more. Lvs. deciduous, $1\frac{1}{2}$–$2\frac{1}{2}$ in. long, obovate to oblong-obovate, bright or bluish-green above, glaucescent or bright green beneath. Fls. appearing with the leaves in clusters of 4–10, about

47

R. atlanticum
(*continued*)

1¼ in. across, tubular-funnel-shaped, white or white flushed with pink or purple, sometimes with yellow blotch, fragrant. Southern Pennsylvania and Delaware south to South Carolina.

In the northern part of its range it intergrades with *R. nudiflorum* and in the southern part with *R. canescens* and pale to rosy-pink flowered forms result.

R. atrorubrum
(*black-red*)

see *R. sanguineum* subsp. *atrorubrum*.

R. augustinii
(After Augustine Henry, 1857–1930, Medical Officer in Chinese Customs, later Professor of Forestry, Dublin)

H3–4 F2–4 L1–2 Pm.–t.

April–May

s. Triflorum. s.s. Augustinii.

Shrub up to 15 ft. or more. Lvs. up to 5 in. long, lanceolate, oblong-lanceolate, oblong-elliptic to obovate. Fls. in clusters of 2–6, up to 2 in. long, up to 2½ in. across, widely funnel-shaped, zygomorphic, varying greatly in colour from rose-pink, white tinged pink, pale lavender-rose to intense violet with yellowish-green or olive-green or brown spots. Hupeh, Szechwan, Yunnan, S. Tibet, 4,300–13,000 ft. B.M. 8479. Much has been written of the different blue colour forms and of their degrees of hardiness. There are bluish forms with almost red stamens, purplish-blue forms with purple stamens and with a darker purplish blotch, and pale blue forms with a green throat and light coloured stamens. The majority of these are considered to be quite hardy in most parts of Britain. Possibly the form raised at Caerhays, Cornwall has the largest flowers with the colour most closely approaching a true pure blue. This form is considered to be less hardy and usually loses its buds in winter. Mr. Lionel de Rothschild at Exbury, and Mr. J. B. Stevenson at Tower Court, Ascot, raised seedlings from intercrossing different colour forms of *R. augustinii* to produce strains combining the richer blue of the supposedly more tender forms with the hardiness of those bearing flowers of the paler, rosy-lilac shades. Several of the best form of these strains, unquestionably hardy, are to be found in some gardens in Britain, notably in the Great Park at Windsor.

At the same time it has been observed that one individual plant may vary considerably in flower colour from year to year.

A.M. 1926 (Dame Alice Godman, Horsham, Sussex).

A.G.M. 1924.

'Marine' is a clone of *R. augustinii* raised by R. M. Bovee, Oswego, Oregon (P.A., A.R.S.).

R. augustinii
(continued)

R. augustinii is a parent of the A.M. clones 'Electra' (1940), 'Eleanore' (1943), 'Bluebird' (1943), 'Blue Diamond' (1935; F.C.C. 1939).

Var. *chasmanthum* (with gaping flowers) H³ F²⁻³ L¹⁻² Pm. is the plant for long known as *R. chasmanthum*. Fls. varying greatly in colour from pale lavender-rose with olive markings to deep intense violet. Yunnan, S.E. Tibet, 10,000 ft.
A.M. 1930 (L. de Rothschild, Exbury).
F.C.C. 1932 (L. de Rothschild, Exbury).
It is a parent of the A.M. cultivar 'Electra' (1940).

Var. *rubrum* H⁴ F²⁻³ L¹⁻² Pm. *March–April* has for long been in cultivation under the number *Forrest* 25914 from Yunnan. It is more compact in habit than *R. augustinii* and has red flowers normally fully open whilst those of *augustinii* are still in bud.

R. auriculatum
eared; referring to the lobes at the base of the leaves)
H⁴ F²⁻³ L²⁻⁴ Pm.–t.
July–Aug.

s. Auriculatum.
A large shrub or tree up to 20 ft. or more. Lvs. up to 12 in. long, 4 in. broad, oblong, oblong-lanceolate, oblong-oblanceolate, rounded and auricled at the base, dark green above, pale green below. Fls. in loose trusses of 7–15, up to 4 ins. long, funnel-shaped, usually white, but sometimes rose-pink, splashed greenish at the base, sweetly scented. Hupeh, 5–7,000 ft. Many plants in cultivation have an unhealthy yellowish-green look. Flowers easily damaged by inclement weather. Very remarkable for its late period of growth and flowering.
A.M. 1922 (Lord Aberconway, Bodnant).
It is a parent of the following A.M. clones: 'Argosy Snow White' (1938), 'Aladdin' (1935), 'Lady Catherine' (1936), 'Blanc-mange' (1947), 'Clotted Cream' (1942), 'Leonore' (1948), 'Wonderland' (1958). 'Polar Bear' is an F.C.C. clone (1946) of *auriculatum × diaprepes*.

R. auritum
(with long ears)
H²⁻³ F²⁻³ L¹⁻² Pd.
April

s. Boothii. *s.s.* Tephropeplum.
Shrub up to 5 ft. Lvs. 1–2½ in. long, elliptic to lanceolate. Fls. in clusters of 4–7, about 1 in. long, tubular-campanulate, pale yellow slightly touched with pink on the lobes, or sulphur-yellow, sepals sharply reflexed. Foliage similar to that of *R. xanthostephanum* but darker; it grows more sturdily and is hardier but the flowers are not so good a yellow. S.E. Tibet, 8,000 ft.
A.M. 1931 (L. de Rothschild, Exbury).

49

R. austrinum
(*southern*)
H³ F²⁻³ L¹⁻² Pm.

May

s. Azalea. *s.s.* Luteum.
Shrub up to 9 ft. Lvs. deciduous, up to 3½ in long, elliptic to oblong or oblong-obovate. Fls opening before or with the leaves, in clusters of 8–15, about 1½ in. across, tubular-funnel shaped cream-yellow, through golden-yellow to shades of orange, carrot-red, apricot, usually with reverse of petal striped with orange-red to purplish with tube of the same colour. The occasional pure yellow limb and tube may suggest the original type before interbreeding with *R. canescens*. Flowers occasionally double. N. Florida and the Georgia–Alabama coastal plain to S.E. Mississippi.

R. baileyi
(After Lt.-Col. F. M. Bailey, traveller in Tibet)
H³⁻⁴ F²⁻³ L¹ Pd.–m.

May

s. Lepidotum. *s.s.* Baileyi.
Shrub, often scraggy, up to 6 ft. Lvs. ¾–2¾ in. long, oblong-oval, elliptic to obovate, covered below with cinnamon or rust coloured scales. Fls. in clusters of 5–9, sometimes up to 18, up to 1¼ in. wide, rotate, scaly without, reddish-purple or deep purple with or without darker spots, style short and sharply bent. S.E. Tibet, Bhutan, 10–14,000 ft. B.M. 8942.
A.M. 1960 (A. C. and J. F. A. Gibson, Glenarn, Rhu, Dunbartonshire).

R. bainbridgeanum
(After Mr. Bainbridge, a friend of George Forrest)
H⁴ F²⁻³ L¹⁻² Pm.

April

s. Barbatum. *s.s.* Crinigerum.
Shrub up to 6 ft. Lvs. up to 5 in. long, oblong-oblanceolate, obovate to elliptic, thinly felted below with grey to tawny indumentum. Fls. 6–8 per truss, about 1½ in. long, campanulate, white or creamy-yellow sometimes flushed with pale or deep rose, blotched with crimson and more or less spotted. S.E. Tibet, 10–13,000 ft. Good forms are very beautiful.

R. bakeri
(After Dr. W. F. Baker, Amory University, U.S.A.)
H⁴ F²⁻³ L¹⁻² Pd.–m.

June

s. Azalea. *s.s.* Luteum.
Shrub usually 2–4 ft. but reaching 9 ft. with certain forms only 6 in. high. Lvs. 1½–2 ins. long, obovate, deep green above, rather glaucous below. Fls. in clusters of 4–7, 1¼–1¾ in. across, tubular-funnel-shaped, usually orange to reddish-orange and red but there are also salmon, salmon-apricot and clear straw-yellow forms. Occasional hybrids with *R. arborescens* occur in clear yellows and pinks. Blooms 2–3 weeks after *R. calendulaceum*. *R. cumberlandense* apparently is identical. Cumberland Plateau from Kentucky, south across Tennessee to mountains of N. Georgia and Alabama.

R. balfourianum

(After Sir Isaac B. Balfour, Regius Professor of Botany, Edinburgh; 1853-1922)

H⁴ F¹⁻² L¹⁻² Pm.

April–May

s. Taliense. s.s. Adenogynum.

Shrub up to 8 ft. Lvs. up to 4 in. long, thick, narrow-ovate to oblong, lower surface with pale-cinnamon or fawn semi-agglutinate silky indumentum. Fls. 1¾-2 in. long, funnel-campanulate, pale rose with crimson markings. Yunnan and Szechwan, 11–12,000 ft. A very shy flowerer but worth growing as a foliage plant. A form with a spongy indumentum is known as var. *aganniphoides*.

R. barbatum

(*bearded*)

H³⁻⁴ F³⁻⁴ L²⁻³ Pt.

March

s. and s.s. Barbatum.

Tree up to 30 ft. Lvs. up to 8 in. long and 3 in. broad, elliptic-lanceolate, lower surface lacking indumentum. Fls. in round compact trusses, up to 2 in. long, tubular-campanulate, bright scarlet. Normally branchlets and leaf-stalks clad with long bristles, though there is a bristleless form. The bark is very beautiful, thin, smooth and reddish-plum coloured. Very closely akin to *R. smithii* but differing in the absence of indumentum on the lower surface of the leaves. Nepal, Sikkim, Bhutan, 10,000 ft.

A.M. 1954 (C. Armytage Moore, Winterfold House, Cranleigh, Surrey).

R. barbatum is a parent of the following A.M. clones:

'Duke of Cornwall' (1907), 'Trelawny' (1936), 'Weirei' (1921), 'Fireball' (1925), 'Titness Park' (1954), 'John Holms' (1957), 'Duchess of Portland' (1903), 'Alix' (1935), 'Kernick Gem' (1928), 'Shilsonii' (1900), 'Tittenhurst' (1933).

R. basilicum

(*royal*)

H³⁻⁴ F²⁻³ L²⁻³ Pt.

April

s. Falconeri.

Tree up to 30 ft. Lvs. up to over 12 in. long and 6 in. broad, broadly ovate to oblanceolate, lower surface deep cinnamon to fawn-grey. Distinguished from *arizelum* by wings to petioles of leaves. Fls. up to 25 in large truss, about 1½ in. long, broadly campanulate, fleshy, pale yellow or creamy-white or tinted crimson, sometimes pink, with crimson blotch. Beautiful young growths at first covered with a rufous tomentum, later grey. Yunnan, N.E. Upper Burma, 10–11,000 ft.

A.M. 1956 (Col. The Lord Digby, Minterne, Dorchester, under *Forrest* 24139).

R. bathyphyllum

(*thickly leafy in allusion to density of foliage*)

H⁴ F¹⁻² L²⁻³ Pm.

April–May

s. Taliense. s.s. Roxieanum.

Shrub up to 5 ft. Lvs. up to 3 in. long and 1 in. broad, thick, leathery, oblong, margin revolute, lower surface with bright rust coloured indumentum. Fls. up to 12 per truss, 1½-2 in. long, campanulate, white with copious crimson spots. S.E. Tibet, Yunnan, Szechwan, 11–13,000 ft.

R. bauhiniiflorum
(with Bauhinia-like flowers)
H³⁻⁴ F¹⁻³ L¹ Pm.

May–June

s. and *s.s.* Triflorum.

Shrub up to 9 ft. with fine reddish-brown bark. Lvs. 1½–2½ in. long, oblong-lanceolate or ovate-lanceolate. Fls. in clusters of 2–3, up to 1¾ in. across, flat saucer-shaped, zygomorphic, lemon-yellow or almost green with or without brown or green spots. Closely allied to *R. triflorum*. Assam, 8–9,500 ft.

R. beanianum
(After W. J. Bean, former Curator, Royal Botanic Gardens, Kew; 1863–1947)
H³⁻⁴ F¹⁻³ L2–3 Pm.s.

April–May

s. Neriiflorum. *s.s.* Haematodes.

Small rather straggling shrub up to 8 ft. with bristly stems. Lvs. up to 4 in. long and 1½ in. broad, oblong-elliptic to oblong, with rich red-brown, woolly indumentum below. Fls. in trusses of 6–10, up to 1½ in. long, tubular-campanulate, scarlet, crimson, or, much inferior, pink. S.E. Tibet, Assam, 9–11,000 ft. B.M. 219 (N.S.).

A.M. 1953 (Col. The Lord Digby, Cerne Abbey, Dorchester, under *K.W.* 6805).

A form with bristleless branches and petioles, less straggly habit and leaves shining above is known as var. *compactum*.

R. beyerinckianum
(After Prof. M. W. Beijerinck)
H¹ F²⁻³ L¹⁻² Pm.s.

April

sect. Vireya. *s.sect.* Phaeovireya of Sleumer.

Straggling shrub up to 9 ft. with young growths tawny. Lvs. up to 2 in. long, elliptic to elliptic-obovate, when young covered with tawny hairs and scales, when mature almost glabrous, dark green above with main nerves impressed, paler and with tawny scales below. Fls. in clusters of 1–5, up to 1½–2 in. long, tubular with spreading lobes, pale rose to scarlet. New Guinea.

R. blepharocalyx
(with fringed calyx)
H⁴ F¹⁻² L¹⁻² Pd.

April–May

s. Lapponicum.

Shrub up to 3 ft. Lvs. about ½ in. long, narrowly oblong-elliptic, densely covered below with pale yellowish-green scales. Fls. in terminal clusters of 3–4, ⅓ in. long, widely funnel-shaped, mauve or rose. Yunnan and Szechwan, 11–14,000 ft.

R. bodinieri
(After Emile Bodinier, French missionary in China; 1824–1901)
H³⁻⁴ F²⁻³ L¹⁻² Pm.

March–April

s. Triflorum. *s.s.* Yunnanense.

Shrub up to 8 ft. Lvs. nearly 3 in. long, lanceolate, apex long-acuminate. Fls. in clusters of 5–8 terminal or axillary in the uppermost leaves, about 1½ in. long, widely funnel-shaped, zygomorphic, rose coloured spotted with purple. Yunnan. Closely related to *R. yunnanense*, differing only in the long-acuminate leaf apex.

R. boothii
(After T. J. Booth, who collected in Bhutan, about 1850)

H¹ F²⁻³ L¹⁻² Pd.–m.s.

April–May

s. and s.s. Boothii.

Shrub, often epiphytic and straggling up to 6 ft. or more, with young branchlets yellow-tomentose. Lvs. 4–5 in. long, ovate to ovate-elliptic, glaucous below. Fls. in clusters of 7–10, 1¼ in. long, broadly bell-shaped with 5 spreading lobes, bright lemon-yellow, unspotted. Bhutan, Assam, 5–8,000 ft. B.M. 7149. Essentially a plant for the cool house. Closely akin to *R. mishmiense* but with more flowers to the truss.

R. boothii is a parent (*R. lepidotum* the other) of the A.M. clone 'Lepidoboothii'.

R. brachyanthum
(*with short flowers*)

H⁴ F¹⁻³ L¹⁻² Pd.

June–July

s. and s.s. Glaucophyllum.

Spreading shrub up to 3 ft. Lvs. up to 2½ in. long, oblong-lanceolate to obovate, glaucous and slightly scaly below. Fls. in trusses of 3–10, about ¾ in. long, broadly campanulate, pale yellow or greenish-yellow, calyx large and leafy, hiding the capsules. Yunnan, S.E. Tibet, 9–11,000 ft. B.M. 8750.

Var. *hypolepidotum* is a form of *R. brachyanthum* with the under surface of the leaves more densely scaly. Yunnan, S.E. Tibet, Burma, 10–14,000 ft. B.M. 9259.

'Blue Light' is an A.M. clone of *R. brachyanthum* var. *hypolepidotum* (Commissioners of Crown Lands, Windsor, 1951).

R. brachycarpum
(*short-fruited*)

H⁴ F²⁻³ L¹⁻² Pm.

June–July

s. Ponticum. *s.s.* Caucasicum.

Shrub up to 10 ft. with young shoots white tomentose and one year old shoots bright green. Lvs. up to 6 in. long and 3 in. broad, oblong to oblong-obovate, with thin felty pale fawn or brownish indumentum below. Fls. 10–20 in elongate truss, up to 1½ in. long, broadly funnel-shaped, creamy-white, sometimes pale yellow, flushed with pink, green spotted. N. & C. Japan. B.M. 7881.

R. brachysiphon
(*short-tubed*)

H¹⁻² F²⁻³ L²⁻³ Pm.

June–July

s. and s.s. Maddenii.

Shrub up to 8 ft. Lvs. up to 6 in. long and 2 in. broad, obovate or elliptic, reticulate above, densely covered with rusty scales below. Fls. in trusses of 2–3, up to 2 in. long, tubular-funnel-shaped, pink, scented. Bhutan, 6–7,000 ft.

R. bracteatum
(*furnished with bracts*)

H⁴ F¹⁻² L¹⁻² Pm.

June

s. Heliolepis.

Shrub up to 6 ft. Lvs. about 2 in. long and up to 1 in. broad, ovate-elliptic, densely scaly below. Fls. in clusters of 3–6, ¾ in. long, campanulate, scaly on the outside, white sometimes tinged pink, with crimson blotch and spots. Szechwan, 7–10,000 ft. B.M. 9031.

R. brevistylum
(*with a short style*)
H⁴ F²⁻³ L¹⁻² Pm.

Late June–July

s. Heliolepis.
Shrub up to 10 ft. Lvs. about 4 in. long and 2 in. broad, elliptic-lanceolate, reticulate above, laxly scaly below. Fls. in trusses of 4–5, 1½ in. long, widely funnel-shaped, pale to deep rose with crimson markings. Yunnan, S.E. Tibet, 11–12,000 ft. B.M. 8898.

R. brookeanum
(After Sir James Brooke, Rajah of Sarawak)
H¹ F³⁻⁴ L¹⁻² Pm.s.

April–May

sect. Vireya. *s.sect.* Euvireya of Sleumer.
Straggling epiphytic shrub. Lvs. 6–9 in. long oblong-lanceolate. Fls. in trusses of 6–14, 1½–2 in. long, tubular-funnel-shaped, orange, orange-yellow or orange-red. Borneo. B.M. 4935. F.C.C. 1869 to form with clear yellow Fls. (J. Veitch).

R. brunneifolium
(*with brown leaves*)

see *R. eudoxum* subsp. *brunneifolium*.

R. bullatum
(*puckered, referring to the upper surface of the leaves*)
H²⁻⁴ F²⁻⁴ L³⁻⁴ Pm.s.

April–May

s. Edgeworthii.
Straggling shrub up to 8 ft. with densely and softly woolly branchlets. Lvs. up to 5 in. long and 2 in. broad, ovate-elliptic, dark green and bullate above, fawn to brown woolly-tomentose below. Fls. 2–5 per truss, 2½ in. long, up to 4 in. diam., widely funnel-shaped, white or white tinged pink, very sweetly scented, calyx large and leafy up to ⅔ in. long, often stained with red. Yunnan, S.E. Tibet, N.E. Upper Burma, 9–13,000 ft. The Chinese equivalent of *R. edgeworthii* with which H. H. Davidian in The Rhododendron and Camellia Year Book, 1964 has suggested it should be merged.
A.M. 1923 (T. H. Lowinsky, Sunninghill) to the white form, under number *Farrer* 842.
A.M. 1946 (Lord Aberconway, Bodnant) to the form blush-pink flushed externally with rose.
F.C.C. 1937 (L. de Rothschild, Exbury) to the white form.
R. bullatum is a parent of the A.M. clones 'White Wings' (1939) and 'Bulbul' (1934).

R. bureavii
(After Edouard Bureau, French Professor; 1830–1918)
H⁴ F²⁻³ L³⁻⁴ Pm.

April–May

s. Taliense. *s.s.* Adenogynum.
Shrub up to 8 ft. with young branchlets clad with a thick rusty-red indumentum. Lvs. thick and leathery, up to 5 in. long and 2 in. broad, ovate or broadly elliptic, under surface clothed with thick bright rusty-red woolly indumentum. Fls. 10–15 in a compact truss, up to 2 in. long, tubular-campanulate, white or rose with crimson markings, 5-lobed calyx about ½ in. long. Yunnan, 11–13,000 ft. One of the finest foliage plants in the Taliense series.
A.M. 1939 (L. de Rothschild, Exbury).

R. bureavii
(continued)

A form of *R. bureavii* with larger leaves and flowers from Szechwan is known as *bureavioides* (*resembling R. bureavii*).

R. burmanicum
(from Burma)
H1–3 F3–4 L1–2 Pd.–m.

April–May

s. Maddenii. s.s. Ciliicalyx.

Shrub up to 6 ft. or more. Lvs. up to 3 in. long, oblanceolate to obovate, densely scaly both above and below. Fls. in trusses of 5–6, up to 1½ in. long, campanulate, yellow, greenish-yellow or greenish-white, sweetly scented. Burma, 9,500 ft.

P.C. 1960 (E. H. M. and P. A. Cox, Glendoick, Perth).

R. burmanicum is a parent of the following A. M. clones: 'Chrysomanicum' (1947), 'Alcesta' (1935), 'Spinbur' (1957), 'Saffron Queen' (1948).

R. caeruleum
(blue)

see *R. rigidum*.

R. caesium
(dullish blue alluding to the lower leaf surface)
H4 F1–2 L1–2 Pm.

May

s. Trichocladum.

Shrub up to 4 ft. with pale brown shining bark. Lvs. 1½–2 in. long, elliptic to oblong-elliptic to oblong-lanceolate, strongly and pleasantly aromatic, bluish-grey and scaly below. Fls. usually in clusters of 3, about ¾ in. long, widely funnel-campanulate, greenish-yellow, with sap-green markings within, scaly without. Yunnan 8–10,000 ft. Described from living plant grown by L. de Rothschild, Exbury, from seeds of *Forrest* 26798.

R. calendulaceum
(like a marigold)
H4 F2–4 L1–2 Pm.

May–June

s. Azalea. s.s. Luteum.

Shrub up to 15 ft. Lvs. up to 3½ in. long, broadly elliptic to elliptic-oblong to obovate-oblong, turning orange and crimson in autumn. Fls. in trusses of 5–7, about 2 in. in diameter, funnel-shaped, in a remarkable range of colour, yellow to orange or scarlet, sometimes partly salmon-pink with orange blotch; orange-red and red forms usually from higher elevations and later flowering. E. North America. B.M. 1721 (var. *croceum*), 2143 (var. *flammeum*), 3439 (var. *fulgidum*).

R. callimorphum
(lovely-shaped)
H4 F3–4 L2–3 Pm.

April–May

s. Thomsonii. s.s. Campylocarpum.

Shrub up to 9 ft. Lvs. 1½–3 in. long, orbicular to broadly elliptic or ovate, dark glossy green above, glaucous below. Fls. in trusses of 5–8, 1½–2 in. long, openly campanulate, deep rose in bud, soft or deep rose when fully open with or without a basal crimson blotch. Yunnan, N.E. Burma, 9–11,000 ft. B.M. 8789. The best forms are extremely beautiful.

R. calophytum
(*beautiful plant*)
H⁴ F²⁻⁴ L²⁻⁴ Pt.

March–April

s. Fortunei. *s.s.* Calophytum.

Tree up to 30 ft. Lvs. up to 15 in. long, 5 in broad, oblong-lanceolate or elongate-lanceolate very striking. Fls. in large loose, flat-topped trusses of 15–30, about 1–2 ins. long, 1½ in. broad, 5–, lobed, open-campanulate, rosy-white, or pale lilac or pink with deep basal blotch and spotted Szechwan, 7–10,000 ft. B.M. 9173. A.M. (G Reuthe, Keston, 1920), to form with white flower heavily flushed with pink. F.C.C. (Dame Alice Godman, South Lodge, Horsham, 1933) to a pale pink form. A parent to the A.M. clones 'Androcles (1948), 'Titness Park' (1954), 'Amalfi' (1939) 'Exbury Calstocker' (1948), 'Calfort' (1932) 'Wayford' (1957), 'Jocelyne' (1954), 'Avalanche (1934), 'Alpine Glow' (1938), 'Our Kate' (1963) 'Avalanche' received the F.C.C. in 1938 and 'Jocelyne' in 1956.

R. calostrotum
(*with a beautiful covering*)
H⁴ F²⁻⁴ L¹⁻² Pd.

May–June

s. Saluenense.

Small shrub up to 4 ft. Lvs. up to 1 in. long ½ in. broad, broadly obovate-elliptic, with green scales above and with numerous pale red o brownish flaky scales below. Fls. in cluster o 1–3, occasionally of 5, about 1 in. long, saucer shaped or rotate, bright rosy-purple or rich purple-crimson with crimson spots, softly pubes cent outside. N.E. Upper Burma, Yunnan, S.E Tibet, Assam, 12–13,000 ft. B.M. 9001. Frequently producing a second flush of flowers.

A form with smaller leaves, up to ½ in. long and with pink flowers, from Upper Burma and Yunnan is known as var. *calciphilum*.

A.M. 1935 (Lt.-Col. L. C. R. Messel, Nymans Handcross, Sussex) to form with deep rosy-mauve to magenta flowers.

R. caloxanthum
(*of a beautiful yellow*)
H³⁻⁴ F²⁻³ L²⁻³ Pm.

April–May

s. Thomsonii. *s.s.* Campylocarpum.

Very free flowering shrub up to 6 ft. Lvs 1½–3 in. long, orbicular, ovate or broadly elliptic dark green above, pale glaucous-green below. Fls in trusses of 4–9, 1–1¾ in. long, campanulate, citron or sulphur-yellow, often tinged pink, orange scarlet in bud. Burma, Tibet, Yunnan, 11–13,000 ft

A.M. 1934 (L. de Rothschild, Exbury) to form with pink flower buds opening to a deep yellow suffused with red.

R. camelliaeflorum
(*with Camellia-like flowers*)
H¹⁻² F¹⁻² L¹⁻² Pm.s.

June–July

s. Camelliaeflorum.

Shrub, usually straggling, up to 6 ft. Lvs. up to 3½ in. long, and 1½ in. broad, narrowly oblong lanceolate, densely scaly below. Fls. 1–3 to the cluster, up to 2 in. diam. campanulate or some

R. camelliaeflorum
(continued)

what rotate, white or white tinged pink or deep rose. Sikkim, Bhutan, 9–11,000 ft. B.M. 4932.

R. campanulatum
(bell-shaped)
H4 F1–4 L2–4 Pm.–t.

April–May

s. Campanulatum.

Very variable shrub up to 18 ft. or more, sometimes tree-like and one of the most common rhododendrons of the Himalayan forests. Lvs. 2–6 in. long, elliptic, oblong-elliptic, to obovate, when unfolding loosely tomentose above, lower surface with thin or thick, felted or woolly, fawn to rusty-brown indumentum sometimes almost glabrous. Fls. in trusses of 6–12, 1–2 in. long, broadly campanulate, sometimes of thin, sometimes of thick texture, in various shades of purple, rosy-white or white, spotted. Kashmir to Bhutan, 9–14,000 ft. B.M. 3759. The bluest forms are regarded as the best; 'Knaphill' is one such. A.M. 1925 (L. de Rothschild, Exbury).

In the form known as var. *aeruginosum* (L4) the young foliage is a metallic silver-green later deepening to a striking soft blue.

R. campbelliae
(After the wife of Dr. Campbell, co-traveller with Hooker in the Himalaya)

see *R. arboreum*.

R. campylocarpum
(with bent fruits)
H3–4 F3–4 L1–2 Pm.

April–May

s. Thomsonii. s.s. Campylocarpum.

A very floriferous shrub up to 12 ft. Lvs. 1½–4 in. long, ovate to shortly elliptic, dark glossy green above, pale glaucous-green below. Fls. in clusters of 6–10, about 1½ in. long, campanulate, canary-yellow with or without basal blotching, pale yellow (or even pink or ivory-white). Nepal, Sikkim, Bhutan, Assam, Tibet, 10–14,000 ft.

F.C.C. 1892 (Messrs. Veitch & Sons, Chelsea).

R. campylocarpum should be in every collection of rhododendrons for it is certainly one of the best yellows for general planting. The type originally introduced by Hooker is a small shrub with clear yellow flowers. The type in common cultivation is a looser growing taller form with orange-vermilion buds, a more pronounced crimson blotch and fewer hairs on the leaf petiole. It is necessary from the point of view of the Stud Book to differentiate between these two forms. In the progeny of the first the pale yellow colour is dominant, and the second throws pink or ivory-whites as well as yellows. The taller form is known as var. *elatum* (B.M. 4968).

R. campylocarpum is a parent of the following A.M. clones:

57

R. campylocarpum
(continued)

'Leonardslee Primrose' (1933), 'Goldsworth Yellow' (1925), 'A. Gilbert' (1925), 'Gladys' (1926), 'Gladys Rose' (1950), 'Logan Damaris' (1948), 'Gilian' (1923), 'Cremorne' (1947), 'Townhill Cremorne' (1947), 'Zuyder Zee' (1936), 'Jersey Cream' (1939), 'Carita' (1945), 'Exminster' (1923), 'Embley Park' (1936), 'Mrs. W. C. Slocock' (1929), 'Penjerrick' (1923).

'Marcia' (1944), 'Lady Bessborough' (1933), 'Roberte' (1936) and 'Letty Edwards' (1948) are F.C.C. clones.

R. campylogynum
(with bent ovary)
H³⁻⁴ F²⁻³ L²⁻³ Pᵈ.

May–June

s. Campylogynum.
Dwarf somewhat spreading shrub 2 in. to 1½ ft. high. Lvs. ½ to 1 in. long, obovate to oblanceolate, usually glaucous beneath. Fls. 1–3 rarely up to 5 in a cluster, ¾ in. long, campanulate, nodding on long flower-stalks, very variable in colour from pale rose-purple or salmon-pink to almost black-purple. An admirable plant for the rock garden. Yunnan, S.E. Tibet, W. Burma, 9–14,000 ft. B.M. 9407A.

A form with smaller flowers, about ½ in. long, from Burma, Tibet, Yunnan is known as var. *myrtilloides* (F³); A.M. 1925 (L. de Rothschild, Exbury); F.C.C. 1943 (E. de Rothschild, Exbury). A form with larger flowers, about 1 in. long, from N.E. Upper Burma is known as var. *charopoeum.*

A form growing much taller than the type, up to 4 ft., from Yunnan, is known as var. *celsum*

A form with the habit of an erect shrub, about 2 ft. high, and with leaves pale green on both surfaces, from Yunnan, is known as var. *cremastum*

R. camtschaticum
(from Kamtschatka)
H⁴ F²⁻³ L¹⁻² Pᵈ.

May

s. Camtschaticum.
Deciduous dwarf shrub up to 1 ft. Lvs. up to 2 in. long, obovate to spathulate-obovate, margin clad with setose hairs. Fls. 1–2 at ends of branchlets, about 1½ in. diam. rotate, reddish-purple spotted within; calyx leafy. Alaska; Bering Straits shores of Okhotsk Sea to N. Japan. It has not proved an easy plant to cultivate in many gardens.

R. canadense
(from Canada)
H⁴ F¹ L¹ Pᵈ.

April

s. Azalea. s.s. Canadense.
Small deciduous shrub up to 3 ft. Lvs. almost 2¼ in. long, usually shorter, elliptic to oblong, dull bluish-green above. Fls. in clusters of 3–6 appearing before the leaves, about ¾ in. long rotate to campanulate, rose-purple, rarely white 2-lipped, the lower divided almost to the base

R. canadense
(*continued*)

N.E. America. The most northern species of the Azalea series. In cultivation thrives in moist situations. B.M. 474.

R. canescens
(*hoary*)
H⁴ F¹⁻² L¹⁻² Pᵐ.

April–May

s. Azalea. s.s. Luteum.
Shrub up to 15 ft. Lvs. up to 3½ in. long, 1½ in. broad, oblong-obovate to oblanceolate or oblong, very hairy beneath except in the form *subglabrum* which is almost hairless. Fls. in clusters of 6–15 appearing with or before the leaves, up to 2 in. diam., tubular-funnel-shaped, with fragrance of honeysuckle, pure white or white flushed pink to pink or purplish with pink or reddish tube, which is covered with pin-head glandular hairs unlike its near relative the eglandular *R. nudiflorum*. N. Carolina to Florida and west to Texas. The so-called Florida Pinxter Azalea.

R. capitatum
(*with flowers in a head*)
H⁴ F¹⁻² L¹⁻² Pᵈ.

April–May

s. Lapponicum.
Shrub up to 3 ft. Lvs. up to 1 in. long, elliptic, densely scaly. Fls. in terminal clusters of 4–5, ½–¾ in. long, funnel-shaped, purple or mauve. Kansu.

R. carneum
(*flesh-coloured*)
H¹⁻² F²⁻³ L¹⁻² Pᵐ·ˢ·

April–May

s. Maddenii. s.s. Ciliicalyx.
Shrub up to 8 ft. Lvs. up to 5 in. long and 1½ in. broad, elliptic to obovate, deep green and reticulate above, glaucous and with yellow scales below. Fls. in trusses of 4–5, 2½–3 in. long, widely expanded to up to 4 in. diam., flesh pink or white faintly stained with pink, fragrant. Upper Burma, 7,500 ft. B.M. 8634.
A.M. 1927 (L. de Rothschild, Exbury).

R. carolinianum
(*from Carolina*)
H⁴ F²⁻³ L² Pᵐ.

May–June

s. Carolinianum.
Compact shrub up to 6 ft. Lvs. up to 3 in. long and 1½ in. broad, obovate-elliptic to elliptic, reticulate above, densely scaly below, Fls. in trusses of 4–10, 1 in. long, tubular, pale rosy-purple or pink, sometimes faintly spotted. S. United States.
A most attractive plant which, though very hardy, requires good drainage for successful cultivation. There is a form with narrower and more pointed leaves and with white flowers having a tan-yellow blotch, known as var. *album*.

R. catacosmum
(*adorned*)
H⁴ F²⁻³ L²⁻³ Pᵐ.

March–April

s. Neriiflorum. s.s. Haematodes.
Shrub up to 9 ft. with young growths clad with brownish or white wool. Lvs. 2½–4½ in. long, obovate, with pale or dark cinnamon thick woolly indumentum below. Fls. in lax trusses of 5–9,

59

3

R. catacosmum
(*continued*)

up to 2 in. long, broadly campanulate, crimson-rose, deep crimson or scarlet with calyx large and petaloid, almost 1 in. long. S.E. Tibet and N. to Yunnan, 13–14,000 ft. A most desirable species.

R. catawbiense
(*from the Catawba river, North Carolina*)
H⁴ F¹⁻² L¹⁻² Pm.–t.

June

s. and s.s. Ponticum.

Shrub up to 15 ft. Lvs. 3–6 in. long and up to 2 in. broad, oblong-ovate to oval. Fls. in trusses of 15–20, about 1½–2 in. long, funnel-campanulate, lilac-purple, reddish-purple, pink or white, with yellow-green spots. Alleghany Mountains, 6,000 ft. B.M. 1671.

In Virginia there is a good albino form (F²). Its chief merit is its extreme hardiness for it will stand 60 degrees of frost.

It is the parent of many of the Waterer hybrids as well as of the F.C.C. clone 'Manglesii' (1885).

R. caucasicum
(*from the Caucasus*)
H⁴ F¹⁻² L¹⁻² Pm.

May

s. Ponticum. *s.s.* Caucasicum.

Shrub up to 10 ft. Lvs. 2–4 in. long, ovate, obovate or oblong, with thin fawn to pale rust indumentum below. Fls. in a many-flowered candelabroid truss, up to 1½ in. long, broadly campanulate, yellowish, creamy-white or tinted rose, spotted within. Caucasus and N.E. Turkey, 6–9,000 ft. B.M. 1145.

'Cunningham's Sulphur' is probably merely a form of *R. caucasicum* which is a parent of the following A.M. clones: 'Goldsworth Yellow' (1925), 'Dr. Stocker' (1900), as well as of the hybrid × *nobleanum*, which received the A.G.M. in 1926.

R. cephalanthum
(*with flowers in a head*)
H⁴ F²⁻³ L¹⁻² Pd.

May

s. Anthopogon.

Shrub up to 4 ft. with persistent leaf bud scales. Lvs. ½–1½ in. long, oblong-elliptic to broadly oblong, impressed-reticulate above, densely covered with several layers of flaky scales below. Fls. in a dense capitate truss, ½–¾ in. long, tubular, white. Yunnan, Szechwan, S.E. Tibet, Upper Burma, 9–15,000 ft. In the very dwarf form known as var. *crebreflorum* from Assam the flowers are pink (F³) and yellow in the form from Upper Burma known as var. *nmaiense*.

R. ceraceum
(*wax-like*)

see *R. lukiangense* subsp. *ceraceum*.

R. cerasinum
(*cherry-coloured*)
H⁴ F¹⁻³ L¹⁻² Pm.

May

s. Thomsonii. *s.s.* Cerasinum.

Shrub up to 12 ft. Lvs. 2–4 in. long, oblong to oblong-elliptic, sub-glaucous below. Fls. pendulous in trusses of 6–7, up to 2 in. long, bell shaped, cherry-red or brilliant scarlet, or creamy-white with broad cherry-red band round the edge

R. cerasinum
(*continued*)

of the lobes, with 5 basal deep purple pouched nectaries. Burma, Tibet, Assam, 10–12,000 ft. Unfortunately most forms tend to hide their flowers. B.M. 9538.

A.M. 1938 (Lt.-Col. L. C. R. Messel, Nymans, Sussex) to that form with bells creamy-white with a cherry-red band round the rim, which Kingdon Ward in the field called "Cherry Brandy" (*K.W.* 6923).

R. chaetomallum
(*with fleecy hair*)
H⁴ F²⁻³ L²⁻³ Pᵐ.

March–April

s. Neriiflorum. *s.s.* Haematodes.

Shrub up to 10 ft., the branchlets covered with bristly hairs. Lvs. up to 4 in. long and 2 in. broad, obovate or oblong-obovate, densely covered below with a thick, pale or dark brown, woolly indumentum. Fls. waxy, in trusses of 4–6, up to 2 in. long, tubular-campanulate, blood-red crimson or deep rose. S.E. Tibet, Yunnan, 11–13,000 ft. B.M. n.s. 25.

A.M. 1959 (E. de Rothschild, Exbury) to form with Turkey Red Fls. H.C.C. 721 from F. 25601.

R. chaetomallum is a variable plant and several forms have been named as follows:

Var. *chaemaephytum*, more or less prostrate, 1–2 ft. high, leaves glabrous beneath. S.E. Tibet, 13,000 ft.

Var. *glaucescens*, upper surface of leaf with a wax-like glaucous sheen. N.E. Upper Burma, 13,000 ft.

Var. *hemigymnum*, under surface of leaf with thin veil of hairs. S.E. Tibet, Upper Burma, 12–14,000 ft. A.M. 1957 (Mrs. R. M. Stevenson, Tower Court, Ascot) to form from F. 25605.

Var. *xanthanthum*, flowers creamy-yellow, flushed rose-pink or striped and margined pale rose. S.E. Tibet, 12–14,000 ft.

R. chamae-thomsonii
(*dwarf thomsonii*)
H⁴ F²⁻³ L¹⁻² Pᵈ.

March–April

s. Neriiflorum. *s.s.* Forrestii.

Shrub up to 3 ft. Lvs. 1½–3½ in. long, ovate to oblong-obovate, usually glabrous beneath. Fls. in trusses of 1–4, 1¼–2 in. long, tubular-campanulate, crimson, bright scarlet or rosy-crimson, sometimes orange-crimson, and occasionally white. Yunnan, S.E. Tibet.

A form from S.E. Tibet and Yunnan with smaller leaves has been named var. *chamaethauma*. This form received the A.M. in 1932 (Lady Aberconway and Hon. H. D. McLaren, Bodnant) under the name of R. *repens* var. *chamaedoxa*.

Sometimes confused with *R. forrestii* and its forms (q.v.).

R. chamaezelum
(*seeking the ground*)
H⁴ F¹⁻² L¹⁻² Pd.

April–May

s. Lapponicum.

A matted shrub up to 8 in. Lvs. $\frac{1}{4}$ in. long, elliptic, rusty-red-scaly below. Fls. single, $\frac{1}{2}$ in. long, openly funnel-shaped, pale yellow. N.W. Yunnan, 12,000 ft.

R. chameunum
(*lying on the ground*)
H⁴ F²⁻³ L¹⁻² Pd.

April–May

s. Saluenense.

Small upright shrub to 2 ft. with bristly branchlets. Lvs. $\frac{1}{4}$–1 in. long, elliptic to ovate-elliptic, pale brown-scaly below. Fls. in clusters of 1–6, 1 in. long, saucer shaped with a frilled edge, deep purple-rose or purple-crimson with crimson spots. Yunnan, Burma, Tibet, Szechwan, 11–12,000 ft.

Closely related to R. *prostratum* which is not of upright habit, but prostrate and creeping.

R. championae
(After Mrs. Champion, wife of its discoverer)
H¹ F²⁻³ L²⁻³ Pm.–t.

April–May

s. Stamineum.

Shrub or small tree up to 8 ft. with bristly branchlets. Lvs. 3–6 in. long, 1–2 in. broad, oblong-oblanceolate, loosely bristly below. Fls. 4–6 to the truss, 4 in. across, widely funnel-shaped, tube mostly white, spreading lobes heavily flushed with pink, or white the upper lip pale yellow in the centre, and copiously dotted with ochre; calyx lobes up to $\frac{1}{2}$ in. long. Kwangtung B.M. 4609.

R. chapmanii
(After A. W. Chapman, American botanist; 1809–99)
H⁴ F²⁻³ L¹⁻² Pm.

April–May

s. Carolinianum.

Rigid shrub up to 6 ft. Lvs. $\frac{3}{4}$–$2\frac{1}{2}$ in. long, oval, olive-green, scaly below. Fls. in dense truss, up to 2 in. long, broadly funnel-shaped, with crisped lobes, rose to clear pink, spotted greenish-brown on upper corolla limb, often with conspicuously chocolate-purple anthers. Heat tolerant and one of the most distinctive of the series. Similar in appearance and garden use to R. *carolinianum*. Sandy pine lands of W. Florida.

R. charianthum
(*with graceful flowers*)

see R. *davidsonianum*.

R. charitopes
(*graceful of aspect*)
H⁴ F²⁻³ L²⁻³ Pd.–m.

April–May

s. and s.s. Glaucophyllum.

A dense shrub up to 4 ft. Lvs. 1–$2\frac{1}{2}$ in. long, obovate, beautifully glaucous below and densely scaly. Fls. often in clusters of 3 but also from 2–6, up to 1 in. long, campanulate with spreading lobes, clear apple-blossom pink, speckled with crimson, with fairly long exserted stamens and a leafy

R. charitopes
(*continued*)

calyx up to $\frac{1}{2}$ in. long. Upper Burma, Yunnan, 10,500–14,000 ft. B.M. 9358.

Frequently flowers in the autumn as well as in April–May.

R. chasmanthum
(*with gaping flowers*)

see *R. augustinii* var. *chasmanthum*.

R. chionanthum
(*with snowy flowers*)
H4 F1–2 L2–3 Pd.

April

s. Neriiflorum. s.s. Haematodes.

Shrub of about 3 ft. Lvs. about $2\frac{1}{2}$ in. long, obovate to oblanceolate, clustered at ends of shoots, covered below with thick tawny, continuous or patchy woolly indumentum. Fls. in trusses of 4–6, $1\frac{1}{2}$ in. long, campanulate, white; calyx $\frac{1}{4}$–$\frac{1}{2}$ in. long, deeply cut into oblong-oval unequal lobes. Upper Burma. 13–14,000 ft.

R. chloranthum
(*with greenish flowers*)
H4 F1–2 L1–2 Pd.–m.

June

s. Trichocladum.

Deciduous shrub up to 7 ft. Lvs. about 1 in. long, obovate, long pilose on margins when young, scaly below. Fls. precocious in 4-flowered trusses, $\frac{3}{4}$ in. long, widely funnel-shaped, yellow, tinged green at base. Yunnan, S.E. Tibet, 11–12,000 ft.

R. chlorops
(*with green eye*)
H4 F2–3 L1–2 Pm.

May

s. and s.s. Fortunei.

Shrub up to 10 ft. Lvs. 3–5 in. long, up to 2 in. broad, oblong to oblong-elliptic, deep green above pale below. Fls. in lax cluster of 6–8, about $1\frac{1}{2}$ in. long, widely campanulate, cream to pale yellow, greenish within at the base and there blotched, some purple spotting, 7-lobed. Yunnan? Described from plants grown from seeds of *Forrest* 16463 (which in the Herbarium is an *Acer*) and cultivated in the Royal Botanic Garden, Edinburgh, and in Lord Stair's garden at Lochinch. Distinctive in the Fortunei series by reason of the yellowish flowers.

R. chrysanthemum
(*golden flowered*)

see *R. temenium* subsp. *chrysanthemum*.

R. chrysanthum
(*golden-flowered*)
H4 F1–2 L1–2 Pd.

May–June

s. Ponticum. s.s. Caucasicum.

Prostrate or semi-prostrate shrub up to 1 ft. Very slow growing. Lvs. up to 3 in. long, $1\frac{1}{2}$ in. broad, broadly oblanceolate or obovate, revolute at margin, dark green and with veins impressed above, pale green or fawn below. Fls. 5–8 to the truss, $1\frac{1}{4}$ in. long, widely campanulate, pale yellow, upper lobe more or less spotted. Siberian-Mongolian Mts. and Manchuria south to Japan. An erect growing form found in Japan is known as var. *niko-montanum*.

R. chryseum
(*golden yellow*)
H⁴ F²⁻³ L¹⁻² Pd.

April–May

s. Lapponicum.
Small alpine shrub up to 2 ft. Lvs. aromatic, ½ in. long, ⅓ in. broad, ovate-elliptic, densely scaly on both surfaces. Fls. in trusses of 4–5, ½ in. long, up to 1 in. across, widely funnel-shaped, bright yellow. Yunnan, S.E. Tibet, Szechwan, 12–14,000 ft. One of the best of the yellow Lapponicums and very pretty when planted among the pale lavender species of the series. B.M. 9246.
One of parents of A.M. 1962 clone 'Chikor'.

R. chrysodoron
(*golden gift—referring to his yellow-flowered plant being given to the Royal Botanic Garden, Edinburgh by Lord Stair*)
H² F²⁻³ L¹⁻² Pm.

s. and s.s. Boothii.
Shrub up to 5 ft. Lvs. 2–3 in. long, elliptic to oblong-elliptic, glaucous, and densely scaly below. Fls. in trusses of 3–6, up to 1½ in. long, widely bell-shaped, bright canary-yellow, unspotted; style bent; calyx small, fringed with white hairs. Yunnan, 6,500–8,500 ft. Akin to *R. sulfureum* but with much reduced calyx. B.M. 9442.
A.M. 1934 (Lord Aberconway, Bodnant).

R. chrysodoron is a parent of the A.M. clones, 'Chrysomanicum' (1947), 'R. W. Rye' (1951), 'Chrysaspis' (1942).

R. chrysolepis
(*with golden scales*)
H² F¹⁻³ L¹⁻² Pd.

June

s. Boothii. s.s. Tephropeplum.
Small, epiphytic shrub with deep red-brown peeling bark. Lvs. 2½–5 in. long, oblong-lance-olate, glaucous-purple and with golden scales below, bell-shaped, bright canary-yellow, with bands of scales outside; style long and straight; calyx a mere rim. Upper Burma 7–8,000 ft.; affinities with *R. chrysodoron*.

R. ciliatum
(*fringed*)
H³⁻⁴ F²⁻³ L¹⁻² Pd.–m.

March–April

s. Maddenii. s.s. Ciliicalyx.
Spreading, often procumbent shrub up to 6 ft. with peeling bark. Lvs. 1½–3½ in. long, up to 1½ ins. broad, elliptic to oblong-elliptic, setose above, fringed with long stiff hairs. Fls. in clusters of 2–4, up to 2 in. long, 2 in. wide, narrow-campanulate, nodding, white or pink tinged. Sikkim, S.E. Tibet, Bhutan, 9–11,000 ft. B.M. 4648 (var. *roseo-album*).
A.M. 1953 (Col. Lord Digby, Dorchester) to a form with the white flowers carrying a faint tinge of pink along the centre of each petal.

R. ciliatum is a parent of the following A.M. clones: 'Rosy Bell' (1894), 'Cilpinense' (1927), 'Delight' (1929), 'Racil' (1957); and of the following F.C.C. clones, 'Countess of Haddington' (1862), 'Princess Alice' (1862).

R. ciliatum
(continued)

R. × praecox (*ciliatum × dauricum*) received the A.G.M. in 1926.

R. ciliicalyx
(fringed calyx)
H$^{1-2}$ F$^{3-4}$ L$^{1-2}$ Pm.s.
March–April

s. Maddenii. s.s. Ciliicalyx.

Shrub, usually straggling, up to 10 ft. with beautiful smooth reddish-purple bark. Lvs. up to 3½ in. long and 1½ in. broad, elliptic, obovate-elliptic to oblong-oblanceolate, reticulate above, glaucous and scaly below. Fls. in trusses of 7–10, 4 in. diam., funnel-shaped, white or suffused with pale rose, especially when freshly opened, sweetly scented. Yunnan, Szechwan, S.E. Tibet, 7,500–9,000 ft. B.M. 7782.

A very floriferous and beautiful species when grown in a cool greenhouse.

A.M. 1923 (Oxford Botanic Garden).

R. ciliicalyx is a parent of the A.M. clones 'Harry Tagg' (1958) and 'White Wings' (1939).

R. cinnabarinum
(cinnabar-red)
H^4 F$^{3-4}$ L$^{2-3}$ Pm.–t.
April–June–July

s. Cinnabarinum.

Shrub up to 15 ft. with purplish young branchlets. Lvs. up to 3 in. long and 1¾ in. broad, obovate-elliptic to broadly oblanceolate, glaucous and scaly below. Fls. in trusses of about 5, up to 2 in. long, tubular, cinnabar-red, much like those of a *Lapageria*. Sikkim, Bhutan, S.E. Tibet, 10–12,000 ft. Very variable in the colour and shape of the flowers and distinct forms have been given the following names:

Var. *pallidum*; fls. widely funnel-campanulate, narrowed at the base and with spreading lobes, pale pinkish-purple. Nepal, Sikkim, Bhutan, 10–12,000 ft. B.M. 4788.

Var. *blandfordiaeflorum*; fls. tubular, red outside and yellow or apricot or greenish within. Nepal, Sikkim, 10–12,000 ft. B.M. 4930.

A.M. 1945 (Lord Aberconway, Bodnant).

Var. *roylei*; fls. more open and rather shorter, deeper plum-crimson. Bhutan, S.E. Tibet, 12,000 ft. 'Vin Rosé' is an A.M. clone (Commissioners of Crown Lands, Windsor, 1953).

'Magnificum' is a clone in which the flowers are exceptionally large.

Var. *aestivale*; fls. similar to type in shape, but appearing in July, cinnabar-red with pale yellow lobes and with narrow oblanceolate leaves.

Var. *purpurellum*; fls. short, bell-shaped, rich plum-purple or bright pinkish-mauve. S. Tibet, 10,000 ft. A.M. 1951 (C. Ingram), L.S. 6349.

R. cinnabarinum
(*continued*)

R. cinnabarinum is the parent of the following A.M. clones: 'Cinncrass' (1935), 'Cinnkeys' (1935), 'Minterne Cinnkeys' (1951), 'Cock of the Rock', (1932), 'Youthful Sin' (1960).

The following are F.C.C. clones: 'Minterne Cinnkeys' (1952), 'Bodnant Yellow' (1944).

Var. *blandfordiaflorum* is the parent of the F.C.C. clone 'Selig' (1937).

Var. *roylei* is the parent of the following A.M. clones: 'Biskra' (1940), 'Conroy' (1950), 'Cinnandrum Tangerine' (1937), 'Lady Rosebery' (1930), 'Revlon' (1957).

The following are F.C.C. clones: 'Lady Chamberlain' (1931), 'Exbury Lady Chamberlain' (1931), 'Golden Queen' (1947), 'Lady Rosebery' (1932).

R. citriniflorum
(*with lemon-yellow flowers*)
H⁴ F¹⁻³ L¹⁻² Pd.–m.

April–May

s. Neriiflorum. *s.s.* Sanguineum.

Shrub up to 4 ft. Lvs. up to 2½ in. long, 1 in. broad, obovate to oblong-obovate, densely covered with a thick, fawn or dark brown indumentum. Fls. in trusses of 4–6, up to 1½ in. long, bell-shaped, fleshy, yellow or yellow flushed with rose, shaded to orange at base; calyx nearly ½ in. long, crimson-yellow, fringed with hairs at margin of lobes. Yunnan, S.E. Tibet, 13–15,000 ft.

A form growing up to 6 ft., with tubular-campanulate fls. in trusses of 3–5, deep crimson or rose-crimson in colour is known as subsp. *horaeum* (H⁴ F¹⁻³ L¹⁻² Pm.; *April–May*). S.E. Tibet, 13,000 ft.

R. clementinae
(After Clementine, wife of George Forrest)
H⁴ F² L²⁻⁴ Pm.

April–May

s. and *s.s.* Taliense.

Shrub up to 10 ft. Lvs. up to 6 in. long, 3 in. broad, oval to oblong-oval, dark mat green above clad below with thick white to pale fawn felty indumentum. Fls. up to 15 to the truss, about 1½ in. long, funnel-campanulate, white, creamy-white, or white tinged rose to dark rose with deeper crimson markings. Yunnan, Szechwan, S.E. Tibet, 11–14,000 ft. A very beautiful foliage plant. B.M. 9392.

R. cloiophorum
(*wearing a collar*)

see *R. sanguineum* subsp. *cloiophorum*.

R. coelicum
(*heavenly*)
H⁴ F²⁻³ L²⁻³ Pm.–t.

April

s. Neriiflorum. *s.s.* Haematodes.

Shrub up to 15 ft. or occasionally a small stout tree. Lvs. about 3 in. long, 1½ in. broad, obovate lower surface with thick cinnamon-coloured indumentum. Fls. about 6–15 in compact rounded truss, about 1½ in. long, tubular-cam-

R. coelicum
(*continued*)

panulate, fleshy, bright scarlet or deep crimson. Yunnan, S.E. Tibet, Upper Burma, 12–14,000 ft.
A.M. 1955 (Col. The Lord Digby, Minterne, Dorchester).

R. collettianum
(After General Sir Henry Collett, 1836–1901)
H^3 F$^{1-2}$ L$^{1-2}$ Pm.

May

s. Anthopogon.
Shrub up to several feet, with very early deciduous leaf bud scales. Lvs. 1½–3 in. long, broadly lanceolate, covered below with hair-like scales. Fls. in many flowered capitate inflorescence, up to 1 in. long, narrowly tubular, white, tinged rose. Afghanistan and Indian Frontier, 10–13,000 ft. B.M. 7019.

R. compactum
(*compact*)
H^4 F$^{1-2}$ L$^{1-2}$ Pd.

April–May

s. Lapponicum.
Shrub up to 3 ft. with stiff erect branches. Lvs. about 1 in. long and ½ in. broad, oblong-lanceolate, scaly above and below. Fls. in a truss of 5–6, about ½ in. long, funnel-shaped, violet-mauve or purplish-mauve. Described from plant grown at Kells, County Meath, N. Ireland from seeds of *Forrest* 13905 probably collected in N.W. Yunnan.

R. complexum
(*interwoven*)
H^4 F$^{1-2}$ L$^{1-2}$ Pd.

April–May

s. Lapponicum.
Matted shrub up to 2 ft. Lvs. ¼ in. long, broadly elliptic, densely scaly on both surfaces. Fls. in trusses of 3, ½ in. long, open funnel-shaped, deep rosy-purple. Yunnan, 11–12,000 ft.

R. concatenans
(*linking together*)
H^4 F$^{2-3}$ L$^{2-3}$ Pm.

April–May

s. Cinnabarinum.
Shrub up to 8 ft. with the young shoots densely scaly and the branches reddish-brown. Lvs. 1½–2½ in. long, oblong or oblong-elliptic, glaucous and purple-tinged below and very scaly. Fls. in trusses of 7–8, 1½–2 in. long, 2 in. across the limb, campanulate with 5 half-spreading lobes, apricot or faintly tinged outside with pale purple or yellow, and conspicuously veined. S.E. Tibet, 10–12,000 ft.
A fine foliage plant in its bluish young growth closely allied to *R. cinnabarinum*.
F.C.C. 1935 (Lt.-Col. L. C. R. Messel, Nymans, Sussex).
'Copper' is an A.M. clone with the inside of the flowers Chinese Coral (H.C.C. 614/1) suffused with shades of red and orange and the outside a bright shade of red that deepens towards the base (Capt. Collingwood Ingram, Benenden, Kent, 1950, under the number L. and S. 6560 and under the name *R. cinnabarinum* 'Cuprea').

R. concinnoides
(like R. concinnum)
H³ F¹⁻² L¹⁻² Pm.

April–May

s. Triflorum. *s.s.* Yunnanense.

Shrub up to 10 ft. Lvs. 1–2 in. long, elliptic, or obovate-elliptic, densely covered with rich brown scales below. Fls. in terminal truss of 3, about 1 in. long, tubular-campanulate, pinkish-purple with darker spotting, fading to white at the base. Assam, where it is often epiphytic on conifers in the rhododendron forest, 8–11,000 ft.

An aberrant species in the Triflorum series by reason of its tubular-campanulate flowers. Flowers in the Triflorum series are usually zygomorphic and widely funnel-shaped. In some respects it approaches the species of the Tephropeplum subseries of the Boothii series.

R. concinnum
(neat)
H⁴ F¹⁻² L¹⁻² Pm.

April–May

s. Triflorum. *s.s.* Yunnanense.

Shrub up to 10 ft. Lvs. 1–3½ in. long, elliptic or obovate-elliptic, scaly on both surfaces. Fls. in clusters of 3–6, up to 1½ in. long, zygomorphic, widely funnel-shaped, pinkish-purple, pale or deep purple, deep rosy-purple, purplish-lavender or white, with or without brownish or crimson spots, usually scaly without. Szechwan, 5,000–14,600 ft. B.M. 8280 (as *R. coombense*), 8620, 8912 (as f. *laetevirens*).

Many plants in cultivation, said to have been raised from seeds of *R. concinnum* would appear to be natural hybrids.

In cultivation *R. concinnum* is very variable and 2 forms have been named as follows:

Var. *benthamianum* with lavender-purple flowers (H⁴ F¹⁻² L¹⁻² Pm.). Szechwan.

Var. *pseudoyanthinum* with ruby-red flowers. Szechwan, 7,500–12,000 ft. (H⁴ F²⁻³ L¹⁻² Pm.).
A.M. 1951 (R.H.S. Gardens, Wisley).

R. consanguineum
(related: i.e. to R. sanguineum)

see *R. sanguineum* subsp. *consanguineum*.

R. cookeianum
(After Mr. R. B. Cooke, V.M.H.)
H²⁻³ F²⁻³ L¹⁻² Pm.-t.

June–July

s. Irroratum. *s.s.* Parishii.

Shrub or tree up to 20 ft. Lvs. up to 6 in. long, up to 2½ in. broad, oblong-lanceolate or oblong-elliptic. Fls. in trusses of 8–15, up to 2 in. long, campanulate, white, pink or red-purple, with or without a crimson blotch at base. Szechwan, 12,000–13,500 ft. Still rare in cultivation.

R. coriaceum
(leathery)
H³⁻⁴ F²⁻³ L²⁻³ Pt.

April

s. Falconeri.

Tree up to 25 ft. with grey-white tomentose foliage buds. Lvs. up to 8 in. long, 2½ in. broad, narrow-elliptic, light green above, at first silvery

68

R. coriaceum
(*continued*)

below, later ash-grey to pale brown. Fls. 15–20 in lax trusses, 1½ in. long, funnel-campanulate, white or white flushed rose with crimson blotch, with or without crimson spots at back within. Yunnan, S.E. Tibet, Upper Burma, 10–13,000 ft. *Forrest 25872* and *Forrest 25622* appear to be the best forms.

'Morocco' is an A.M. clone (Commissioners of Crown Lands, Windsor, 1953) form with white flowers, crimson blotched and very little spotting.

R. coryanum
(After Reginald R. Cory, 1871–1934)
H4 F2–3 L1–2 Pm.–t.
April–May

s. Arboreum. s.s. Argyrophyllum.
Shrub up to 20 ft. Lvs. 3–7 in. long, up to 2 in. broad, narrow elliptic to oblong-oblanceolate, leathery, light green above, with thin pale cinnamon indumentum below. Fls. 20–30 in lax truss, 1½ in. long, funnel-campanulate, creamy-white, spotted with crimson. Yunnan, S.E. Tibet, 12–14,000 ft.

R. coryphaeum
(*leading, alluding to its large size*)
H3–4 F2–3 L2–3 Pt.
April

s. Grande.
Shrub up to 20 ft. Lvs. up to 18 in. long and 5 in. broad, oblong-obovate to oblanceolate, mat green above, white, grey or fawn below. Fls. 20 or more to the truss, 2 in. long, obliquely campanulate, creamy-white with purple blotch and numerous spots. Yunnan, S.E. Tibet, 11–14,000 ft.

A.M. 1963 (E. de Rothschild, Exbury) to 'Exbury' clone with white fls. tinged with translucent shade of very pale yellow, throat blotched ruby-red.

R. cowanianum
(After Dr. J. M. Cowan, notable authority on rhododendrons; 1892–1960)
H3–4 F1 L1 Pm.
May

s. Trichocladum.
Shrub up to 5 ft. Lvs. deciduous, 1–2 in. long, up to 1 in. broad, obovate to oblong-obovate, pilose at the margin, covered with yellow-green scales below. Fls. in clusters of 2–4, up to ¾ in. long, shortly campanulate, reddish-purple; calyx large, up to ⅓ in. long, margin of lobes sometimes pilose. Nepal, 10–12,000 ft.

R. crassum
(*fleshy*)
H2–4 F2–3 L2–3 Pm.
June–July

s. and s.s Maddenii.
Shrub up to 15 ft. Lvs. up to 5 in. long and 3 in. broad, lanceolate or obovate-oblanceolate, thick and rigid, glossy and dark green and veiny above, densely rusty-scaly below. Fls. in trusses of 3–5, up to 3½ in. long, tubular-funnel-shaped, white, creamy-white, rosy-white or pink with or without a yellow blotch, sweetly scented; calyx up to ½ in. long. Yunnan, S.E. Tibet, Upper Burma, 7,500–12,000 ft. The hardiest of the Maddenii rhododendrons and a very desirable

R. crassum
(*continued*)

species flowering as it does in June–July, when other rhododendron flowers are scarce. B.M. 9673.

A.M. 1924 (T. H. Lowinsky, Sunninghill) white-flowered form.

R. crinigerum
(*bearing hairs*)
H⁴ F²⁻³ L²⁻³ Pm.

April–May

s. Barbatum. s.s. Crinigerum.

Shrub up to 12 ft. with young shoots very viscid with long-stalked glands. Lvs. 3–7 in. long, up to 2 in. broad, lanceolate or oblong-oblanceolate, dark green and often glossy and slightly bullate above, covered below with dense white to deep buff indumentum. Fls. in trusses of about 12, up to 1½ in. long, campanulate, white or white flushed rose or pale pink or cream with an intense dark red basal blotch; calyx often nearly ½ in. long, densely glandular. Yunnan, S.E. Tibet, 10,000–14,500 ft. B.M. 9464.

A.M. 1935 (L. de Rothschild, Exbury) to pale pink form rather heavily spotted and blotched with red.

A form with the indumentum on the lower surface of the leaves thinner than in the type is known as var. *euadenium;* S.E. Tibet, Yunnan, 12–14,000 ft.

R. cubittii
(After G. E. S. Cubitt, who collected in North Burma)
H²⁻³ F³⁻⁴ L¹⁻² Pm.s.

March–April

s. Maddenii. s.s. Ciliicalyx.

Shrub up to 12 ft. with smooth purplish-brown bark sparingly peeling. Lvs. about 4 in. long, 1½ in. broad, elongate-oblong-elliptic, mucronate apex, glaucous and scaly below. Fls. in trusses of 3–4, about 4 in. diam., widely funnel-shaped, white, deeply flushed rose without, reddish-brown markings sometimes orange-yellow blotch on back of tube within, lobes somewhat crisped at margin. N. Burma, 5,800 ft. B.M. 9502.

Plants growing out of doors have flowers more deeply stained with pink.

A.M. 1935 (Lt.-Col. E. H. W. Bolitho, Penzance) to a form with the flowers deeply flushed with rose.

'Ashcombe' is an F.C.C. clone (Crown Estate Commissioners, Windsor, 1962) with large white flowers orange-yellow blotched in the throat.

R. cuffeanum
(After Lady Wheeler Cuffe)
H¹ F³⁻⁴ L¹⁻² Pm.s.

April–May

s. Maddenii. s.s. Ciliicalyx.

Shrub up to 9 ft., loosely branched and often straggling. Lvs. up to 4 in. long, oblanceolate or oblong-oblanceolate, reticulate above, densely scaly below. Fls. about 5 to the truss, up to 3 in. long, tubular-campanulate, white with yellow blotch. S.W. Burma, 6,000 ft. B.M. 8721.

R. cuneatum
(*wedge-shaped*)
H4 F2–3 L1–2 Pm.

April

s. Lapponicum.
Shrub up to 10 ft. Lvs. large for the series, about 1 in. long, ⅔ in. broad, elliptic, densely scaly on both surfaces. Fls. the largest in the series and in clusters of 3–6, 1 in. long, widely funnel-shaped, rose-lavender, deep rose, deep rose-purple or pink. Yunnan, 11–13,000 ft.

R. cyanocarpum
(*with blue fruits*)
H4 F2–3 L2–3 Pm.–t.

March–April

s. *and* s.s. Thomsonii.
Shrub or small tree up to 20 ft. with young vegetative shoots glaucous-green. Lvs. 2–5 in. long, broadly elliptic to orbicular, dark mat green above, glaucous-green below, resembling those of *R. thomsonii*. Fls. 8–10 in loose truss, up to 2½ in. long, widely funnel-campanulate, white, creamy-white flushed rose, or a rich soft rose; calyx cup-like about ½ in. long. Yunnan, 10,000–13,500 ft. B.M. n.s. 155.
A.M. 1933 (Lady Loder, Leonardslee, Sussex) to form with white flowers flushed with rose.
A form with a glandular ovary has been named var. *eriphyllum:* Yunnan, 11,000 ft.

R. dalhousiae
(After Lady Dalhousie, wife of the Governor-General of India)
H1–2 F3–4 L2–3 Pm.s.

May–June

s. Maddenii. s.s. Megacalyx.
Straggly, leggy shrub up to 10 ft. Lvs. up to 6 in. long, 2½ in. broad, obovate or oblanceolate, glaucous below and very scaly. Fls. about 5 to the truss, about 4 in. long, tubular-campanulate and funnel-shaped, fragrant, pale yellow or white, golden at the base, or white flushed pink. Sikkim, Bhutan, S.E. Tibet, 6–8,000 ft. B.M. 4718.
A.M. 1930 (Vice-Adm. A. Walker Heneage-Vivian, Swansea).

R. dalhousiae is a parent of the F.C.C. clones 'Countess of Haddington' (1862), 'Henryanum' (1865).

R. dasycladum
(*with hairy boughs*)
H4 F2–3 L1–2 Pm.

April–May

s. Thomsonii. s.s. Selense.
Shrub up to 8 ft., with setose-glandular branch-lets and leaf-stalks. Lvs. 1¼ to nearly 5 in. long, oblong to oblong-elliptic, dark mat-green above, pale green below. Fls. in trusses of 5–8, about 1½ in. long, funnel-shaped, rose or white with or without a blotch, sometimes spotted. Yunnan, S.E. Tibet, 10–14,000 ft.

R. dasypetalum
(*with hairy petals*)
H4 F1–2 L1–2 Pd.

April

s. Lapponicum.
Shrub up to 3 ft. Lvs. ⅔ in. long, oblong-elliptic, light green and densely scaly below. Fls. in clusters of 1–4, ¾ in. long, open funnel-shaped, purple-rose or deep blue-purple, hairy outside the tube. Yunnan, Szechwan, 11–14,000 ft.

R. dauricum

(from Dauria, part of S.E. Siberia, east of Lake Baikal, N.E. Asia, now partly in U.S.S.R. and partly in China)

H4 F2–3 L1–2 Pm.c.

Jan.–Feb.–March

s. Dauricum.

Shrub up to 8 ft., semi-deciduous or evergreen. Lvs. up to 1¼ in. long, elliptic, dark green above, densely scaly below. Fls. in trusses of 1–3, about ¾ in. long, widely funnel-shaped, bright rose-purple. N. Asia—Altai, east to Korea. B.M. 636.

There are two forms, one semi-deciduous, the other evergreen (called *sempervirens*—B.M. 8930).

A.M. 1963 (Crown Estate Commissioners) to semi-deciduous clone 'Midwinter'.

R. dauricum is one of the parents of *R.* × *praecox* (A.G.M. 1926) and as both forms have been used this hybrid varies in the amount of foliage retained during the winter. It is also a parent of 'Early Gem' (F.C.C. 1874) and of the A.M. clones 'Olive' (1942), 'Fittra' (1949).

R. davidii

(After L'Abbé Armand David, an early collector in W. China; 1826–1900)

H4 F2–3 L2–3 Pm.–t.

April–May

s. Fortunei. s.s. Davidii.

Shrub up to 15 ft. Lvs. up to 8 in. long, 1½ in. broad, leathery, narrowly oblong-lanceolate, green on both surfaces. Fls. in an elongate truss of 8–12, up to 2 in. long, open campanulate, rose-red or lilac, spotted purple within. Szechwan, 5–10,000 ft.

R. davidsonianum

(After Dr. W. H. Davidson, Friends Mission in China)

H3–4 F2–4 L1–2 Pm.–t.s.

April–May

s. Triflorum. s.s. Yunnanense.

Shrub up to 10 ft. sometimes with straggly leggy branches. Lvs. 1–3 in. long, usually lanceolate, laxly scaly below, like a V in section. Fls. terminal and axillary in the uppermost leaves, in clusters of 2–6, 1–1½ in. long, 2 in. diameter, widely funnel-shaped or rotate, zygomorphic, white tinged pink, pink, pale rose or pale purplish-rose, with or without red spots. Szechwan, Yunnan, 6,500–11,500 ft. Most beautiful in its better forms. B.M. 8605; 8759, as *R. siderophyllum*; 8665, as *R. charianthum*. A.M. 1935 (Lord Aberconway, Bodnant) to pale rose form. F.C.C. 1955 (Lord Aberconway and the National Trust, Bodnant) to pale rose form.

'Ruth Lyons' is a clone with a truss of up to 10 flowers of Rhodamine Pink (H.C.C. 527/1–527/2). P.A. (A.R.S.). The plant known as *R. charianthum* and figured in B.M. 8665 belongs here.

R. decipiens

(deceptive)

H3 F2–3 L2–3 Pt.

April–May

s. Falconeri.

Small tree up to 20 ft. Lvs. up to 7 in. long, elliptic or obovate-elliptic, at first rusty below, later paler. Fls. in trusses of up to 30, purple-rose, very similar to those of *R. hodgsonii* and possibly a hybrid between this species and *R. falconeri*. Sikkim, 10–11,000 ft.

72

R. decorum
(*ornamental*)

H$^{3-4}$ F$^{2-3}$ L$^{2-3}$ P$^{m.-t.}$

April–May–June

s. and *s.s.* Fortunei.

Shrub or tree up to 20 ft. Lvs. up to 6 in long, 3 in. broad, oblong, oblong-ovate to oblong-obovate, pale glaucous-green below. Fls. in lax trusses of 8–14, up to 3 in. long, open funnel-shaped, white, sometimes shell-pink, with or without spots. Yunnan, Szechwan, 8–11,000 ft. The forms sent home by Wilson & Ward are said to be the hardiest. Farrer's form, with flowers larger than in the type is regarded as tender. 'Cox's Uranium Green' is a clone with distinctive greenish-yellow flowers.

R. decorum is a parent of the following A.M. clones:

'Mrs. J. Comber' (1932), 'Sheila Moore' (1948), 'Cerisette' (1954), 'Dorothea' (1925), 'Kewdec White Lady' (1938), 'W. Leith' (1935), 'Decsoul' (1937).

R. degronianum
(After M. Degron, Director of the French Posts in Yokohama in 1869)

H^4 F$^{1-2}$ L$^{2-3}$ P$^{m.c.}$

May

s. Ponticum. *s.s.* Caucasicum.

Compact rounded shrub up to 5 ft., clad almost to the base with foliage. Lvs. up to 6 in. long, 1½ in. broad, oblong, oblong-elliptic to obovate, felty fawn to rufous below. Fls. in trusses of 10–12, up to 2½ in. across, widely funnel-campanulate, 5-partite clear soft pink with deep pink lines along the middle of the petals. Japan. B.M. 8403. Has been grown in gardens under the name of *R. metternichii*, from which it differs in its 5-partite corolla, that of *metternichii* being 7-partite.

R. delavayi
(After L'Abbé Jean M. Delavay, an early collector in W. China; 1838–95)

H$^{2-3}$ F$^{2-4}$ L$^{2-3}$ P$^{m.-t.}$

March–April–May

s. and *s.s.* Aboreum.

Tree up to 30 ft. with white-floccose young shoots. Lvs. up to 8 in. long oblong-lanceolate to oblong-oblanceolate, dark green and glossy above with white or grey or fawn indumentum of spongy texture below. Fls. in round compact trusses of up to 20, 2 in. long, campanulate, blood-red, or in inferior forms, white and pink. Yunnan, Burma, 6–10,000 ft. B.M. 8137.

The Chinese equivalent of the Himalayan *R. arboreum* but tender and only suitable for the south and west.

F.C.C. 1936 (Capt. A. M. Talbot Fletcher, Margam Castle, Port Talbot, S. Wales).

R. dendricola
(*dweller on trees*)

H^1 F$^{3-4}$ L$^{2-3}$ P$^{m.s.}$

May

s. Maddenii. *s.s.* Ciliicalyx.

Straggling shrub up to 9 ft.; in nature generally epiphytic. Lvs. 3–4½ in. long, 1¼–2 in. broad, oblong-elliptic, densely scaly below. Fls. 2–4 per truss, 3½–4 in. long, widely funnel-shaped, white

R. dendricola
(*continued*)

tinged pink with an orange or greenish mark towards the base. Burma. B.M. 9682.

R. desquamatum
(*bereft of scales*)
H4 F2–3 L1–2 Pm.–t.

March–April

s. Heliolepis.

Shrub or tree up to 25 ft. Lvs. up to $3\frac{1}{2}$ in. long, $1\frac{1}{2}$ in. broad, oblong-elliptic, densely dark brown scaly below. Fls. in loose clusters, $1\frac{1}{2}$ in. long, widely funnel-shaped or almost flat, mauve or pinkish-purple, spotted crimson. Yunnan, Szechwan, Burma, S.E. Tibet, 10–14,000 ft. B.M. 9497.

A.M. 1938 (Capt. A. M. Talbot Fletcher, Margam Castle, Port Talbot, S. Wales) to five different plants showing five different colour forms from clear pale mauve to reddish-mauve, with variable red spotting, raised from F. 24535 Forrest.

R. desquamatum is a parent of the A.M. clone 'Eleanore' (1943).

R. detersile
(*clean*)
H4 F2–3 L2–3 Pd.–m.

April–May

s. Taliense. s.s. Adenogynum.

Shrub up to 3 ft. with young shoots clothed with rufous wool. Lvs. clustered at ends of shoots, $1\frac{1}{2}–2\frac{1}{2}$ in. long, up to 1 in. broad, elliptic to oblanceolate, revolute at margin, loose woolly indumentum below. Fls. in compact truss of about 8, up to $1\frac{1}{2}$ in. long, funnel-campanulate, reddish. Szechwan, 7–8,000 ft.

R. detonsum
(*shorn*)
H4 F1–3 L1–3 Pm.

May

s. Taliense. s.s. Adenogynum.

Shrub up to 12 ft. Lvs. 3–5 in. long, up to 2 in. broad, oblong to oblong-elliptic, pale cinnamon to brown below. Fls. in lax trusses of about 10, 2 in. diam. funnel-campanulate, rose-pink with crimson spots. Yunnan, 9–11,000 ft. B.M. 9359.

A very attractive shrub and certainly one of the best of the series.

R. diacritum
(*distinguished*)
H4 F1–2 L1–2 Pd.

April

s. Lapponicum.

Matted shrub up to 2 ft. Lvs. about $\frac{1}{4}$ in. long, broadly elliptic, densely scaly. Fls. single, $\frac{1}{3}$ in. long, openly funnel-shaped, deep rose-purple with white throat. Yunnan, 13–14,000 ft.

R. diaprepes
(*distinguished*)
H3 F2–3 L2–3 Pm.–t.

June–July

s. and s.s. Fortunei.

Shrub or tree up to 25 ft., with current year shoots glaucous-green. Lvs. up to 12 in. long and 4 in. broad, oblong-elliptic to oblong-oblanceolate, light green above, pale glaucous-green below. Fls. in lose trusses of 7–10, as much as 4 in. long and 6 in. diam. open funnel-campanulate, fleshy, slightly fragrant, white or faintly flushed with rose. Yunnan, S.E. Tibet, 9–11,000 ft. B.M. 9524.

Forrest 11958 is regarded as the hardiest form.

A.M. 1926 (L. de Rothschild, Exbury).

'Gargantua' is an A.M. clone and a triploid plant ($2n = 39$) grown from seeds of *Forrest* 11958, with very large flowers, white with a green flush at the base, strongly and pleasantly scented (Mrs. R. M. Stevenson, Tower Court, Ascot, 1953).

R. diaprepes is a parent of 'Polar Bear' (F.C.C. 1946), 'Mrs. J. Comber' (A.M. 1932).

R. dichroanthum
(with two-coloured flowers)
H4 F1–3 L1–2 Pd.–m.
May–June

s. Neriiflorum.   s.s. Sanguineum.

Shrub up to 6 ft. Lvs. up to 4 in. long and $1\frac{1}{2}$ in. broad, oblong to obovate to oblanceolate, with white to grey indumentum. Fls. in loose trusses of 4–8, up to $1\frac{1}{2}$ in. long, tubular-campanulate, deep or dull orange, orange-rose, creamy-rose or salmon-pink; calyx large and fleshy, over $\frac{1}{2}$ in. deep, coloured orange-pink or salmon. Yunnan, 9–12,000 ft. B.M. 8815.

A.M. 1923, (Lady Aberconway and the Hon. H. D. McLaren, Bodant) to form with orange-red flowers. Much used by the hybridizer in his search for colour-breaks and as a parent in the following A.M. clones: 'Margela' (1948), 'Piccaninny' (1956), 'Kingcup' (1943), 'Break of Day' (1936), 'Berryrose' (1934), 'Golden Horn' (1945), 'Fabia' (1934), 'Fabia Tangerine' (1940), 'Francis Hanger' (1950), 'Astarte' (1931), 'Mohamet' (1945).

R. dichroanthum is a most variable species and certain forms have been named as follows:

Subsp. *apodectum* (H4 F1–2 L1 Pd.–m.). Fls. orange flushed rose or crimson, or crimson tinged with orange or bright cherry-scarlet. Yunnan, 10–11,000 ft. B.M. 9014.

Subsp. *herpesticum* (H4 F1–2 L1–2 Pd.); dwarf shrub up to 2 ft. with dull yellow to orange-red fls. N. Burma, 12–13,000 ft. It is a parent of the A.M. cultivars 'Icarus' (1947), 'Organdie' (1947).

Subsp. *scyphocalyx* (H4 F1–2 L1–2 Pm.); Fls. in trusses of 3–5, orange, rose-orange, yellowish-crimson or copper-yellow. N. Burma 10–13,000 ft.

Subsp. *septentrionale* (H4 F1–2 L1–2 Pd.–m.); Fls. yellow flushed rose or lemon-yellow. N. Burma, Yunnan, 12–14,000 ft.

R. dictyotum
(net-veins)
H4 F1–2 L1–2 Pm.–t.
May

s. Lacteum.

Shrub up to 12 ft. Lvs. 2–5 in. long, 1–2 in. broad, oblong, oblong-elliptic or oblanceolate, under surface with thin brown, rust or cinnamon felty indumentum. Fls. in loose truss of 8–15, $1\frac{1}{2}$–2 in. long, bell-shaped, white or white flushed

R. dictyotum
(*continued*)

rose, unspotted or spotted with crimson, with or without a crimson blotch. Yunnan, Szechwan S.E. Tibet, 11–14,000 ft. A rather rare plant in cultivation.

R. didymum
(*two-fold*)

see *R. sanguineum* subsp. *didymum*.

R. dimitrum
(*with double cap alluding to the very large calyx*)
H3–4 F1–2 L1–2 Pm.

April

s. *and s.s.* Irroratum.

Shrub up to 7 ft. Lvs. 1½–3 in. long up to 1 in. broad, oblong or oval-oblong, yellowish-green below. Fls. 10–12 per truss, about 1½ in. long tubular-campanulate, deep rose, spotted crimson calyx nearly ½ in. deep and unusually large for the Series. Yunnan, 10,000 ft.

R. diphrocalyx
(*with calyx wide and flat like the basal board of a chariot on which the riders stood.*)
H4 F1–2 L1–2 Pm.–t.

April

s. Barbatum. *s.s.* Glischrum.

Shrub up to 15 ft. with young stems clad with long setose glands. Lvs. up to 6 in. long, 2¼ in. broad, oblong-oval, oval, or obovate, pale glaucous-green below. Fls. in a truss of about 20, 1½ in. long, broadly tubular-campanulate, rosy-crimson with crimson spots and basal blotch; calyx large and fleshy, bright red. Yunnan, 10–11,000 ft.

R. discolor
(*of various colours*)
H3–4 F2–4 L2–3 Pm.–t.

June–July

s. *and s.s.* Fortunei.

A robust shrub up to 20 ft. or more, with the new growths often produced at the same time as the flowers. Lvs. up to 8 in. long, 3 in. broad, oblong-elliptic to oblong-oblanceolate, dark green above, pale below. Fls. in a loose truss of about 10, up to 3½ in. long and 4 in. across the mouth, funnel-shaped, white, or white faintly flushed pink or pale pink, seven-lobed, fragrant. Szechwan, Hupeh, 4–7,000 ft. B.M. 8696.

Some forms are at first shy to flower. A mature plant in full flower is a beautiful sight and especially valuable in July.

F.C.C. 1922 (Royal Botanic Gardens, Kew) to a form with white flowers slightly tinged with pink.

A.M. 1922 (Hon. H. D. McLaren, Bodnant) to a form with beautiful pale-pink flowers, crimson-blotched at the base.

R. discolor has been much used in hybridization and four of its progeny have received the F.C.C.: 'Lady Bessborough' (1933), 'Roberte' (1936), 'Exbury Angelo' (1947), 'Exbury Albatross' (1935); 'Azor Sister' is a *discolor* hybrid which has received the F.C.C. after trial at Wisley (1960).

76

R. discolor
(*continued*)

R. *discolor* is a parent of the following A.M. clones:

'Celeste' (1944), 'Argosy Snow White' (1936), 'Norman Shaw' (1926), 'A. Gilbert' (1925), 'Ladybird' (1933), 'Margaret Dunn' (1946), 'Antonio' (1939), 'Exbury Antonio' (1939), 'Azor' (1933), 'Angelo' (1935), 'Sheffield Park Angelo' (1950), 'Solent Queen' (1939), 'Pink Domino' (1925), 'Repose' (1956), 'Albatross' (1934), 'Townhill Albatross' (1945), 'Akbar' (1952), 'Bonito' (1934).

'Ice Cream' is a *discolor* hybrid which has received the A.M. after trial at Wisley (1960).

R. doshongense
(*from the Doshong La, S.E. Tibet*)
H4 F1-2 L1-2 Pd.–m.
March–May

s. *and* s.s. Taliense.
Tangled shrub up to 3 ft. Lvs. up to 2½ in. long, 1½ in. broad, oval to ovate to obovate, rugulose above, at first silvery-white later pale fawn below. Fls. in clusters of up to 15, about 1½ in. long, campanulate, pink with many dark purple spots. S.E. Tibet, 12–13,000 ft.

R. drumonium
(*from woods*)
H4 F1-2 L1-2 Pd.c.
April

s. Lapponicum.
Tufted compact shrub up to 2 ft. Lvs. about ¼ in. long, elliptic, rich-brown-scaly below. Fls. solitary or in pairs, nearly ½ in. long, widely funnel-shaped, purplish-blue, deep rose-purple or mauve. Yunnan, 10–12,000 ft.

R. dryophyllum
(*oak-leaved*)
H4 F1-3 L2-3 Pm.–t.
April–May

s. Lacteum.
Shrub or small tree up to 25 ft., young shoots with thin buff coloured indumentum. Lvs. 2–3 in. long, ½–2 in. broad, oblong, oblong-elliptic or lanceolate, glossy above, covered below with suede-like, fawn-brown, yellow-brown, cinnamon or yellow indumentum. Fls. in trusses of 8–16, ¾–1¾ in. long, funnel-campanulate or campanulate, white, creamy-white, white flushed rose, pink or pinkish-purple, with or without crimson spots, occasionally with a crimson blotch. Yunnan, Szechwan, S.E. Tibet, Bhutan, Burma, 11–14,000 ft.

The best forms of this very variable species are most desirable.

R. dumicola
(*dweller in thickets*)
H4 F1-2 L1-2 Pd.–m.
April

s. Taliense. s.s. Adenogynum.
Shrub up to 4 ft. Lvs. up to 3 in. long, 1½ in. broad, oblong-elliptic, with thin tawny indumentum below. Fls. in a 5–7 flowered truss, about 1½ in. long, campanulate, white flushed rose with a faint blotch of crimson; calyx large and foliaceous. Yunnan, 14,000 ft.

R. dumosulum
(*small and bushy*)
H⁴ F¹⁻² L²⁻³ Pd.–m.
April

s. Lacteum.

Shrub up to 4 ft. Lvs. 1½–3 in. long, oblong or lanceolate, slightly rugulose above, covered below with suede-like brown or rust continuous indumentum. Fls. in trusses of 7–8, ⅓–1¾ in. long, funnel-campanulate, white faintly flushed rose, with crimson spots. Yunnan, S.E. Tibet, 13,000 ft. A small growing and small-leaved expression of *R. dryophyllum*.

R. eclecteum
(*to be chosen out*)
H⁴ F¹⁻³ L²⁻³ Pm.
Jan.–April

s. and s.s. Thomsonii.

Shrub up to 8 ft. Lvs. 2–5 in. long, 1–2 in. broad, obovate or obovate-oblong, glaucous above pale green below. Fls. in trusses of about 12, up to 2 in. long, tubular-campanulate, fleshy, white, yellow, pink or rose, sometimes rose-magenta with or without crimson spots. Yunnan, Szechwan, S.E. Tibet, 10–14,000 ft. Often flowers so early as to be frosted.

A.M. 1949 (E. de Rothschild, Exbury) to a primrose-yellow form.

Of many forms of *R. eclecteum*, two have been named as follows:

Var. *bellatulum*, with rather smaller, oblong, long-stalked leaves and bright rose flowers. Yunnan, S.E. Tibet, 10–14,000 ft.

Var. *brachyandrum*, with deep rose or crimson flowers. Yunnan, S.E. Tibet, Burma, 12–14,000 ft.

Certain forms of *R. eclecteum* and *R. stewartianum* are very similar.

R. edgarianum
(After Rev. J. H. Edgar, China Inland Mission)
H⁴ F¹⁻³ L¹⁻² Pd.
May–June

s. Lapponicum.

Shrub up to 3 ft. Lvs. ⅓ in. long, broadly elliptic, densely scaly on both surfaces, reddish-brown below. Fls. in clusters of 1–3, about ½ in. long, open funnel-shaped, blue-purple or rose-purple. Szechwan, Yunnan, S.E. Tibet, 12–15,000 ft.

R. edgeworthii
(After M. P. Edgeworth, Bengal Civil Service; 1812–81)
H²⁻³ F³⁻⁴ L²⁻³ Pm.s.
April–May

s. Edgeworthii.

Occasionally compact but usually a thin straggling shrub up to 10 ft. with the branchlets densely woolly tomentose. Lvs. about 4 in. long, and up to 2 in. broad, elliptic to ovate-elliptic, dark green shining and bullate above, brown cobwebby-tomentose below. Fls. in trusses of 2–3, up to 4 in. long and as much across, open funnel-shaped, white or tinged with pink, very fragrant. Sikkim, Bhutan, 7–10,000 ft. B.M. 4936. Some forms are very much hardier than others.

R. edgeworthii
(*continued*)

F.C.C. 1933 (Lt.-Col. L. C. R. Messel, Hand-cross, Sussex).

R. edgeworthii is a parent of the two F.C.C. clones 'Princess Alice' (1862) and 'Purity' (1888); 'Purity' also received the A.M. in 1908.

R. elliottii
(After Mr. Elliott, friend of
Sir George Watt, its discoverer)
H$^{2-3}$ F$^{3-4}$ L$^{2-3}$ Pm.–t.s.

May–June

s. Irroratum. *s.s.* Parishii.

Shrub or small straggling tree up to 12 ft. Lvs. up to 10 in. long and 4 in. broad, elliptic-oblong, glossy green above, paler below. Fls. in trusses of 10–15, up to 3 in. long and wide, tubular-campanulate, scarlet or crimson with darker spots. Manipur, 9,000 ft. B.M. 9546.

A.M. 1934 (J. J. Crosfield., Embley Park, Romsey, Hampshire).

F.C.C. 1937 (Admiral Walker Heneage-Vivian, Blackpill, Swansea).

Some of the many splendid hybrids which have been raised from this beautiful species are:

'Kilimanjaro' (F.C.C. 1947), 'Fusilier' (F.C.C. 1942), 'Grenadier' (F.C.C. 1943), 'Morvah' (F.C.C. 1959).

The following are A.M. clones:

'Kiev' (1950), 'Jutland' (1947), 'Leo' (1948), 'Shiela Moore' (1948), 'Cerisette' (1954), 'Golden Horn' (1945), 'Elros' (1948), 'Beefeater' (1958), 'Billy Budd' (1957), 'Delius' (1946), 'Querida' (1952), 'Royal Blood' (1954), 'Gaul' (1939), 'Rouge' (1950).

R. eriogynum
(*with a woolly ovary*)
H$^{2-3}$ F$^{3-4}$ L$^{2-3}$ Pm.–t.

June

s. Irroratum. *s.s.* Parishii.

Shrub or small tree up to 10 ft. or more, with young shoots covered with whitish indumentum. Lvs. up to 8 in. long, and 3 in. broad, oblong-elliptic to oblong-lanceolate when young with white stellate indumentum below, later glaucous. Fls. in trusses of 12–16, up to 3 in. long and broad, tubular-campanulate, a magnificient clear bright red. Yunnan, 9–10,000 ft. B.M. 9337.

A.M. 1924 (T.H. Lowinsky, Sunninghill).

R. eriogynum is hardly to be distinguished from *R. facetum*. Growth is naturally late and it does not like being transplanted. It is suitable for outdoor cultivation only in favourable localities, but grown in a cool house it is a marvellous plant.

R. eriogynum is a parent of the F.C.C. clones: 'Firetail' (1937), 'Tally Ho' (1933), 'Romany Chal' (1937), and of the A.M. clones: 'Townhill Red Cap' (1945), 'Beau Brummell' (1938), 'Panoply' (1942), 'Grosclaude' (1945), 'Damask' (1932), 'Rosenkavalier' (1959), 'Fancy Free' (1938).

R. eritimum
(*highly prized*)
H³ F¹⁻² L¹⁻² Pm.–t.

April

s. *and* s.s. Irroratum.

Shrub or small tree up to 18 ft. Lvs. up to 7 in. long and 2 in. broad, narrowly oblong or oblong-oblanceolate, rather glaucous below. Fls. about 15 to the truss, up to 2 in. long, tubular-campanulate, 7-lobed, dark crimson or lighter rose-magenta, blotched at base but not conspicuously spotted. Yunnan, S.E. Tibet, 9–13,000 ft.

This is rather a variable species and forms of it have been named as follows:

Subsp. *gynnogynum* (H³⁻⁴ F¹⁻² L¹⁻² Pm.); a shrub up to 8 ft., with smaller leaves than the type and with crimson flowers. Yunnan, S.E. Tibet, 11–12,000 ft.

Subsp. *heptamerum* (H³⁻⁴ F¹⁻² L¹⁻² Pm.); a shrub up to 8 ft. and with flowers larger than in the type and deep crimson. N.E. Upper Burma, 10,000 ft.

R. erosum
(*eaten away*)
H⁴ F²⁻³ L¹⁻³ Pm.–t.

March–April

s. Barbatum. s.s. Glischrum.

Shrub or small tree up to 20 ft. Lvs. up to 4 in. long and 3 in. broad, obovate to oblong-oval, rather reticulate above, at first softly brown-woolly below, later glabrous. Fls. in trusses of up to 15, 1½ in. long and broad, campanulate, deep rich crimson to a fine shade of rose-pink, with large, irregularly lobed deep pink calyx. S.E. Tibet, 10–12,000 ft.

A striking plant in flower and foliage resembling *R. barbatum* but with more rounded leaves.

R. erubescens
(*blush-red*)
H⁴ F²⁻³ L²⁻³ Pm.

April

s. Fortunei. s.s. Oreodoxa.

Shrub up to 10 ft. with smooth purplish bark. Lvs. up to 6 in. long, and 2 in. broad, oblong-elliptic, dark mat green above, pale yellowish-green below. Fls. about 8 to the truss, up to 2 in. long, and 1–1½ in. broad, funnel-campanulate, white inside, rose-carmine outside or a deep rich rose. Szechwan, 12,000 ft. B.M. 8643.

Related to *R. fargesii*.

R. erythrocalyx
(*with a red calyx*)
H⁴ F¹⁻² L²⁻³ Pm.

April–May

s. Thomsonii. s.s. Selense.

Shrub up to 8 ft. Lvs. up to 4 in. long, elliptic to ovate, mat olive-green above, pale below. Fls. in trusses of 4–10, about 2 in. long, funnel-campanulate, white or pink, rarely yellow, with or without a crimson blotch, crimson spotted or unspotted; calyx about ⅓ in. long, reddish. S.E. Tibet, Yunnan, 11–13,000 ft.

Closely allied to *R. selense* and as in this species the leaves tend to hide the flowers.

esetulosum
(airless)

H4 F1-2 L2-3 Pm.

April–May

. euchaites
(with beautiful hairs)

. eudoxum
(of good report)

H4 F1-3 L1-2 Pm.

April–June

. eurysiphon
(with broad tube)

H4 F1-3 L2-3 Pm.

May

. exasperatum
(rough)

H3-4 F1-2 L2-3 Pm.-t.

April–May

---

s. Thomsonii.   *s.s.* Selense.

Shrub up to 6 ft. Lvs. 2–4 in. long, half as broad, oblong, oblong-elliptic or elliptic, minutely rugulose above, pale below. Fls. in lax truss of up to 10, up to 2 in. long, campanulate, creamy-white or white, or flushed rose or purplish, spotted with crimson or unspotted. Yunnan, S.E. Tibet, 10–14,000 ft.

Very similar to *R. erythrocalyx.*

see *R. neriiflorum* subsp. *euchaites.*

s. Neriiflorum.   *s.s.* Sanguineum.

Shrub up to 6 ft. with thin twiggy branches. Lvs. 1½–3 in. long and about half as broad, obovate or oblong-oval, glaucous below or with a thin veil of hairs. Fls. in truss of 5–6, up to 1½ in. long, campanulate or tubular-campanulate, deep clear crimson-rose, rose, or white flushed with rose, frequently half hidden among the leaves. Yunnan, S.E. Tibet, 11–13,000 ft.

A.M. (E. H. M. and P. A. Cox, Glendoick, Perth, 1960).

There is a form of this species which has been named:

Subsp. *brunneifolium* (H3-4 F1-2 L1-2 Pm.) which differs in the marked indumentum on the lower leaf surface, in the small calyx and usually in the eglandular ovary. The flowers are crimson or rose-crimson and unspotted. S.E. Tibet, Yunnan, 11–12,000 ft.

s. Thomsonii.   *s.s.* Selense.

Shrub up to 5 ft. Lvs. 1–3 in. long and half as broad, oblong to oblong-elliptic, pale glaucous-green below. Fls. in loose truss of 3–5, about 1½ in. long, campanulate, creamy-white or very pale rose, more or less heavily flushed with deep magenta, copiously spotted with crimson. S.E. Tibet, 13,000 ft.

Allied to *R. selense* and *R. martinianum.*

s. Barbatum.   *s.s.* Glischrum.

Shrub or small tree up to 15 ft. with young shoots bronze and densely clad with glandular bristles. Lvs. up to 7 in. long and 4 in. broad, broadly ovate to subobovate, dark green above, paler below, mid-rib bristly as is the petiole. Fls. in a truss of 10–12, about 1½ in. long, bell-shaped, rusty brick-red. Assam, S.E. Tibet, 9,500–12,000 ft. Very attractive young and old foliage.

R. eximium
(excellent)

H^{3-4} F^{2-3} L^{3-4} Pm.–t.

April–May

s. Falconeri.

Tree up to 30 ft. with young shoots and foliag
buds covered with rusty tomentum. Lvs. re
sembling those of *R. falconeri*, up to 12 in. lon
and 6 in. broad, oval to obovate-elliptic, for
year covered above with rusty tomentum and the
dark green with the nerves deeply impressed
mature leaves covered below with cinnamon c
rust indumentum. Fls. up to 2 in. long, campanu
late, fleshy, rose or pink-tinted. Bhutan 10–11,00
ft. B.M. 7317. A fine foliage plant.

R. faberi
(After Rev. Ernst Faber, who
collected in China during 1887–
91)

H^4 F^{1-2} L^{1-2} Pm.–t.

May

s. Taliense. *s.s.* Adenogynum.

Shrub or small tree up to 18 ft. with youn
shoots covered with rust-coloured wool. Lvs. u
to 6 in. long and 2 in. broad, oblong-oval, lowe
surface light brown to buff to rusty-brown. Fl
in a truss of up to 10, about $1\frac{1}{2}$ in. long, cam
panulate, white, with or without crimson spot
Szechwan.

R. facetum
(elegant)

H^{2-3} F^{3-4} L^{2-3} Pm.–t.

*June–Aug. or even
into Nov.*

s. Irroratum. *s.s.* Parishii.

Shrub or small tree up to 30 ft. with youn
shoots at first covered with white or tawny mea
Lvs. up to 12 in. long and 3 in. broad, oblong
elliptic to oblong-oblanceolate, dull mat gree
above, light green below. Fls. usually in trusses o
8–10, occasionally up to 20, about $2\frac{1}{2}$ in. long, 3 i
diam., tubular-campanulate, scarlet, crimson-scar
let or deep rose, with or without deeper coloure
spots. Burma, Yunnan, 8–11,000 ft.

A.M. 1938 (Adm. A. Walker Heneage-Vivia
Swansea).

R. facetum is a parent of the A.M. clon
'Lady Digby' (1946).

R. falconeri
(After Hugh Falconer, 1808–65,
Supt. Saharanpur Gardens, India
in 1832)

H^{3-4} F^{3-4} L^{3-4} Pm.–t.

April–May

s. Falconeri.

Large shrub or tree up to 50 ft. with reddish
brown flaking bark and young shoots covered wit
grey-fawn tomentum. Lvs. 12 in. or more lor
and about half as wide, oblong-oval to elliptic t
broadly obovate, dark mat green and the nerve
deeply impressed above, under-surface dotted wit
dense rust-coloured indumentum. Fls. 20 or mor
to the truss, $2\frac{1}{2}$ in. long, 1–2 in. across, oblique
campanulate, 8–10 (usually 8), lobed, creamy-whit
to pale yellow with a purple blotch. Sikkin
Nepal to Bhutan, 8–11,000 ft. B.M. 4924.

In the south and west it is an extremely hand
some plant; in the east the leaves tend to b
smaller.

R. falconeri
(continued)

A.M. 1922 (Messrs. Gill, Falmouth).

R. falconeri is a parent of the F.C.C. clone 'Fortune' (1935), and the A.M. clones 'Muriel' (1925) and 'Faltho' (1954).

R. fargesii
(After Père Farges, 1844–1912, French Foreign Missions in N.W. Szechwan)

H⁴ F²⁻⁴ L²⁻³ Pm.-t.

March–April

s. Fortunei. s.s. Oreodoxa.

Shrub up to 20 ft. Lvs. up to 3½ in. long and 2 in. broad, elliptic to oblong-elliptic, dark green above, pale and glaucous below. Fls. in trusses of 6–10, 1½–2 in. long, open campanulate, rose, rosy-lilac, pink, or white, spotted or unspotted, 5–7 lobed. Hupeh, Szechwan, Yunnan, 7–13,000 ft. B.M. 8736.

Very closely allied to *R. oreodoxa*. Its floriferousness may be such that unless the dead flowers are picked off, the plant is apt to suffer a severe check.

A.M. 1926 (G. W. E. Loder, Ardingly) to a form with rose pink flowers with dark crimson dots on the inside.

'Barto Rose' is an American selection with flowers approaching Rose Madder and with deep purple spots in the upper half.

R. fargesii is a parent of the A.M. clones 'Carex' (1932), 'Rosalind' (1938).

R. farinosum
(mealy)

H³⁻⁴ F¹⁻² L²⁻³ Pm.

May

s. Arboreum. s.s. Argyrophyllum.

Shrub up to 6 ft. with young shoots at first clothed with thin grey tomentum. Lvs. up to 3 in. long and up to half as broad, oblong-elliptic to obovate, bullate above, white to fawn tomentose below. Fls. few to the truss, about 1½ in. long, campanulate, white. Yunnan, 9–10,000 ft. A very little known species.

R. farrerae
(After Mrs. Farrer, wife of Capt. Farrer, East India Company, in 1829)

H¹ F¹⁻² L¹⁻² Pd.

June

s. Azalea. s.s. Schlippenbachii.

Low shrub with short rigid shining brown branchlets. Lvs. deciduous or subpersistent, usually in 3's at the ends of the branchlets, 1–1½ in. long, ovate. Fls. single or in pairs, usually expanding before the leaves, about 2 in. across, rotate-funnel-shaped, pale to deep rose with red-purple spots. E. China.

R. fastigiatum
(erect)

H⁴ F²⁻³ L¹⁻² Pd.c.

April–May

s. Lapponicum.

Compact shrub up to 3 ft. Lvs. 3 in. long, elliptic-oblanceolate, densely scaly on both surfaces. Fls. in clusters of 4–5, about ½ in. long, widely funnel-shaped, light purple to deep purple-blue. Yunnan, 11–14,000 ft.

A.M. 1914 (G. Reuthe, Keston) to form with bluish-lilac flowers.

83

R. fauriei
(After Père Louis F. Faurie,
French Foreign Missions, China)

H⁴ F¹⁻² L¹⁻² Pm.

June

s. Ponticum. s.s. Caucasicum.

Shrub up to 10 ft. Lvs. 3–5 in. long and 1½ in.
broad, oblong-elliptic to obovate, pale green
below. Fls. 12–15 per truss, about 1–1½ in. long,
funnel-campanulate, white or yellowish with a
pinkish flush and green spots. Japan.

R. ferrugineum
(*rusty-coloured*)

H⁴ F¹⁻² L¹⁻² Pd.–m.s.

June

s. Ferrugineum.

Spreading sometimes straggling shrub up to
4 ft. Lvs. 1–1½ in. long, oblanceolate, densely
reddish-brown scaly below. Fls. in small trusses,
about ¾ in. long, tubular, rosy-crimson, loosely
scaly but not hairy on the outside. The Alpenrose.
Alps of S. Europe from the Pyrenees to the
Austrian Alps.

There is a form with white flowers. See
R. hirsutum.

R. fictolacteum
(*false R. lacteum*)

H⁴ F²⁻⁴ L²⁻³ Pm.–t.

April–May

s. Falconeri.

Shapely tree up to 40 ft. with the young shoots
cinnamon-tomentose. Lvs. very variable in size up
to 12 in. long and 4 in broad, oblong-obovate to
oblanceolate, dark green above, with a buff to rusty
indumentum below. Fls. in a truss of up to 25, up to
2 in. long and broad, oblique-campanulate, white,
creamy-white, or tinted rose, with a dark crimson
blotch. Yunnan, Szechwan, S.E. Tibet, 10–13,000
ft. B.M. 8372 (as *R. lacteum*). The first introduc-
tions bore rather small flowers, but later forms with
fine large flowers are a magnificent sight.

Closely allied to *R. rex*, but differs usually in
the shorter and narrower leaves and often in the
smaller flowers and truss.

A.M. 1923 (G. Reuthe, Keston) to a form with
white flowers with a crimson blotch at the base
and with a few spots of the same colour.

A.M. 1953 (Col. The Lord Digby, Cerne Abbey,
Dorchester) to a form called 'Cherry Tip';
grown from seeds of *Rock* 59255; the flowers are
white with some pink flushes, while the upper
segments are stained with a deep crimson blotch
and numerous spots up to the base of the lobes.

R. fimbriatum
(*minutely fringed*)

H⁴ F¹⁻² L¹⁻² Pd.

April–May

s. Lapponicum.

Dwarf shrub up to 2 ft. with yellowish-green
young shoots. Lvs. up to nearly 2 in. long and
¾ in. broad, lanceolate to oblong-lanceolate, pale
green above, rather glaucous below. Fls. about 8
per truss, about ⅓ in. long, campanulate, deep
mauve-purple. Szechwan, 12,000 ft.

Very similar to *R. scintillans*.

R. flavidum
(somewhat yellow)
I4 F2–3 L1–2 Pd.

March

s. Lapponicum.

Small much branched shrub. Lvs. about ½ in. long and ¼ in. broad, elliptic to oblong, glaucous and scaly below. Fls. 3–5 per truss, ⅔ in. long, open funnel-shaped, pale yellow. W. Szechwan and S.E. Tibet, 10,000 ft. B.M. 8326.

There is a form with broader leaves, smaller calyx and glabrous style which has been called var. *psilostylum*.

There is also a form with white flowers.

R. flavorufum
(red-yellow, alluding to the hairs changing from yellow to red-brown)
I4 F1–2 L1–2 Pm.

April–May

s. and s.s. Taliense.

Shrub up to 6 ft. Lvs. up to 5 in. long and 2½ in. broad, oval, elliptic or oblong-oval, lower surface at first covered with pale yellow indumentum which later changes to reddish. Fls. in truss of up to 10, up to 1½ in. long, funnel-campanulate, white or soft rose with a few crimson spots. Yunnan, S.E. Tibet, 11–14,000 ft.

R. fletcherianum
(After H. R. Fletcher, Regius Keeper, Royal Botanic Garden, Edinburgh, 1958–)
I4 F2–3 L1–2 Pm.

March–April

s. Maddenii. s.s. Ciliicalyx.

Shrub up to 4 ft. with bristly branchlets. Lvs. up to 2 in. long and 1 in. broad, oblong-lanceolate or oblong-elliptic, bristly at the margin, pale brown scaly below. Fls. in trusses of 2–5, nearly 2 in. long, widely funnel-shaped, pale yellow; calyx up to ½ in. long, deeply 5-lobed. S.E. Tibet, 14,000 ft.

For long grown under the name of R. *valentinianum* with the number *Rock* 22302.

R. floccigerum
(woolly)
I4 F1–3 L1–2 Pm.

March–April

s. and s.s. Neriiflorum.

Twiggy shrub up to 6 ft. Lvs. 2–5 in. long, up to 1 in. broad, narrowly oblong, oblong-elliptic to semi-lanceolate, dark-green above, with curious floccose indumentum covering a glaucous lower surface which later becomes almost bare. Fls. in trusses of 4–7, 1½ in long, tubular-campanulate, deep or lighter crimson, but varying to rose or yellow margined with rose. Yunnan, S.E. Tibet, 10–13,000 ft. B.M. 9290.

A.M. 1957 (Col. The Lord Digby, Minterne, Dorchester) to a form lacking the characteristic indumentum and known as var. *appropinquans*.

R. floribundum
(free flowering)
I4 F1–3 L2–3 Pm.–t.

April

s. Arboreum. s.s. Argyrophyllum.

Shrub or tree up to 15 ft. with young shoots hoary with a floccose indumentum. Lvs. 3–6 in. long and up to 2 in. broad, lanceolate, dark green and bullate above, whitish tomentose below. Fls. in trusses of 5–12, 1½ in. long, widely campanulate, purplish-lavender, rose or pink, with a

R. floribundum
(*continued*)

dark crimson blotch and spots. Szechwan
4–8,000 ft. B.M. 9609.

Good forms well grown, are most attractive.

A.M. 1963 (E. de Rothschild Exbury) to clon
'Swinhoe' with Roseine purple fls. (H.C.C. 629/1
with blotch of dark crimson.

R. fordii

see *R. simiarum*.

R. formosum
(*beautiful*)
H2–3 F3–4 L1–2 Pm.–s.

May–June

s. Maddenii. s.s. Ciliicalyx.

Shrub often straggly up to 10 ft. with bristly
young branchlets. Lvs. up to 3 in. long and 1½ in
broad, oblanceolate to obovate, fringed with long
white hairs at the margin, scaly below. Fls. in
trusses of 2–3, about 2½ in. long, widely funnel
shaped, white tinged yellow and rose and often
with 5 reddish stripes on the outside, sometime
scented. Assam, 5–5,500 ft. B.M. 4457.

A.M. 1960 (Royal Botanic Garden, Edinburgh
to a form with flowers white with pale orange tinge
in throat with reverse with a light staining of pale
pink.

R. formosum is a parent of the F.C.C. clones
'Purity' (1888), 'Tyermannii' (1925). 'Purity'
received the A.M. in 1908.

R. forrestii
(After George Forrest, 1873–
1932)
H4 F1–4 L1–2 Pdp.

April–May

s. Neriiflorum. s.s. Forrestii.

Prostrate creeping shrub up to 12 in. Lvs
up to 1½ in. long and ¾ in. broad, broadly obovate
to orbicular, dark green and shining above
purple below. Fls. single or in pairs, about 1½ in
long, tubular-campanulate, bright scarlet. S.E
Tibet, Yunnan, Burma. B.M. 9186.

A very slow growing plant and when well
flowered quite beautiful. Unfortunately there are
many forms in cultivation which are shy of flower
ing and which in fact have never flowered although
they are quite aged. Two forms have been named
as follows:

Var. *repens* with the lower surface of the leaves pale
or glaucous-green. A form of this received the
F.C.C. in 1935 (J. B. Stevenson, Esq., Tower
Court, Ascot).

Var. *tumescens* with dome shaped habit with the
outer branches creeping and larger flowers and
leaves. This form received the A.M. in 195?
(Mrs. R. M. Stevenson, Tower Court, Ascot—
under *Rock* 59174).

R. forrestii var. repens is a parent of the F.C.C
clones 'Ethel' (1940), 'Elizabeth' (1943), 'Little

. forrestii
(ontinued)

Ben' (1937) and of the A.M. clones 'Yeoman' (1947) 'Little Bert' (1939), 'Fascinator' (1950), 'Euchelia' (1935).

. fortunei
fter Robert Fortune, early llector in China; introduced a plant to India; 1812–80)

4 F³⁻⁴ L¹⁻³ Pm.–t.

May

s. and s.s. Fortunei.

Tree up to 30 ft. Lvs. up to 7 in. long and 3 in. broad, dark mat green above, pale glaucous-green below. Fls. in loose truss of 6–12, up to 2 in. long and $3\frac{1}{2}$ in. across, funnel-campanulate, pale pink-lilac, with 7 rather undulate lobes, fragrant. Chekiang, 3,000 ft. B.M. 5596.

R. fortunei which, strangely enough, has not had an award has been much used in hybridization and is the parent of the following F.C.C. and A.M. clones: 'Letty Edwards' (F.C.C. after trial at Wisley, 1948), 'Loderi Pink Diamond' (F.C.C. 1914), 'Loderi White Diamond' (F.C.C. 1914), 'Naomi Stella Maris' (F.C.C. 1939).

All the following have received the A.M.: 'Ernest Gill' (1918), 'Naomi' (1933), 'Naomi Nautilus' (1938), 'Calfort' (1932), 'Gladys' (1926), 'Gladys Rose' (1950), 'Pilgrim' (1926), 'Loderi Julie' (1944), 'Loderi Sir Edmund' (1930), 'Lavender Girl' (1950), 'Pink Rosette' (1956), 'Dot' (1945), 'Duke of York' (1894), 'Betty' (1927), 'Prelude' (1951), 'China' (1940, A.M. after trial at Wisley, 1948).

. fragariflorum
(trawberry-flowered)

3–4 F¹⁻² L¹⁻² Pd.

May–June

s. Saluenense.

Shrublet forming carpet up to 1 ft. Lvs. up to $\frac{1}{2}$ in. long, elliptic-obovate, strongly aromatic, laxly golden-scaly above and below. Fls. in clusters of 2–6, about $\frac{3}{4}$ in. long, widely funnel-shaped or almost rotate, pinkish-purple or purplish-crimson or crushed-strawberry, slightly fragrant. S.E. Tibet and Assam, 13–15,000 ft. A link between the Saluenense and Lapponicum series.

. fulgens
hining)

4 F¹⁻³ L¹⁻² Pm.

Feb.–March–April

s. Campanulatum.

Shrub up to 12 ft. Lvs. 2–5 in. long, broadly obovate or oval or oblong-elliptic, dark green and glossy above, below clothed with thick brown or tawny indumentum. Fls. 10–12 in compact round truss, up to $1\frac{1}{2}$ in. long, tubular-campanulate, bright scarlet with large almost black nectaries in the 5 basal pouches. Sikkim, Bhutan, Assam, Tibet, 11–14,000 ft. B.M. 5317.

A.M. 1933 (G. W. E. Loder, Esq., Ardingly).

R. fulgens is a parent of the A.M. clone 'Fulgarb' (1937).

R. fulvastrum
(*somewhat tawny*)
H⁴ F¹⁻² L¹⁻² Pm.

May

s. Neriiflorum. s.s. Sanguineum.
Shrub up to 5 ft. Lvs. up to 2½ in. long, oblong
oval, covered below with thin cobweb-like in
dumentum. Fls. in a truss of about 4, about 1½ in
long, bell-shaped, pale lemon-yellow or creamy
yellow. S.E. Tibet, 12–14,000 ft.

Subsp. *mesopolium* (H⁴ F¹⁻² L¹⁻² Pᵈ·) is a form
growing about 2 ft. high with campanulate c
tubular-campanulate, rose, pink or crimson
flowers. S.E. Tibet, 12–13,000 ft.

R. fulvum
(*tawny*)
H⁴ F²⁻⁴ L²⁻⁴ Pm.-t.

March–April

s. Fulvum.
Small tree up to 20 ft. with fulvous or greyish
tomentose young growths. Lvs. up to 10 in. lon
and 3 in. broad, oblanceolate or oblong or obovat
dark green and shining above, with a yellowis
to brilliant cinnamon indumentum below. Fl
up to 18 to the truss, about 1½ in. long, funne
campanulate, white flushed rose to deep rose wit
or without a crimson blotch and spots. Yunna
Szechwan, Burma, Assam, S.E. Tibet, 8,000
14,500 ft. B.M. 9587.
A.M. 1933 (Hon. H. D. McLaren, Bodnant) t
a form with pink flowers blotched with crimson

R. fumidum
(*smoke-coloured*)
H⁴ F¹⁻² L¹⁻² Pm.

June

s. Heliolepis.
Shrub up to 6 ft. Lvs. up to 3 in long, oblon
or ovate-oblong, scaly below. Fls. in a truss c
5–7, about 1 in. long, bell-shaped, dull viole
densely scaly without, Yunnan, Szechwan, 10
12,000 ft.

R. galactinum
(*milky*)
H⁴ F¹⁻² L¹⁻² Pm.-t.

April–May

s. Falconeri.
Tree up to 20 ft. Lvs. up to 8 in. long and 3 in
broad, oblong-ovate to lanceolate or oblanceolate
dark green above, buff-grey or pale cinnamo
below. Fls. in trusses of about 15, about 1½ in
long, bell-shaped, white or pale rose with crimso
blotch which breaks into lines and spots. Szechwan
9–10,000 ft. Though less attractive than som
other Chinese species it is well worth growing in
cold garden. B.M. n.s. 231.

R. genestierianum
(After Père A. Genestier, b. 1858,
of the French R.C. Tibetan
Mission, friend of G. Forrest)
H²⁻³ F¹⁻² L²⁻³ Pm.

April

s. Glaucum. s.s. Genestierianum.
Shrub up to 12 ft. with purplish branchlet
Lvs. 4–6 in. long, 1–1½ in. broad, lanceolate t
oblanceolate, very glaucous even white below
giving good autumn colour. Fls. in clusters c
4–15, about ½ in. long, shortly and broadly tubula
plum-purple covered with a glaucous bloom
Yunnan, S.E. Tibet, Upper Burma, 8–14,500 f
B.M. 9310.

R. giganteum
(*gigantic*)
I¹⁻² F²⁻⁴ L³⁻⁴ Pm.–t.

Feb.–March–April

s. Grande.

Large tree up to 80 ft. with young branchlets clothed with thin greyish felt-like indumentum. Lvs. up to 16 in. long and up to half as broad, elliptic or oblanceolate, bright mat green above, pale green below. Fls. a compact truss of up to 25, about 2½ in. long and broad, funnel-campanulate, deep rose-crimson with a slight blotch of deeper crimson. The giant of the race. Yunnan, 9–11,000 ft. Only suitable for outdoor cultivation in very few gardens. Much of the best representation is in the garden of the National Trust for Scotland, Brodick Castle, Isle of Arran. B.M. n.s. 253.

F.C.C. 1953 (Her Grace the Duchess of Montrose, Brodick—under number *Forrest* 19335).

R. gilvum
(*pale yellow*)

see *R. temenium* subsp. *gilvum*.

R. glaphyrum
(*polished*)

see *R. temenium* subsp. *glaphyrum*.

R. glaucopeplum
(*with shining covering*)
I⁴ F¹⁻² L¹⁻² Pm.

May

s. and s.s. Taliense.

Shrub up to 8 ft. Lvs. up to 3 in. long and 1½ in. broad, oval to oblong-oval, with greyish-white indumentum below. Fls. in a truss of up to 10, about 1½ in. long, funnel-campanulate, bright rose with conspicuous crimson marking. Yunnan, 11,000 ft.

R. glaucophyllum
(*with bluish-grey leaf*)
I³⁻⁴ F²⁻³ L¹⁻² Pd.–m.

May

s. and s. s. Glaucophyllum.

Small shrub up to 4 ft. Lvs. 1½–3½ in. long, lanceolate to oblong-lanceolate or elliptic-lanceolate, white underneath, very aromatic. Fls. in trusses of 4–10, up to 1 in. long, and 1½ in. wide, campanulate, pink, pale rose or pinkish-purple; calyx large and leafy, densely scaly outside. Sikkim, Bhutan, S.E. Tibet, 9–12,000 ft. B.M. 4721.

Two forms of this species have been named as follows:

Var. *tubiforme* with tubular corolla about 1½ in. long. Assam, Bhutan, 10–11,000 ft.

Var. *luteiflorum* with lemon-yellow flowers (Dresden Yellow H.C.C. 64/2) N. Burma, 10–11,000 ft.

A.M. (National Trust for Scotland, 1960) under *K.W.* 21556.

R. glaucophyllum is a parent of the A.M. clone 'Rosy Bell' (1894).

89

R. glischroides
(*resembling R. glischrum*)
H³⁻⁴ F²⁻³ L²⁻³ Pm.–t.

March–April

s. Barbatum. *s.s.* Glischrum.

Shrub up to 15 ft. young shoots densely bristl with gland-capped setae. Lvs. up to 6 in long an 2 in. broad, oblong-lanceolate to oblong, dar. green and with main veins impressed above densely clothed below with long setae. Fls. i loose trusses of 6–10, 1½–2 in. long, campanulate white or creamy-white, more or less flushed ros with a crimson blotch; calyx up to ¾ in. long purplish, cut almost to base into unequal gland ciliate oblong to lanceolate lobes. N.E. Uppe Burma, 10–11,000 ft.

There is a form known as var. *arachnoideum* i which the whole under surface of the leaf i covered with a cobweb of white hairs.

R. glischrum
(*sticky*)
H⁴ F¹⁻³ L²⁻³ Pm.–t.

April–May

s. Barbatum. *s.s.* Glischrum.

Shrub or tree up to 25 ft. with bristly-glandula branchlets and leaf stalks. Lvs. 4–10 in. long an 1–2½ in. broad, oblanceolate, bright green above pale green below and there densely covered wit hispid long curved setae. Fls. in trusses of abou 10, about 1½ in. long, campanulate, plum-rose rose, pink or white, with crimson blotch and spots calyx about ½ in. long with unequal oblong lobe ciliate at the margin. Yunnan, Upper Burma S.E. Tibet, 13–14,000 ft. B.M. 9035.

A form which differs from the type in havin short bristly glands on the under surfaces of th leaves, in the short calyx, and usually in th smaller leaves is known as var. *adenosum*. S.E Tibet.

R. globigerum
(*bearing a globe*)
H⁴ F¹⁻³ L¹⁻² Pm.

April–May

s. Taliense. *s.s.* Roxieanum.

Shrub up to 8 ft. with thick gnarled branches persistent perulae and young shoots clad wit whitish to fawn felted indumentum. Lvs. 1½–3½ ir long, up to 1½ in. broad, oblong-oval or obovate dark green opaque above, clothed below wit thick woolly fulvous indumentum. Fls. in compac truss of about 15, 1–1½ in. long, campanulate white with crimson markings. Szechwan, 11 12,000 ft.

R. glomerulatum
(*with small clusters*)
H⁴ F¹⁻² L¹⁻² Pd.

April–May

s. Lapponicum.

Shrub up to 3 ft. Lvs. up to ¾ in. long and ½ ir broad, ovate or ovate-elliptic, densely scaly abov and below. Fls. in clusters of 4–6, girt by per sistent scales, about ⅔ in. long, widely funnel shaped, light purple-mauve. Yunnan.

R. grande
(*large*)

H$^{2-3}$ F$^{3-4}$ L$^{3-4}$ Pm.–t.

Feb.–March–April

s. Grande.

Tree up to 30 ft. Lvs. 6–12 in. long, up to 5 in. broad, oblong-lanceolate to oblanceolate or oblong-elliptic, deep green and shining above with the main nerves strongly impressed, usually silvery-white or sometimes tawny below. Fls. in rounded truss of up to 25, up to 3 in. long, ventricose-campanulate, pale rose in bud opening to white or creamy-white with a purple blotch, 8-lobed. Sikkim, Bhutan, 7,500–10,000 ft. B.M. 5054, 6948 (var. *roseum*).

F.C.C. 1901 (F. D. Godman, South Lodge, Horsham) to form with creamy-white flowers stained purple at the base and touched with rose on the exterior in the young state; leaves silvery beneath.

R. grande is a parent of the following A.M. clones: 'Muriel' (1925), 'Elsae' (1925), 'Clyne Elsae' (1940), 'Fulbrook' (1961).

R. griersonianum
(After R. C. Grierson, of the Chinese Maritime Customs at Tengyueh, friend of G. Forrest)

H$^{3-4}$ F$^{3-4}$ L$^{2-3}$ Pm.s.

June

s. Griersonianum.

Shrub often straggling, up to 10 ft., with young shoots clad with floccose hairs and setose glands, and with long, tapered, conical flower buds, the outer scales having long tapering tips. Lvs. up to 8 in. long and 2 in. broad, lanceolate, dull mat green above, with loose whitish to buff woolly tomentum below. Fls. in trusses of 5–12, up to 3½ in. long, and 4 in. broad, funnel-campanulate, 5-lobed, bright geranium-scarlet and quite unlike any other species of rhododendron. Yunnan, N. Burma, 7–9,000 ft. B.M. 9195.

F.C.C. 1924 (T. H. Lowinsky, Sunninghill, and L. de Rothschild, Exbury).

The long tapered flower buds are very similar to those of *R. auriculatum* otherwise there seems little relationship between these two species and the species has recently been moved into a separate series.

One of the most striking of the Chinese rhododendrons and an eminently desirable one, especially in the south and west, but worth a trial in any sheltered position in all but the coldest districts. Rather tender while young.

R. griersonianum has been much used in hybridization and is a parent of the following F.C.C. and A.M. clones:

F.C.C. 'Laura Aberconway' (1944), 'Azor Sister' (1960—Wisley Trials), 'Fusilier' (1942), 'Tally Ho' (1933), 'Elizabeth' (1943), 'Sunrise' (1942), 'Dorinthia' (1938), 'Vanessa' (1929), 'Matador' (1946).

R. griersonianum
(*continued*)

A.M. 'Damozel' (1948), 'Fire Flame' (1942), 'Toreador' (1942), 'Ouida' (1936), 'Aladdin' (1935), 'Mrs. Leopold de Rothschild' (1933), 'Rosefinch' (1939), 'Goblin' (1939), 'Ivanhoe' (1945), 'Siren' (1942), 'Fabia' (1934), 'Arthur Osborn' (1933), 'Fire Glow' (1935), 'Jibuti' (1949), 'Tortoiseshell Wonder' (1947), 'Brookside' (1962), 'May Day' (1932), 'Winsome' (1950), 'Infanta' (1941), 'Romarez' (1953), 'Day Dream' (1940), 'Diva' (1937), 'Sarita Loder' (1934), 'Glamour' (1946), 'Arthuria' (1952), 'Romany Chai' (1932), 'F.C. Puddle' (1932), 'Agnes' (1943), 'Grenadine' (1956), 'Rosabel' (1936), 'Ibex' (1948), 'Gretia' (1946), 'Captain Blood' (1947), 'Karkov' (1947), 'Vanessa Pastel' (1946), 'Amor' (1951), 'Gwilt King' (1952), 'Bonfire' (1933).

R. griffithianum
(After William Griffith, 1810–45, Supt. of Calcutta Botanic Garden)

H¹⁻³ F³⁻⁴ L²⁻³ Pm.–t.

May

s. Fortunei. *s.s.* Griffithianum.

Large shrub or small tree up to 20 ft., with beautiful smooth, thin, reddish-brown peeling bark and pale green young shoots. Lvs. up to 12 in. long and 4 in. broad, oblong to oblong-elliptic or oblong-ovate, yellowish-green with a glaucous tint below. Fls. in lax truss of up to 6, up to 3 in. long, and 6 in. across, widely campanulate, white, sometimes with green spotting, or white tinged with pink, beautifully veined, sometimes fragrant; calyx saucer-shaped, as much as $\frac{3}{4}$ in. deep, green or pink-tinted. Sikkim, Bhutan, 7–9,000 ft. B.M. 5065.

F.C.C. 1886 (Mr. Brown, Elmclon, Hull, Nr. Birmingham, as *R. aucklandii* and Mr. Standish as *R. griffithii*).

Several forms of this magnificent rhododendron exist, but unfortunately they are usually hardy, only in the extreme south and west and in the most sheltered of gardens.

It has been used a very great deal in hybridization and is a parent of the following F.C.C. and A.M. clones:

F.C.C. 'Beauty of Tremough' (1902), 'Manglesii' (1885), 'Exbury Angelo' (1947), 'Loderi Pink Diamond' (1914), 'Sunrise' (1942), 'Tip-the-Wink' (1936), 'Alice Mangles' (1882), 'Touchstone' (1939).

A.M. 'Gill's Triumph' (1906), 'Glory of Penjerrick' (1904), 'William Watson' (1925), 'Yvonne Opaline' (1931), 'Yvonne Pride'

R. griffithianum
(*continued*)

(1948), 'Norman Gill' (1922), 'Gillian' (1923), 'Penjerrick' (1923), 'Dr. Stocker' (1900), 'Gay Lady' (1938), 'Tittenhurst Belle' (1925), 'Dorothea' (1925), 'Angelo' (1945), 'Sheffield Park Angelo' (1950), 'Solent Queen' (1939), 'The Don' (1920), 'Loderi Julie' (1944), 'Loderi Sir Edmund' (1930), 'Pink Bride' (1931), 'Pink Shell' (1923), 'Jeritsa' (1951), 'Gill's Gloriosa' (1925), 'Leonardslee Giles' (1948), 'Exbury Cornish Cross' (1935), 'Pengaer' (1911), 'St. Keverne' (1922), 'Lady Montagu' (1931).

R. gymnanthum
(*with naked flowers*)

see *R. lukiangense* subsp. *gymnanthum*.

R. gymnocarpum
(*with naked fruit*)
H⁴ F²⁻³ L²⁻³ Pd.–m.

April

s. Taliense. s.s. Roxieanum.
Shrub up to 4 ft. Lvs. up to 4½ in. long, and to just over 1½ in. broad, oblong-elliptic to oblong-oblanceolate, thick, leathery, covered below with fawn semi-woolly indumentum. Fls. in loose truss of up to 6, 1½–2 in. long, broadly campanulate, pale or deep claret-crimson and with deeper markings. S.E. Tibet, 12–14,000 ft.
A.M. 1940 (L de Rothschild, Exbury) to form with deep, rich crimson flowers.

R. gymnogynum
(*with naked pistils*)

see *R. eritimum* subsp. *gymnogynum*.

R. habrotrichum
(*with soft hairs*)
H⁴ F²⁻³ L²⁻³ Pm.

April

s. Barbatum. s.s. Glischrum.
Shrub up to 10 ft. with densely bristly-glandular young shoots. Lvs. up to 7 in. long and 3 in. broad, elliptic-oblong, dark green and slightly rugulose above, pale green below with mid-rib bristly towards the base. Fls. in compact truss of up to 20, up to 2 in. long, funnel-campanulate, white or pale rose, with or without markings and faintly blotched. Yunnan, 10,000 ft.
A.M. 1933 (H. White, Sunningdale) to pink-flowered form.

R. haemaleum
(*blood-red*)

see *R. sanguineum* subsp. *haemaleum*.

R. haematodes
(*blood-like*)
H⁴ F³⁻⁴ L²⁻³ Pd.–m.

May–June

s. Neriiflorum. s.s. Haematodes.
Dwarf shrub or bush as much as 10 ft. high with young shoots woolly-tomentose. Lvs. up to 3 in. long and 1½ in. broad, oblong to obovate, dark green above, densely rufous-woolly-tomentose below. Fls. in a truss of 6–12, up to 2 in. long, tubular-campanulate, fleshy, glistening, brilliant

R. haematodes
(*continued*)

scarlet-crimson, occasionally deep pink; calyx up to $\frac{1}{3}$ in. long, commonly red. Yunnan, 11–12,000 ft. B.M. 9165.

F.C.C. (A.M. Williams, Launceston, 1926).

This is one of the finest Chinese rhododendrons ever introduced. Perfectly hardy and flowering late, it should be grown in every collection of rhododendrons. It takes some years before it is free-flowering, but is well worth the trouble and patience.

R. haematodes has been much used in hybridization and is a parent of the following F.C.C. and A.M. clones:

F.C.C.   'Choremia' (1948), 'Welkin' (1951).

A.M.   'Aspansia' (1945), 'Sussex Bonfire' (1934), 'Grosclaude' (1945), 'May Day' (1932).

'Red Imp' is a seedling of *R. haematodes*, raised by Bovee, Oregon, with flowers moderate red outside (2.57 4/10 Nickerson), lighter inside.

R. hanceanum
(After H. F. Hance, 1827–86, Consul at Canton, etc.)

H⁴ F²⁻³ L¹⁻² Pd.–m.

April

s. Triflorum. *s.s.* Hanceanum.

Shrub up to 4 ft. with bronze-brown young growths. Lvs. $1\frac{1}{2}$–5 in. long, up to 2 in. broad, ovate-lanceolate to obovate, finely scaly below. Fls. in a 5–11 flowered raceme, up to 1 in. long, funnel-shaped, creamy white or pale yellow, slightly scented; calyx nearly $\frac{1}{4}$ in. long, 5-lobed to the base. Szechwan, 5–13,000 ft. B.M. 8669.

'Nanum' (H⁴ F³ L¹⁻² Pd.), known in cultivation as *R. hanceanum* var. *nanum*, is a compact shrub, 6 in. high with an inflorescence of 5–10 yellow flowers; it is an excellent compact growing plant suitable for the rock or peat garden.

'Canton Consul' is a form of 'Nanum' with creamish-green buds and cream flowers, which received the A.M. 1957 (Crown Estate Commissioners).

R. hardingii
(After H. I. Harding, H.M. Consul at Tengyueh, 1923–5, to whom Forrest was indebted for the material of the flowering specimen of the type number)

H²⁻³ F¹⁻² L¹⁻² Pm.s.

April–May

s. and s.s. Irroratum.

Shrub, somewhat straggling up to 8 ft. Lvs. up to 4 in. long and 1 in. broad, lanceolate, slightly recurved at margin, pale green below. Fls. in lax truss of up to 12, about $1\frac{1}{2}$ in. long, cup-shaped or open, campanulate, white more or less flushed rose-pink and more or less crimson-spotted. Yunnan, 7,000 ft.

R. headfortianum
(After the late Marquess of Headfort)

H²⁻³ F²⁻³ L²⁻³ Pm.s.

May–June

s. Maddenii. *s.s.* Megacalyx.

Shrub about 3 ft. high (?). Lvs. up to 5 in. long, 2 in. broad, narrow oblong to oblong-lanceolate, margins recurved, glaucous and scaly below. Fls. solitary, about 3 in. long, widely funnel-shaped,

94

R. headfortianum
(continued)

cream, slightly tinged with pink outside the tube; calyx $\frac{3}{4}$ in. long, 5-lobed almost to the base. S.E. Tibet, Assam, 8,000 ft. B.M. 9614.

R. heliolepis
(with glittering scales)
H4 F1–3 L1–2 Pm.–t.

May–June

s. Heliolepis.

Shrub up to 10 ft. or more. Lvs. intensely aromatic, 3–4 in. long, up to $1\frac{1}{2}$ in. broad, oblong-elliptic, long-mucronate, closely reticulate above, scaly below. Fls. in small loose trusses of 4–6, about 1 in. long, widely funnel-shaped, rosy-purple or of a charming shade of pale old rose, or white, with dark blotch. Yunnan, 10–11,000 ft. Useful in that it is in bloom when most of the other species have finished flowering.

A.M. 1954 (Mrs. R. Stevenson, Tower Court, Ascot) to form with white flowers with green and brown spotting, under the number *Forrest* 26961.

R. hemidartum
((half-flayed, alluding to patchy indumentum))
H4 F2–3 L2–3 Pm.

April

s. Neriiflorum. s.s. Haematodes.

Shrub up to 6 ft. with young shoots clothed with shaggy gland-tipped hairs. Lvs. up to 4 in. long, $1\frac{1}{2}$ in. broad, oblong to obovate, green with a glaucous bloom above, with brown patchy indumentum below. Fls. in compact trusses of 6–10, about 2 in. long, tubular-campanulate, deep rich crimson. S.E. Tibet, 13–14,000 ft.

R. hemitrichotum
(half-hairy)
H4 F2–3 L1–2 Pd.–m.

April

s. Scabrifolium.

Shrub up to 4 ft. Lvs. about 1 in. long, $\frac{1}{2}$ in. broad, oblanceolate, softly hairy above, glaucous below and densely scaly. Fls. in groups of 1 or 2, axillary, crowded near the apex of the shoot, up to $\frac{3}{4}$ in. long, widely funnel-shaped, white or pale pink, deeper on the margin, in bud tipped bright brick-red. Szechwan, 12,000 ft.

R. hemsleyanum
(After W. B. Hemsley, English botanist, 1843–1924)
H4 F2–3 L2–3 Pm.–t.

May–June

s. and s.s. Fortunei.

Small tree up to 18 ft. Lvs. up to 8 in. long, and 4 in. broad, oblong to oblong-ovate, deeply auricled-cordate at base, dark green above, pale below. Fls. in truss of up to 10, sometimes more, $3\frac{1}{2}$–4 in. long, widely funnel-shaped, white. Szechwan. Cultivated in the U.S.A.

R. heptamerum
(with seven parts)

see *R. eritimum* subsp. *heptamerum*.

R. herpesticum
(spreading)

see *R. dichroanthum* subsp. *herpesticum*.

R. himertum
(lovely)

see *R. sanguineum* subsp. *himertum*.

R. hippophaeoides
(*resembling sea buckthorn*)
H⁴ F²⁻³ L²⁻³ Pd.–m.

March–April

s. Lapponicum.

Shrub, up to 5 ft. Lvs. up to $1\frac{1}{4}$ in. long and $\frac{1}{3}$ in. broad, oblanceolate, scaly, densely so below. Fls. in trusses of 6–8, nearly 1 in. across, flat funnel-shaped, lavender-blue, pale lilac to rose. Yunnan, 9–11,000 ft. where it is often found in boggy ground. B.M. 9156.

A.M. 1927 (Lady Aberconway and the Hon. H. D. McLaren, Bodnant) to form with lavender-blue flowers.

A.G.M. 1925.

R. hirsutum
(*hairy*)
H⁴ F¹⁻² L¹⁻² Pd.–m.

June

s. Ferrugineum.

Shrub, with short twiggy branchlets, up to 5 ft. Lvs. $\frac{1}{2}$–1 in. long, oblanceolate to elliptic-oblanceolate, crenulate on the margin and fringed with bristly hairs. Fls. in small trusses, about $\frac{1}{2}$ in. long, tubular with lobes fringed with short hairs, rose-pink to nearly scarlet. C. Europe. B.M. 1853.

Since it grows on limestone it may be attempted in calcareous soils. There is a form with white flowers and one with double flowers (F²).

R. hirtipes
(*shaggy-footed*)
H⁴ F¹⁻³ L¹⁻³ Pm.–t.

April

s. Barbatum. s.s. Glischrum.

Shrub or small tree up to 25 ft. with bristly young shoots. Lvs. $2\frac{1}{2}$–5 in. long, $1\frac{1}{2}$–3 in. broad, oblong-oval, oval, or broadly elliptic, glossy above, paler below and with prominent setose-glandular mid-rib. Fls. in loose truss of 3–5, up to 2 in. long, campanulate, almost white to rose-pink with carmine spots, broadly striped with pink on the outside; calyx almost $\frac{1}{3}$ in. long, unequally 5-lobed to near base. S.E. Tibet, 13,000 ft.

R. hodgsonii
(After B. H. Hodgson, one time the East India Co.'s resident in Nepal)
H⁴ F²⁻³ L²⁻³ Pm.–t.

April

s. Falconeri.

Shrub or often a small tree up to 20 ft. with smooth reddish-brown peeling bark. Lvs. up to 12 in. long and 5 in. broad, oblong-elliptic to broadly oblong-oblanceolate, dark mat green and with mica-like spots above, covered below with grey to fawn, sometimes darker, indumentum. Fls. in compact rounded truss of up to 20, up to 2 in. long, tubular-campanulate, dark magenta-purple fading to a paler and duller tint of magenta-lilac. Sikkim, Nepal to Bhutan, 10–12,000 ft. B.M. 5552.

R. hodgsonii is a parent of the A.M. clones 'Elsae' (1925), 'Clyne Elsae' (1940), 'Ronald' (1958).

R. hookeri

After Sir J. D. Hooker, 1817–1911) Director of Kew, botanist and traveller in the Himalayas.

H3 F2–4 L2–3 Pm.–t.

March–April

s. and *s.s.* Thomsonii.

Shrub, with young growths at first glaucous, and with thin smooth reddish-brown bark. Lvs. up to 6 in. long, up to 2½ in. broad, oblong or oblong-oval, mat and with primary nerves impressed above, light glaucous-green below with lateral veins studded with isolated hair-tufts like small hooks, at first white, later brown. Fls. in truss of up to 15, 1½–2 in. long, tubular-campanulate or funnel-shaped, of the most intense blood-red or pink; calyx up to ¾ in. long, often coloured. Bhutan, Assam, 10–12,000 ft. M.B. 4926.

Closely allied to *R. thomsonii* and *R. meddianum* but easily distinguished by the tufts of hairs like small barbs on the lower surface of the leaf. Pink forms are rather poor compared to the deep red forms.

F.C.C. 1933 (Hon. H. D. McLaren, Bodnant) to fine form with flowers of the darkest red and with large calyx of the same colour.

It is a parent of the A.M. clones 'Eureka' (1939), 'Alix' (1935).

R. horaeum

beautiful)

see *R. citriniflorum* subsp. *horaeum*.

R. hormophorum

bearing a necklace)

H4 F1–3 L1–2 Pm.

May

s. Triflorum. *s.s.* Yunnanense.

Shrub up to 8 ft. Lvs. completely deciduous, 1–3 in. long, lanceolate or oblanceolate, with pale yellow scales below. Fls. in trusses of 3–6, terminal, or terminal and axillary in the uppermost leaves, up to 1½ in. long, widely funnel-shaped, zygomorphic, white tinged pink, rose, lilac or lavender, with or without brown markings. Yunnan, Szechwan, 8–12,000 ft.

A.M. 1943 (Col. The Lord Digby, Minterne) to a white form with a few buff spots on the upper petal.

The plant which used to be known as *R. chartophyllum* var. *praecox* belongs here.

R. houlstonii

After G. Houlston, Chinese Imp. Maritime Customs, friend E. H. Wilson)

H4 F2–3 L2–3 Pm.–t.

May

s. and *s.s.* Fortunei.

Tree up to 20 ft. Lvs. 3–6 in. long and 1–2 in. broad, oblong-oblanceolate to oblong-elliptic, dark green above, pale below. Fls. in trusses of 6–10, up to 2½ in. long, funnel-campanulate, 7-lobed, white or pale pink, faintly lined and spotted. Hupeh, Szechwan, 4,500–7,000 ft. It is a parent of the A.M. clone 'Arthur J. Ivens' (1944).

R. hunnewellianum
(After a well-known New England family)
H⁴ F²⁻³ L²⁻³ Pm.–t.

March–April

s. Arboreum. *s.s.* Argyrophyllum.
Shrub or small tree up to 25 ft. Lvs. 3–6 i
long, about 1 in. broad, narrow-oblanceolate, ligl
green and rugulose above, with white or gr
floccose tomentum below. Fls. in truss of 7–8, u
to 2 in. long, widely campanulate, white tint
pink (much deeper pink in bud) pink spotte
within. W. Szechwan, 6–10,000 ft.

R. hylaeum
(*belonging to forests*)
H⁴ F¹⁻³ L²⁻³ Pm.–t.

May

s. and *s.s.* Thomsonii.
Shrub or tree up to 25 ft., with densely glandul
young shoots. Lvs. up to 7 in. long and 2 i
broad, oblong or oblanceolate, when youn
floccose and glandular above later glabrous, pa
green semi-glaucous and when mature glabro
below. Fls. in truss of 10–12, up to 2 in. lon
tubular-campanulate, fleshy, pale rose with deep
spots; calyx about ⅓ in. long, greenish. W. Burm
Tibet, Yunnan, 7–12,000 ft.
Distinct from *R. thomsonii* by reason of th
oblong or oblanceolate leaves.

R. hylothreptum
(*growing on wood*)

see *R. anthosphaerum* subsp. *hylothreptum*.

R. hypenanthum
(*bearded flowers*)
H³⁻⁴ F¹⁻² L¹⁻² Pd.

April–May

s. Anthopogon.
Shrub up to 2 ft. with short twiggy branches an
with the bud-scales persisting for several year
Lvs. about 1½ in. long and ⅓ in. broad, obovat
elliptic, densely scaly below. Fls. in a sma
compact truss, ¾ in. long, narrowly tubula
yellow. N.W. Himalayas, 11–18,000 ft., ve
similar to *R. anthopogon*.

R. hyperythrum
(*reddish*)
H³⁻⁴ F²⁻³ L¹⁻² Pm.

April–May

s. Ponticum. *s.s.* Caucasicum.
Shrub up to 5 ft. Lvs. up to 5 in. long and 1½ i
broad, oblong to elliptic-oblong or elliptic-lance
late, lower surface dotted with reddish punctul
tions. Fls. in trusses of 7–10, up to 2 in. lon
funnel-campanulate, white, with or withou
purple spots. Formosa. B.M. n.s. 109.

R. hypoglaucum
(*blue-grey underneath*)
H⁴ F¹⁻³ L¹⁻² Pm.–t.

May

s. Arboreum. *s.s.* Argyrophyllum.
Shrub or small tree up to 20 ft. Lvs. up to 5 i
long and 1½ in. broad, oblong-elliptic, oblon
lanceolate or oblanceolate, bright green, glossy an
with veins slightly impressed above, with thi
smooth white tomentum below. Fls. in truss
of up to 8, about 1½ in. long, funnel-campanulat
white flushed rose and with numerous deep ro
spots. E. China, Hupeh, 5–7,000 ft. B.M. 864

R. hypophaeum
(*grey beneath*)
H⁴ F¹⁻² L¹⁻² Pm.

   May

s. Triflorum. s.s. Yunnanense.
   Shrub up to 5 ft. Lvs. 1–2½ in. long, usually lanceolate, densely scaly and glaucous below. Fls. in clusters of 3–5, terminal or terminal and axillary in uppermost leaves, about 1 in. long, widely funnel-shaped, zygomorphic, white faintly tinged with rose, or pink, or purplish-blue or purple or pale lavender. Rather rare in cultivation. Akin to *R. davidsonianum*.

R. idoneum
(*suitable*)
H⁴ F¹⁻² L¹⁻² Pd.c.

   April–May

s. Lapponicum.
   Small compact cushion-like shrub up to 1½ ft. Lvs. ¼ in. long, broadly elliptic, very pale yellow-green-scaly below. Fls. in pairs, about ½ in. long, open funnel-shaped, deep blue-purple with a white throat, Yunnan, Szechwan, 11–14,000 ft.

R. imberbe
(*not bearded*)
H⁴ F¹⁻² L²⁻³ Pm.

   March

s. and s.s. Barbatum.
   Shrub up to 8 ft. Lvs. up to 5 in. long and 2 in. broad, obovate-elliptic, dark green above, pale and glabrous below. Fls. in truss of up to 15, about 2 in. long, tubular-campanulate, red, with lines of darker spots within. West Central Himalaya, 9,000 ft.

R. impeditum
H⁴ F³⁻⁴ L¹⁻² Pd.
(*tangled*)
   April–May

s. Lapponicum.
   Low shrub with short branchlets covered with black scales. Lvs. about ½ in. long and ¼ in. broad, broadly elliptic, densely scaly on both surfaces. Fls. single or in pairs, about ⅔ in. long, open funnel-shaped, mauve or light purplish-blue. Yunnan, Szechwan, 15–16,000 ft. A fine species for the rock garden.
   A.M. 1944 (Sunningdale Nurseries, Windlesham, Surrey) to form grown under number *Rock* 59263.
   R. impeditum is a parent of the F.C.C. clone 'Impeanum' (1934).

R. imperator
(*Emperor*)
H³⁻⁴ F²⁻³ L¹⁻² Pd.p.

   May

s. Uniflorum.
   Dwarf, sometimes prostrate shrub, up to 1 ft. Lvs. up to 1 in. long, narrow, oblanceolate, glaucous-green below. Fls. solitary or in pairs, very freely borne, over 1 in. long, about ½ in. across, funnel-shaped, pink or pinkish-purple or rosy-purple. Burma 10–11,000 ft. A splendid plant for the rock garden. It would appear that many plants in the trade named *R. imperator* are really *R. uniflorum*.
   A.M. 1934 (Lord Swaything, Townhill Park, Southampton) to form with rosy-purple flowers.

R. inaequale
(*of unequal size*)
H¹ F³⁻⁴ L¹⁻³ Pm.s.

March–May

s. Maddenii. s.s. Ciliicalyx.

Shrub, often straggly, up to 10 ft. Lvs. up to 5 in. long and 1½ in. broad, lanceolate or elliptic-oblanceolate, dull dark green above, scaly below, ciliate at margin. Fls. in truss of up to 6, about 2 in. long, 4 in. broad, widely funnel-shaped, white with upper petal marked with broad orange-yellow band, very fragrant. Assam, 4–5,000 ft. B.M. n.s. 295. A plant for the cool house.

A.M. 1947 (Lord Aberconway, Bodnant).

R. indicum
(*Indian*)
H²⁻³ F²⁻³ L¹⁻² Pd.–m.p.

June

s. Azalea. s.s. Obtusum.

Spreading evergreen shrub, sometimes prostrate, up to 6 ft. Lvs. up to 1½ in. long, narrow lanceolate to oblanceolate, remotely crenulate-serrulate at the margin, ciliate, with scattered adpressed red-brown hairs on both surfaces, often changing in the autumn to crimson or vinous-purple. Fls. single or in pairs, about 2½ in. across, broad funnel-formed, red to scarlet or rose-red. S. Japan, where it is called the Satsuki or Fifth* month (June) Azalea, by reason of its blooming during the month. There are numerous forms and the Japanese Satsuki Society has selected 162 of them.

A well-known form which has been in the trade for many years, with double salmon-red flowers is known as *balsaminaeflorum* (F³), or *Azalea rosaeflora*.

The *Azalea indica* of the trade is not this species but belongs to *R. simsii* and allied forms. B.M. 4726 (var. *crispiflorum*).

R. inopinum
(*unexpected*)
H⁴ F¹⁻² L¹⁻² Pm.

April–May

s. Taliense.

Shrub up to 6 ft. with young growths covered with floccose scurfy indumentum, at first white, later brown. Lvs. 1½ to 4 in. long and up to 7½ in. broad, oval-oblong, dark green above, pale green and clad with patches of indumentum below. Fls. in trusses of about 10, about 1 in. long, funnel-campanulate, white, with or without a deep crimson blotch and crimson spots. Szechwan.

R. insigne
(*remarkable*)
H⁴ F³⁻⁴ L³⁻⁴ Pm.

May–June

s. Arboreum. s.s. Argyrophyllum.

Slow growing shrub up to 12 ft. Lvs. 2½–5 in. long, up to nearly 2 in. broad, oblong-lanceolate or oblong-oblanceolate, margin slightly reflexed, dark green above, covered below with a tawny-grey, skin-like indumentum with a coppery sheen. Fls

---

*Under the old Chinese calendar, the equivalent of our June, is the fifth month of the year.

in a truss of 8 or more, up to 2 in. long, widely campanulate, pinky-white with crimson spots within. Szechwan, 7–10,000 ft. B.M. 8885. A very beautiful species.

A.M. 1923 (Lady Aberconway and the Hon. H. D. McLaren, Bodnant).

R. intricatum
(entangled)
4 F2–3 L1–2 Pd.
April

s. Lapponicum.

Intricately-branched shrub up to 3 ft. Lvs. about ⅓ in. long, oblong-elliptic, densely greenish-grey-scaly. Fls. in small subglobose truss, ⅓ in. long, narrowly tubular, rose-lilac to mauve. Szechwan, 12–15,000 ft. B.M. 8163. A good plant for the rock garden.

F.C.C. 1907 (Messrs. J. Veitch, Chelsea).

It is a parent of the A.M. clone 'Bluebird' (1943).

R. iodes
(rust-coloured)
4 F1–2 L1–2 Pd.–m.
April–May

s. Taliense. s.s. Roxieanum.

Shrub up to 8 ft., with young shoots rusty-tomentose. Lvs. up to 4½ in. long, 1 in. broad, usually lanceolate, lower surface rust-coloured. Fls. in truss of 10–12, about 1½ in. long, funnel-campanulate, white with crimson spots but usually not with a basal blotch. S.E. Tibet, 12,000 ft.

R. irroratum
*(covered with dew,
minutely spotted)*
4 F2–4 L2–3 Pm.–t.
March–May

s. and s.s. Irroratum.

Large shrub or small tree up to 25 ft. with young shoots thinly tomentose and glandular. Lvs. 2½–5 in. long and up to 1½ in. broad, lanceolate to oblanceolate or narrowly elliptic, pale green above and even paler below. Fls. in truss up to 15, about 1¼ in. long, tubular-campanulate, white or creamy-yellow, often suffused a pale or a deeper rose with many or few crimson or greenish spots. Yunnan, Szechwan, 9–11,000 ft. B.M. 7361.

A.M. 1957 (Col. The Lord Digby, Minterne, Dorchester) to form with flowers white with a faint bluish-pink tinge and flower buds tinged with bright bluish-pink.

'Polka Dot' is an A.M. clone with flowers white, heavily marked throughout with spots of Paeony Purple (H.C.C. 729/1) and suffused with a shade of pink (E. de Rothschild, Exbury, 1957).

R. iteophyllum
(willow-leaved)
1 F1–2 L1–2 Pm.
May

s. Maddenii. s.s. Ciliicalyx.

Shrub up to 6 ft. with young shoots densely scaly. Lvs. up to 3½ in. long and up to ⅔ in. broad, linear or linear-lanceolate, scaly especially below. Fls. in trusses of 2–3, about 2¼ in. long, funnel-shaped, white or white tinged with pink. Assam, 2–6,000 ft. A plant for the cool greenhouse.

R. japonicum
(*from Japan*)
H4 F3-4 L1-2 Pd.-m.

May

s. Azalea. s.s. Luteum.

Deciduous shrub up to 10 ft. Lvs. up to 4 i
long, 1¼ in. broad, obovate to obovate-oblon
dark dull-green above, lighter green below an
strongly nerved, ciliate at the margin. Fl
precocious, in trusses of 6–12, up to 2½ in. di
meter, broadly funnel-shaped, orange or salmon
red to brick-red, with large orange blotch. C. & N
Japan. B.M. 5905.

Formerly known as *R. molle* or *Azalea moll*
this is one of the parents of the numerous hybric
which do so much to beautify our gardens.

R. jasminiflorum
(*jasmine-flowered*)
H1 F2-3 L1-2 Pm.

May–Sept.

Sect. Vireya. *Subsect.* Solenovireya of Sleume

Shrub up to 10 ft. Lvs. crowded towards th
end of the branchlets, up to 3 in. long and 1 i
broad, ovate to elliptic. Fls. in terminal loos
trusses of up to 20, 1½–2 in. long, narrow, tubul
with spreading lobes, white, sometimes tinge
rose. Malayan Peninsula and Sumatra. B.M
4524.

Essentially a plant for a warm greenhouse.

R. johnstoneanum
(After Mrs. Johnstone, wife of
Political Agent, Manipur, 1882)
H2-3 F3-4 L1-2 Pm.-t.

May

s. Maddenii. s.s. Ciliicalyx.

Large shrub up to 15 ft. Lvs. 2–4 in. long an
up to 1½ in. broad, elliptic or obovate-ellipti
bristly-ciliate when young, dark green abov
glaucous to brownish-olive-green and dense
scaly below. Fls. in trusses of 3–4, 2 in. or mo
long, 3 in. across, open funnel-campanulat
fragrant, pale yellow or white, or sometimes whi
tinged pink, spotted with red, yellow blotche
Assam, Manipur, 6–11,000 ft.

A.M. 1934 (Col. Spender Clay, Ford Mano
Lingfield, Surrey, and Lt.-Col. L. C. R. Messe
Nymans, Hand Cross, Sussex) form with flowe
pale creamy-white, yellow blotched at the bas

'Rubeotinctum' is an A.M. clone (Lt.-Co
E. H. W. Bolitho, Trengwainton, Heamoo
Cornwall), raised from seeds of *K.W.* 7732, wit
the flowers white with a deep pink stripe alor
the middle of each petal, the same colour supe
imposed on yellow forming a patch towards th
base of the back petal; A.M. 1941, as var. *rube*
tinctum.

There are also forms with double or semi-doub
flowers:

'Double Diamond' is an almost complete
double form, the colour white with a vestige
orange in the throat. A.M. 1956 (Commissione
of Crown Lands).

R. johnstoneanum
(continued)

R. johnstoneanum is a parent of the A.M. clones 'R.W. Rye' (1951) and *R. johnstoneanum* 'Double Diamond' a reputed parent of the A.M. cultivar 'Johnnie Johnston' (1956).

R. jucundum
(pleasant)

H4 F1-2 L1-2 Pm.-t.

May–June

s. Thomsonii. *s.s.* Selense.

Shrub up to 20 ft. with young shoots covered with stalked setose glands. Lvs. 1½–3 in. long, up to 1½ in. broad, elliptic to oblong-elliptic, dark green above, glaucous below. Fls. in trusses of 5–8, up to 1½ in. long, funnel-campanulate, rose, pink or white, with or without a crimson blotch. Yunnan, S.E. Tibet, 9–12,000 ft.

R. kaempferi
After E. Kaempfer, 1651–1716, who travelled in China but wrote about Japanese plants).

H4 F3-4 L1-2 Pm.

May–June

s. Azalea. *s.s.* Obtusum.

Deciduous or semi-evergreen, loosely branched shrub up to 10 ft. Lvs. up to 3 in. long, strigose-pubescent on both sides. Fls. in clusters of 1–4, 1¾–2½ in. long and wide, funnel-shaped, salmon-red, orange-red, pink to rosy-scarlet, white with somewhat frilled lobes, sometimes semi-double, sometimes hose-in-hose. Great variability also in time of flowering. C. & N. Japan.

A.M. 1953 (Commissioners of Crown Lands, Windsor.)

'Eastern Fire' is an F.C.C. clone (Commissioners of Crown Lands, Windsor, 1955) with flowers of Camellia Rose (H.C.C. 622/1) with the tips of the lobes a darker shade, which also received the A.M. in 1953.

R. keiskei
After Ito Keisuke, 1803–1900, a Japanese botanist)

H3-4 F2-3 L1-2 Pd.-m.c.

March–May

s. and *s.s.* Triflorum.

Mostly a low growing compact shrub, almost deciduous. Lvs. 1–3 in. long, lanceolate or oblong-lanceolate, scaly below, when young often bronze-brown. Fls. in trusses of 3–5, about 1 in. long zygomorphic, widely funnel-shaped, lemon-yellow, unspotted. Japan, 2–6,000 ft. B.M. 8300.

Of small stature for the Triflorum Series this species is very free-flowering and very suitable for the small garden.

A.M. 1929 (Mr. Harry White, Windlesham, Surrey).

R. keiskei is a parent of the A.M. clone 'Chink' (1961).

R. keleticum
(charming)

H4 F1-3 L1-2 Pd.p.

May–June

s. Saluenense.

Semi-prostrate spreading shrub up to about 1 ft. with sub-persistent leaf bud scales. Lvs. up to 1 in. long, oblong to ovate-elliptic, densely scaly below. Fls. in clusters of 1–3, up to 1 in. long, funnel-shaped or rotate, deep purplish-crimson

R. keleticum
(*continued*)

with red or deep crimson spots. S.E. Tibet, Yunnan, Upper Burma, 11–15,000 ft.

Allied to *R. radicans* but less prostrate and matted and with larger leaves of different shape

A.M. 1928 (Messrs. Gill, Falmouth) to form with lilac flowers with red spots.

R. kendrickii
(After Dr. Kendrick, friend of the botanist, Dr. Nuttall)
H² F¹⁻² L¹⁻² Pm.-t.

April–May

s. and s.s. Irroratum.

Shrub or small tree up to 25 ft. Lvs. up to 5 in. long and 1½ in. broad, oblong-lanceolate or lanceolate. Fls. in truss of 15 or more, up to 1½ in. long, tubular-campanulate, pink, scarlet or crimson, with red or deep crimson spots. Bhutan 7–9,000 ft. B.M. 5129.

R. keysii
(After a Mr. Keys)
H³⁻⁴ F²⁻³ L¹⁻² Pm.s.

June

s. Cinnabarinum.

A leggy or straggly shrub up to 12 ft. or more Lvs. 3–4 in. long, up to 1½ in. broad, oblong-lanceolate, densely scaly on both surfaces. Fls. from clustered lateral and terminal buds, ¾ in long, tubular, slightly ventricose, bright red tipped yellow or bright orange tipped a deep red. S.E Tibet, Bhutan, Assam, 9–16,000 ft. B.M. 4875.

A.M. 1933 (L. de Rothschild, Exbury) to form raised from seeds of *K.W.* 6257, from S.E. Tibet and known as var. *unicolor*; the tubular flower are of an almost uniform red with the tips of the short erect teeth being slightly yellowish. (This form is said to be hardier than the one from Bhutan.)

R. keysii is a parent of the following clones 'Minterne Cinnkeys' (F.C.C. 1952), 'Cinnkeys' (A.M. 1935).

R. kiusianum
(*from the mountains of Kyushu, Japan*)
H³⁻⁴ F¹⁻² L¹⁻² Pd.

May–June

s. Azalea. *s.s.* Obtusum.

Evergreen or semi-evergreen densely branched spreading shrub up to 3 ft. Lvs. up to 1½ in. long oval to elliptic-ovate, bright green above, paler beneath. Fls. in clusters of 2–5, funnel-shaped almost tubeless, 1–1½ in. across, salmon-red, pink to crimson or purple, rarely white. Japan.

There are numerous natural hybrids between *R. kiusianum* and *R. kaempferi*.

Regarded as the species from which the Kurume Azaleas originally introduced by Wilson, were developed.

R. kongboense
(*from Kongbo, S.E. Tibet*)
H⁴ F¹⁻² L¹⁻² Pd.

April–May

s. Anthopogon.

Twiggy shrub or undershrub up to 2 ft. or more Lvs. up to 1 in. long, oblong to oblong-oblanceolate. Fls. in a small tight truss, up to ⅜ in. long tubular, bright-rose, densely hairy on the tube without. Tibet–Bhutan border, 11–15,000 ft. B.M. 9492.

R. kotschyi

(After Theodor Kotschy, 1813–56, Austrian botanist)

H4 F2–3 L1–2 Pd.

May–July

s. Ferrugineum.

Dwarf twiggy shrub up to 2 ft. Lvs. about ½ in. long, ¼ in. broad, oblanceolate, crenulate at margin, densely scaly below. Fls. in clusters of 4–8, about ½ in. long, tubular with spreading lobes, rosy-pink, rarely white. C. Europe, 5–7,500 ft. B.M. 9132.

R. kotschyi is a parent of the A.M. clone 'Silverburn', 1958.

R. kyawi

(After Maung Kyaw, a Burmese collector)

H2–3 F3–4 L2–3 Pm.–t.

July

s. Irroratum. s.s. Parishii.

Shrub or tree up to 20 ft. Lvs. 6–12 in. long, up to 4 in. broad, oblong to oblong-oval, bright green and rather bullate above, pale green below. Fls. in a truss of up to 20, up to 2½ in. long, tubular-campanulate, bright crimson or rose-scarlet. Burma, Yunnan, 6–12,000 ft. B.M. 9271.

A magnificent rhododendron, especially when grown in a cool greenhouse, introduced and grown under the name of *R. prophantum*.

R. kyawi is a parent of the following A.M. clones: 'Leonore' (1948), 'Romarez' (1953), 'Iliad' (1949).

R. lacteum

(milky)

H4 F2–4 L2–3 Pm.–t.

April–May

s. Lacteum.

Shrub or tree up to 30 ft. with very conspicuous scars of the fallen leaves. Lvs. 3–7 in. long, 1½–4 in. broad, obovate, oblong-elliptic, rarely oblanceolate, covered below with thin suede-like fawn or brown indumentum. Fls. in trusses of up to 20, sometimes more, 1½–2 in. long, broadly campanulate, sulphury-white, pale or clear yellow, often stained pink, with or without a crimson blotch. Yunnan, Szechwan, Burma, 10–13,000 ft. B.M. 8988.

Very beautiful when well-grown, but on the whole of poor constitution, often not long lived, slow growing, reluctant to set seeds and difficult to propagate by layering.

F.C.C. 1926 (A. M. Williams, Launceston) to form with suphury-white flowers, dark crimson-blotched at the base.

R. lacteum is a parent of the following F.C.C. and A.M. clones:

F.C.C. 'Jocelyne' (1956).

A.M.   'Guepier' (1961), 'Repose' (1956), 'Mariloo Eugenie' (1950), 'Mariloo Gilbury' (1943), 'Robert Keir' (1957), 'Lionel's Triumph' (1954).

R. lanatum
(*woolly*)
H⁴ F²⁻³ L²⁻³ Pm.

April–May

s. Campanulatum.

Shrub up to 6 ft. with young shoots densel
clothed with soft adpressed white to tawny cotton
indumentum. Lvs. tending to be confined to th
tops of the branchlets, 2½–5 in. long, elliptic o
obovate or oblong-obovate, covered below wit
brown or rust woolly indumentum. Fls. in trusse
of up to 10, 1¼–2 in. long, broadly campanulate
pale yellow, spotted with crimson-purple. Sikkim
Bhutan, Assam, Tibet, 12–14,000 ft.

Not the easiest of rhododendrons to grow, bu
very attractive when well grown. A form wit
larger and narrower leaves from S.E. Tibet i
known as var. *luciferum* so named because th
Tibetans use the wool from the undersides of th
leaves as wicks for their lamps.

Closely allied to *R. tsariense* which has smalle
leaves and white or pink flowers.

R. lanigerum
(*woolly*)
H⁴ F³⁻⁴ L²⁻³ Pm.–t.

March–April

s. and s.s. Arboreum.

Shrub or small tree up to 20 ft. with the youn
shoots at first grey-tomentose, later glabrous an
with the large round flower-buds covered wit
russet indumentum and very attractive. Lvs. u
to 9 in. long and 3 in. broad, oblong-lanceolate o
oblong-oblanceolate, dark green above, covere
below with white or grey or light cinnamon-brow
to olive-brown indumentum. Fls. in round com
pact trusses of up to 25 or more, up to 2 in. long
campanulate, rose-purple to reddish-purple t
dark magenta. Assam, S.E. Tibet, 10–11,000 f

A.M. 1949 (Col. E. H. Bolitho, Trengwaintor
Heamoor, Cornwall).

A.M. 1951 (Mrs. R. M. Stevenson, Towe
Court, Ascot, under number *K.W.* 6258, and th
name *silvaticum*).

The following are A.M. clones:

'Silvia' (1954). R. Olaf Hambro, Logan House
Stranraer; a seedling, grown under the name o
R. silvaticum with flowers of a pale shade o
crimson (H.C.C. 22/1) suffused with white an
with a dark crimson ring round the base of th
throat.

'Round Wood' (1951). Crown Estate Commis
sioners, Windsor; a seedling grown under th
name of *R. silvaticum* and under the numbe
K.W. 6258, with crimson flowers.

'Chapel Wood' (1961). Crown Estate Com
missioners, Windsor; a seedling of *Rock* 0391
with flowers of Neyron Rose (H.C.C. 623/1–623/2
in a truss of up to 50 flowers.

R. lanigerum
(*continued*)

'Stonehurst' (1961). Robert Strauss, Stonehurst, Ardingly, Sussex; a seedling with flowers of a light shade of Cherry (H.C.C. 722/3) in a truss of about 35 flowers.

R. lapponicum
(*from Lapland*)
H⁴ F¹ L¹ Pᵈ.

Jan.–Feb.

s. Lapponicum.

Small shrublet a few inches high with densely scaly branchlets. Lvs. $\frac{1}{3}$–$\frac{1}{2}$ in. long, obovate-oblanceolate, densely scaly especially below. Fls. in clusters of up to 3 about $\frac{1}{3}$ in. long, funnel-shaped, purple. Arctic Europe, Asia and America. B.M. 3106.

A most difficult plant in cultivation, especially in the South.

R. lasiopodum
(*woolly-footed*)
H² F²⁻³ L¹⁻² Pᵐ.⁻ᵗ.

June

s. Maddenii. s.s. Ciliicalyx.

Shrub up to 16 ft. Lvs. up to 5 in. long, 2$\frac{1}{2}$ in. broad, broadly elliptic, glaucous and densely rusty-scaly below. Fls. usually in pairs, up to 2$\frac{1}{2}$ in. long, narrowly funnel-shaped, white, stained with yellow at the base within; fragrant. Yunnan, 8–9,000 ft.

R. laudandum
(*praiseworthy*)
H⁴ F¹⁻² L¹⁻² Pᵈ.

April

s. Anthopogon.

Small shrub up to 3 ft. with deciduous and sub-persistent leaf-bud scales. Lvs. up to $\frac{3}{4}$ in. long, oval to oblong-oval, covered with dark red scales below. Fls. in small compact head, about 1$\frac{1}{2}$ in. long, narrowly tubular, pale shade of pink or almost white, densely covered without with long whitish hairs. A form with white flowers and persistent leaf-bud scales is known as var. *temoense*. Tibet–Bhutan border, 12–15,000 ft.

R. laxiflorum
(*loose-flowered*)
H⁴ F¹⁻² L¹⁻² Pᵐ.⁻ᵗ.

April

s. and s.s. Irroratum.

Shrub up to 15 ft. or more. Lvs. up to 6 in. long and 2 in. broad, oblong to oblong-elliptic, bright green and mat above, paler below and minutely red-punctulate. Fls. in a loose truss of about 12, 1$\frac{1}{2}$ in. long, campanulate, pure white sometimes suffused with rose, unspotted. Yunnan, 8–11,000 ft.

R. lepidostylum
(*with scaly styles*)
H⁴ F¹ L³⁻⁴ Pᵈ.

May–June

s. Trichocladum.

Compact shrub up to about 3 ft. with densely bristly and scaly branchlets. Lvs. about 1$\frac{1}{2}$ in. long and $\frac{2}{3}$ in. broad, ovate to obovate, margin setulose, for most of the year a fine bluish-green colour. Fls. single or in pairs, about 1 in. long, widely funnel-shaped, pale yellow, often hidden by the foliage. Yunnan, 11–12,000 ft. With *R. campanulatum* var. *aeruginosum*, it has the bluest foliage in the genus and is a fine foliage plant, especially for the small garden.

R. lepidotum
(*beset with scales*)
H³⁻⁴ F¹⁻² L¹⁻² Pd.–m.

June

s. *and* s.s. Lepidotum.

A shrub from a few inches to 5 ft. Lvs. up to 1½ in. long, narrowly oblanceolate, densely covered below with more or less fleshy scales. Fls. in clusters of 1–3, occasionally 4, about 1 in. diameter, rotate, densely scaly-glandular on the outside, pink, purple, crimson, yellow, greenish-yellow or white. From N.W. Himalayas and Nepal through Tibet and Burma to Szechwan and Yunnan, 8–16,000 ft.

There are numerous forms of this widely distributed, variable species and formerly some of the more distinctive were named as follows:

R. *lepidotum*; with pink, purple or crimson flowers. B.M. 4657.

R. *elaeagnoides*; sometimes almost deciduous and with yellow or greenish-yellow flowers. B.M. 4802, as *lepidotum* var. *chloranthum*.

R. *obovatum*; with longer, broader obovate or broadly elliptic leaves and with purple or crimson flowers. B.M. 6450, as *lepidotum* var. *obovatum*.

R. *lepidotum* is a parent of the A.M. clone 'Lepidoboothii' (1919).

R. leptothrium
(*with thin leaves*)
H²⁻³ F¹⁻² L²⁻³ Pd.

April–May

s. Ovatum.

Shrub up to 6 ft. Lvs. up to 2 in. long, lanceolate to oblong-lanceolate, very thin in texture and very bright green in colour. Fls. single from axillary buds, up to 1 in. diam. almost rotate, deep magenta-rose. Yunnan, Upper Burma, 7–11,000 ft.

R. leucaspis
(*white shield*)
H³⁻⁴ F³⁻⁴ L²⁻³ Pd.

Feb.–March

s. Boothii. s.s. Megeratum.

Bushy undershrub up to 2 ft. with pilose and scaly branchlets. Lvs. up to 2½ in. long and 1¼ in. broad, elliptic to obovate, dark green and pilose above and glaucous and scaly below, ciliate at the margin. Fls. in clusters of up to 3, usually in pairs, 2 in. diam., rotate, milky-white, contrasting sharply with the chocolate-brown stamens. Burma–Tibet frontier, 8–10,000 ft. B.M. 9665.

When raised from seeds it flowers at a very early stage. Flowering so early in the year the flowers are always liable to be frosted.

Closely akin to R. *megeratum* which has yellow, campanulate to campanulate-rotate, flowers.

F.C.C. 1944 (E. de Rothschild, Exbury).

A.M. 1929 (L. de Rothschild, Exbury) to form with touch of sulphur yellow at the base within.

R. *leucaspis* is a parent of the A.M. clones 'Chrysaspis' (1942), 'Bric-à-Brac' (1945), 'Valaspis' (1935).

R. leucopetalum
(with white petals)

see *R. sanguineum* subsp. *leucopetalum*.

R. lindleyi
(After Dr. John Lindley, 1799–1865) botanist and Secretary R.H.S.

H¹⁻³ F⁴ L²⁻³ Pm.–s.

April–May

s. Maddenii. *s.s.* Megacalyx.

Straggly shrub, often epiphytic, up to 15 ft. Lvs. up to 6 in. long and 2½ in. broad, elliptic to oblong-elliptic, dark green and laxly reticulate above, glaucous and sparsely scaly below. Fls. usually in trusses of 4–6, occasionally up to 12, up to 4 in. long and 5 in. broad, tubular-funnel-shaped, almost lily-like, fragrant, white or creamish with an orange or yellowish blotch; calyx nearly ⅔ in. long, 5-lobed to near the base. Sikkim, Bhutan, Assam, 6–10,000 ft. B.M. n.s. 363.

A magnificent rhododendron, some forms of which are clearly more hardy than others. Possibly the best representation of this species, growing out of doors, is in the garden of the Gibson family, Glenarn, Rhu, Dunbartonshire.

F.C.C. 1937 (Adm. A. Walker Heneage-Vivian, Clyne Castle, Swansea) form with flowers with a tinge of pink at the ends of the petals.

A.M. 1935 (L. de Rothschild, Exbury) form with flowers delicately flushed with rose-magenta towards the apex of the petals, yellow at the base within.

R. lindleyi is a parent of the A.M. clone 'Lord Stair' (1952).

R. linearifolium
(with linear leaves)
H³⁻⁴ F¹ L¹⁻² Pd.–m.

April–May

s. Azalea. *s.s.* Obtusum.

Shrub up to 3 ft. Lvs. up to 3 in. long and ¼ in. broad. Fls. pink, deeply divided into linear-lanceolate segments. Cultivated in Japan, apparently unknown in the wild. Usually regarded as an abnormal form of *R. linearifolium* var. *macrosepalum*, and sometimes called *R. macrosepalum* var. *linearifolium*, and probably is only entitled to the status of a clone.

Var. *macrosepalum* (H³ F¹⁻² L¹⁻² Pd.–m.); lvs. up to 2½ in. long, ovate-elliptic or ovate to lanceolate, rich crimson-purple in autumn. Fls. in truss of 2–10, 2 in. diam., funnel-shaped, lilac-pink to rose-purple. Japan. B.M. 5769.

R. litangense
(from Litang, S.W. Szechwan)
H⁴ F¹⁻² L¹⁻² Pd.

April–May

s. Lapponicum.

Small shrub up to 2 ft. Lvs. about ½ in. long, oblong-elliptic, loosely scaly on both surfaces. Fls. in clusters of 2–4, about ½ in. long, widely funnel-shaped, plum-purple. Szechwan, Yunnan, 11–14,000 ft.

R. litiense
(*from the Li-ti-ping,*
Yunnan)
H⁴ F²⁻³ L²⁻³ Pm.

   May

s. Thomsonii. s.s. Souliei.

Shrub up to 12 ft. with densely glandular young shoots. Lvs. up to nearly 4 in. long, oblong or oblong-oval, mat green above, waxy glaucous below, when young very blue. Fls. in truss of about 6, up to almost 2 in. diam., widely campanulate or saucer-shaped, yellow, without blotch or spots. Yunnan, 9–13,000 ft. Close to *R. wardii*, differing in the oblong or oblong-oval leaves, waxy glaucous beneath and in the rather smaller flowers tending to be campanulate and less openly cup-shaped.

F.C.C. 1953 (Col. The Lord Digby, Minterne, Dorchester).

A.M. 1931 (L. de Rothschild, Exbury).

R. litiense is a parent of the A.M. clones: 'Moonshine' (1952), 'Moonshine Supreme' (1953), 'Moonshine Crescent' (1960, Wisley Trials), 'Lascaux' (1954), 'Tosca' (1959).

R. lochae
(After Lady Loch, patroness of horticulture in 19th century)
H¹ F²⁻³ L¹⁻² Pm.–t.

   April–May

Sect. Vireya. *Subsect.* Euvireya. *Series* Javanica of Sleumer.

Shrub or small tree up to 20 ft., often epiphytic. Lvs. up to 2 in. long and 1 in. broad, broadly obovate, dark green, shining and rather rugulose above, paler below and laxly scaly. Fls. pendulous, in clusters of 2–7, up to 2 in. long, tubular-funnel-shaped, scaly outside, pilose inside, scarlet. Queensland, Australia, 3,500–4,000 ft. B.M. 9430.

A plant for the cool greenhouse.

A.M. 1957 'Down Under' (Crown Estate Commissioners).

R. lochmium
(*from a coppice*)
H⁴ F¹⁻² L¹⁻² Pm.s.

   May

s. Triflorum. s.s. Yunnanense.

Shrub up to 10 ft. somewhat straggling. Lvs. up to 2½ in. long and 1 in. broad, recurved from the mid-rib (in distinction to the similar *R. davidsonianum*), densely scaly below. Fls. in trusses of 3–4, up to 1½ in. long, funnel-shaped, zygomorphic, white flushed with rosy-purple. Probably W. Szechwan.

Raised from seeds of *Wilson* 1220 (= *R. villosum* = *trichanthum*) from Szechwan and thus possibly a natural hybrid. Possibly a seedling of *R. davidsonianum* × *R. trichanthum*.

R. longesquamatum
(*with long scales*)
H⁴ F¹⁻³ L²⁻³ Pm.–t.

   May

s. Barbatum. s.s. Maculiferum.

Shrub up to 12 ft. or more, with long brown or black scales persisting for several years and with young shoots densely clothed with pale fawn or rusty tomentum. Lvs. up to 5 in. long and 2 in. broad, oblong, oblong-obovate or oblong-oblan-

R. longesquamatum
(*continued*)

ceolate, dark green and lustrous above, pale green below, with shaggy tawny hairs on mid-rib. Fls. in truss of 6–12, about 1½ in. long, more or less bell-shaped, pink to rose with crimson blotch; calyx over ½ in. deep. Szechwan, 10–12,000 ft. B.M. 9430.

R. longistylum
(*long-styled*)
H3 F1–2 L1–2 Pm.

April

s. Triflorum. s.s. Yunnanense.
Shrub up to 7 ft. Lvs. up to 2½ in. long, oblanceolate-lanceolate or oblong-lanceolate, laxly scaly below. Fls. terminal or terminal and axillary in upper leaves, in clusters of 3–10, about ¾ in. long, funnel-shaped, zygomorphic, pink or white. Szechwan, 3,300–7,500 ft.
Allied to *R. yunnanense* and to *R. hypophaeum.*

R. lophogynum
(*with crested ovary*)
H3 F1–2 L1–2 Pd.

May

s. Trichocladum.
Deciduous shrub up to 3 ft. Lvs. about 1 in. long and ⅓ in. broad, oblanceolate, pilose on both surfaces, laxly scaly below. Fls. in clusters of 2–4, about 1 in. long, widely funnel-shaped, yellow and precocious. Yunnan, 10–11,000 ft.

R. lopsangianum
(After Nga-Wang Lopsang Tup-Den Gyatso, the late Dalai Lama of Tibet)
H4 F1–3 L2–3 Pm.

April

s. and s.s. Thomsonii.
Low compact shrub up to 6 ft. with glandular branchlets. Lvs. up to 2½ in. long and 1½ in. broad, elliptic or oblong-elliptic or oval, very glaucous below. Fls. in a loose truss of 3–5, up to 1¼ in. long, tubular-campanulate or funnel-campanulate, fleshy, deep crimson with a small 5-lobed calyx of the same colour. S.E. Tibet, 8,500–14,000 ft.
Closely allied to *R. thomsonii* with deep crimson flowers and leaves of similar shape. But the leaves and the flowers of *R. lopsangianum* are smaller than those of *R. thomsonii* which attains larger proportions.

R. lowndesii
(After Col. D. G. Lowndes, who discovered it in 1950)
H3–4 F1–2 L1 Pd.

June–July

s. and s.s. Lepidotum.
A dwarf shrublet up to about 1 ft. Lvs. deciduous, bristly all over, up to 1 in. long, oblanceolate or obovate, bristly at the margin. Fls. solitary or in pairs, about 1 in. in diameter, rotate-campanulate, pale yellow, lightly spotted with carmine. Nepal, 10–15,000 ft.
If it proves to be of good constitution it will be a valuable rock garden plant.

R. ludlowii
(After F. Ludlow, who has collected widely in the Himalayas)
H3–4 F2–3 L1 Pd.

April–May

s. Uniflorum
Small shrub up to 1 ft. Lvs. about ½ in. long, obovate, undulate or crenulate at margin. Fls. single or in pairs, about 1 in. long and 1 in. diameter, saucer-shaped, yellow, spotted

R. ludlowii
(*continued*)

reddish-brown at the base within; calyx large, leafy. S.E. Tibet, 13,500 ft. B.M. n.s. 412.

Allied to *R. pumilum*.

Parent of A.M. clone 'Chikor', 1962.

R. lukiangense
(*from Lukiang, Yunnan*)
H³⁻⁴ F¹⁻² L¹⁻² Pm.

March–April

s. and s.s. Irroratum.

Medium-sized shrub up to 12 ft. with purplish young shoots. Lvs. up to 5 in. long, oblong-lanceolate or oblanceolate, dark green above, paler below. Fls. in truss of 8–12, about 2 in. long, tubular-campanulate, rose to magenta rose with a small blotch and more or less spotted with crimson; calyx over ½ in. long. N.W. Yunnan, S.E. Tibet, 8–12,000 ft.

Forms of this species have been named as follows:

Subsp. *adroserum* (H⁴ F¹⁻² L¹⁻² Pm.); lvs. smaller and less pointed and flowers light rose at base, flushed magenta-rose at margins and conspicuously spotted outside. Yunnan, 11–12,000 ft.

Subsp. *ceraceum* (H²⁻³ F¹ L¹⁻² Pm.); Fls. magenta-rose, with small blotch, with or without a few spots. Yunnan, S.E. Tibet, 10–11,000 ft.

Subsp. *gymnanthum* (H⁴ F¹⁻² L¹⁻² Pm.); fls. pale or deep claret-crimson and with deeper markings. S.E. Tibet, 13,000 ft.

R. lutescens
(*becoming yellow*)
H³⁻⁴ F¹⁻⁴ L²⁻³ Pm.

Feb.–Mar.–April

s. and s.s. Triflorum.

Shrub up to 12 ft. with long branches and attractive bronzy-red new growths. Lvs. up to 3½ in. long, lanceolate, oblong-lanceolate or ovate-lanceolate, dull green above, pale green and scaly below. Fls. in trusses of 3–6, terminal and axillary among uppermost leaves, up to 2 in. across, widely funnel-shaped, zygomorphic, pale or rather deeper primrose-yellow spotted with light green. Szechwan, Yunnan, 2,000–9,800 ft. B.M. 8851.

Good forms of this species are extremely desirable for they give a fine show early in the year as well as in the autumn when the leaves turn to yellow and bronze.

F.C.C. 1938 (L. de Rothschild, Exbury; a form with clear lemon-yellow flowers, up to 2 in. across and for long known as 'Exbury F.C.C. var.'.

'Bagshot Sands' is an A.M. clone (Mrs. R. M. Stevenson, Ascot 1953); a form with primrose-yellow flowers (H.C.C. 601/2) with darker spotting chiefly at the base, 13 flowers to the truss.

R. lutescens is a parent of the A.M. clones 'Alcesta' (1935), 'Bo-peep' (1937).

R. luteum
yellow)
H4 F3-4 L2-3 Pm.

   May

s. Azalea. *s.s.* Luteum.

   Deciduous shrub up to 12 ft. with glandular-villous young shoots and sticky winter buds. Lvs. 2–4 in. long and up to 1½ in. broad, oblong to oblong-lanceolate, ciliate and serrulate. Fls. in trusses of 12, precocious, 2 in. across, funnel-form, densely viscid without, yellow, very fragrant. Caucasus and E. Europe. B.M. 433.

   Its fragrant yellow flowers and particularly fine autumn leaf colour make *R. luteum*, often known as *R. flavum* or *Azalea pontica*, a most desirable plant. In some parts of the country it has become naturalized. A.G.M. (1930).

R. lyi
After J. Ly, a Chinese collector)
H2-3 F2-3 L2-3 Pm.

   Apr.–May–June

s. Maddenii. *s.s.* Ciliicalyx.

   Shrub up to 6 ft. with scaly and bristly branch-lets. Lvs. up to 3 in. long, oblanceolate or oblong-oblanceolate, glossy and reticulate above, scaly below. Fls. in truss of up to 4, about 2 in. long, white with a yellow blotch, fragrant. Kweichow. B.M. 9051.

R. lysolepis
with loose scales)
H4 F2-3 L1-2 Pd.–m.

   April–May

s. Lapponicum.

   Shrub up to 4 ft. Lvs. about ¾ in. long, ½ in. broad, oblong-elliptic, glistening glandular, scaly above, and below. Fls. in clusters of 2–3, nearly 1 in. diameter, widely funnel-shaped, purple, deep violet or pinkish-violet. Szechwan, 12,000 ft.

R. macabeanum
After Mr. McCabe, Deputy Commissioner, Naga Hills)
H3-4 F3-4 L3-4 Pm.–t.

   March–April

s. Grande.

   Tree, as much as 45 ft., with young shoots of silver and bud scales of red. Lvs. up to 12 in. long and up to 6 in. or more broad, oblong-elliptic, dark green and with the main veins impressed above, white or greyish-white tomentose below. Fls. many in a compact, occasionally rather loose truss, up to 3 in. long, ventricose-campanulate, deep yellow or very pale cream-yellow, blotched with purple at the base. Manipur, 8–9,000 ft. Collected twice in recent years by Kingdon Ward this is undoubtedly one of the best of the woodland species. B.M. n.s. 187.

   F.C.C. 1938 (Lt.-Col. E. H. W. Bolitho, Treng-wainton, Cornwall); A.M. 1937 (Trengwainton).

R. macrophyllum
with big leaves)
H4 F1-2 L1-2 Pm.–t.

   May–June

s. and *s.s.* Ponticum.

   Stout shrub up to 20 ft. Lvs. 3–6 in. long and up to 2½ in. broad, oval, oblong-obovate to elliptic, dark green above, paler below. Fls. about 20 in dome-shaped truss, about 1½ in. long and 2¼ in. across, broadly campanulate, rosy-purple, through pink shades to white, with reddish-brown

R. macrophyllum
(*continued*)

spots on the upper lobes and the margins of the petals usually crimped. British Columbia to California, 1,500 ft. B.M. 4863. Formerly called *R. californicum*.

R. maculiferum
(*bearing spots*)

H⁴ F²⁻³ L¹⁻² Pm.–t.

April

s. Barbatum. s.s. Maculiferum.

Shrub or small tree up to 20 ft. with pale green young shoots. Lvs. 3–5 in. long, 1–2 in. broad, oblong-oval, elliptic to obovate, light green above, pale glaucous-green below. Fls. in lax truss of up to 10, about 1½ in. long, open-campanulate, white or white flushed rose, with deep black-purple blotches at the base. Szechwan, Hupeh, 8–10,000 ft.

R. maddenii
(After Lt.-Col. E. Madden, traveller in India; d. 1856)

H²⁻³ F²⁻⁴ L²⁻³ Pm.

June

s. and s.s. Maddenii.

Shrub up to 8 ft. with papery bark. Lvs. 4–5 in. long, up to 1½ in. broad, lanceolate to oblanceolate, sometimes elliptic, dull green above, densely reddish-brown scaly below. Fls. in truss of 2–4, up to 3 in. long, widely tubular, fleshy, white with faint flush of rose on the outside, scented. Sikkim, Bhutan, 5–9,000 ft. B.M. 4805.

A number of plants grown under the name of *R. calophyllum* are really *R. maddenii*; the true *R. calophyllum* is not in cultivation.

A.M. 1938 (Lt.-Col. E. H. W. Bolitho, Trengwainton, Cornwall) to form with up to 6 flowers in the truss, white, greenish within the tube.

R. magnificum
(*distinguished, magnificent*)

H²⁻³ F²⁻⁴ L³⁻⁴ Pm.–t.

Feb.–Mar.–April

s. Grande.

Tree up to 45 ft. Lvs. up to 18 in. long and 8 in. broad, oblong to oblong-obovate, mat green above, covered below with thin white or greyish-brown indumentum. Fls. in compact trusses of up to 30, about 2 in. long, tubular-campanulate rosy-purple. Burma-Tibet frontier, 6–8,000 ft.

Allied to *R. protistum* and *R. giganteum* and probably best represented in the open in the garden at Brodick Castle, Isle of Arran.

A.M. 1950 (Lt.-Col. D. R. Carrick-Buchanan, Corsewell, Stranraer, Wigtownshire) to form with flowers Fuchsine Pink (H.C.C. 627/1) with darker veining, grown under number *K.W.* 9200.

R. makinoi
(After T. Makino, Japanese botanist)

H⁴ F²⁻³ L²⁻³ Pm.

June

s. Ponticum. s.s. Caucasicum.

A rounded shrub up to 8 ft. and with young growths clothed with white—later tawny—woolly tomentum and appearing in Aug.–Sept. Lvs. up to 7 in. long and 1 in. broad, narrow lanceolate recurved, upper surface bright green and semi bullate, lower surface with thick woolly-tawny

R. makinoi
(*continued*)

indumentum. Fls. in a truss of up to 8, nearly 2 in. long, funnel-campanulate, clear soft pink with or without crimson dots. Japan.

Remarkable for its very late, beautiful annual growths. For long grown as *R. metternichii* var. *angustifolium*.

R. malayanum
(*from Malaya*)
H¹ F²⁻³ L¹⁻² Pm.–t.

Sect. Vireya. *Subsect.* Malayovireya of Sleumer.

Shrub or small tree up to 15 ft. Lvs. 3–4 in. long, elliptic to elliptic-lanceolate, dark green above, red-brown below. Fls. in trusses of 3–8, nodding, ¾ in. long, slightly curved, tubular with spreading lobes, scarlet. Siam, Malay Peninsula, Sumatra, Java, Borneo, Celebes, up to 9,000 ft. B.M. 6045.

R. mallotum
(*fleecy*)
H⁴ F²⁻⁴ L³⁻⁴ Pm.–t.

March–April

s. Neriiflorum. s.s. Haematodes.

Shrub or small tree up to 20 ft. with young shoots clothed with grey or cinnamon-grey indumentum. Lvs. up to 6 in. long and 3 in. broad, stiff, obovate, dark green and rough rugulose above, covered below with cinnamon-brown woolly indumentum. Fls. in compact truss of up to 15, 1½–2 in. long, tubular-campanulate, dark crimson. Yunnan, Upper Burma, 11–12,000 ft. B.M. 9419.

A.M. 1933 (Col. R. Stephenson Clarke, Borde Hill, Sussex).

R. manipurense
(*from Manipur*)
H³ F²⁻³ L¹⁻² Pm.

June

s. and s.s. Maddenii.

Shrub up to 15 ft. Lvs. up to 7 in. long and 3 in. broad, elliptic to oblong-elliptic, shining above, densely scaly below. Fls. in trusses of 4–6, up to 4 in. long, tubular-funnel-shaped, pure white, scaly without, fragrant. Assam, Burma–Tibet frontier, 7–10,000 ft.

B.M. 8212 (as *R. maddenii* var. *obtusifolia*)

R. manopeplum
(*with a loose covering*)
H³ F¹⁻² L¹⁻² Pm.

April–May

s. Thomsonii. s.s. Selense.

Shrub up to 5 ft. Lvs. up to 4 in. long and 2 in. broad, oblong-oval to ovate, pale green below and with a thin yellowish indumentum. Fls. in truss of up to 8, about 1½ in. long, widely campanulate, creamy-white flushed rose, faintly spotted. S.E. Tibet. Now generally merged with *R. esetulosum*. See Rhod. Year Book, 1951–2, p. 147.

R. mariesii
(After Charles Maries, a collector for Messrs. Veitch, d. 1902)
H³ F¹⁻² L¹⁻² Pm.

April

s. Azalea. s.s. Schlippenbachii.

Deciduous shrub up to 10 ft. with young shoots covered at first with appressed yellowish silky hairs. Lvs. in twos or threes at the ends of the branchlets, up to 3 in. long and 1½ in. broad,

R. mariesii
(continued)

ovate-lanceolate or broad ovate or elliptic, prominently reticulate below. Fls. single or in pairs, 2 in. across, rotate-funnel-shaped, pale rose-purple with red-purple spots on upper lobes. S.E. & C. China, Formosa, 1–4,000 ft. B.M. 8206.

R. martinianum
(After John Martin, gardener at Caerhays, Cornwall)

H4 F2–3 L1–2 Pm.

April–May

s. Thomsonii. s.s. Selense.

Shrub up to 6 ft. with stiff branches densely glandular when young. Lvs. about 1½ in. long, oblong to oblong-elliptic, pale and glaucous below. Fls. in loose clusters of 1–3, on pedicels up to 1½ in. long, about 1½ in. long, funnel-campanulate, pale rose, white or creamy-white, with or without crimson spots. Yunnan, S.E. Tibet, Burma, 10–13,500 ft.

Allied to *R. selense*, but with fewer flowers to the truss.

R. maximum
(very large)

H4 F1–2 L1–2 Pm.–t.

July

s. and s.s. Ponticum.

Shrub or small tree up to 15 ft. or more. Lvs. 4–12 in. long, 1½–3 in. broad, ovate-lanceolate or obovate-lanceolate, dark green above, pale below, and then with a fugitive indumentum very often. Fls. in trusses of 15–20, about 1½ in. across, broad funnel-shaped, pale to deeper pink, with yellow-green spots, pink-tipped in bud, sometimes rose-red or white. Eastern United States. B.M. 951.

Very hardy and shade tolerant.

R. meddianum
(After Geo. Medd, Agent I.F. Company, Bhamo, Upper Burma)

H3–4 F2–4 L2–3 Pm.

April

s. and s.s. Thomsonii.

Shrub up to 8 ft. or more, with glaucous young shoots. Lvs. 2–7 in. long, up to 3 in. broad, oval, oblong-oval or obovate, dark glaucous-green above, pale below. Fls. in truss of up to 12, 1½–2½ in. long, tubular-campanulate, fleshy, deep crimson or bright scarlet. Yunnan, 10–11,000 ft. B.M. 9636. A form known as var. *atrokermesinum* from Burma sometimes has flowers larger and darker and glandular branchlets, pedicels and ovary; it received the A.M. in 1954 (R. Olaf Hambro, Logan House, Stranraer) to form with flowers a pale shade of Turkey Red (H.C.C. 721) with a little dark spotting on the upper lobes.

R. meddianum is a parent of the A.M. clones 'Queen of Hearts' (1949), 'Kenlis' (1948), 'Rocket' (1954).

R. megacalyx
(large calyx)

I2-3 F3-4 L1-2 Pms.-t.

April–May

s. Maddenii. *s.s.* Megacalyx.

Shrub, often straggly, or small tree up to 16 ft. Lvs. up to 6 in. long and 3 in. broad, elliptic or obovate-elliptic, round at apex and base, glaucous and densely lepidote below. Fls. in truss of up to 5, up to $3\frac{1}{2}$ in. long, tubular or broadly funnel-shaped, the two lower petals usually larger than the others, white, fragrant; calyx as much as 1 in. long with broadly ovate lobes, green or tinged with pink. N.E. Upper Burma, 7–9,000 ft. B.M. 9326. A very beautiful rhododendron.

A.M. 1937 (Adm. A. Walker Heneage-Vivian, Clyne Castle, Swansea).

R. megeratum
(passing lovely)

I3 F2-3 L1-2 Pd.

March–April

s. Boothii. *s.s.* Megeratum.

Shrub up to 2 ft. with densely pilose branchlets and purple scaling bark. Lvs. up to $1\frac{3}{4}$ in. long, elliptic to oval, very glaucous and scaly below, bristly at the margin. Fls. single or in clusters of up to 3, $1\frac{1}{4}$ in. long, campanulate or rotate-campanulate, yellow; calyx rather large, $\frac{1}{3}$ in. long, almost membranous. Yunnan, Tibet, Assam, Burma, 8–13,000 ft. B.M. 9120. Rather fastiduous as to situation.

It is a parent of the A.M. clones 'Moth' (1955), 'Sulfmeg' (1940).

R. mekongense
(from the Mekong River, China)

I4 F1-2 L1-2 Pd.-m.

May

s. Trichocladum.

Deciduous shrub up to 4 ft. Lvs. up to $1\frac{1}{4}$ in. long and $\frac{1}{3}$ in. broad, oblanceolate, scaly below, ciliate on margin. Fls. precocious, in trusses of 3–4, about 1 in. long, widely funnel-shaped, pale yellow tinged with green; calyx about $\frac{1}{4}$ in. long, with the oblong lobes fringed with long bristles. E. Tibet, Yunnan, 11,000 ft.

R. melinanthum
(honey flowered)

I4 F2-3 L1-2 Pm.

April–May

s. Trichocladum.

Deciduous shrub up to 8 ft., branchlets with long bristles. Lvs. up to $1\frac{1}{2}$ in. long, $\frac{2}{3}$ in. broad, narrow obovate to oblanceolate, scaly below, pilose on margin when young. Fls. precocious, in trusses usually of 3–4, $\frac{3}{4}$ in. long, widely funnel-shaped, yellow. Upper Burma, 12–14,000 ft. B.M. 8903. Regarded as the finest species in the Trichocladum series.

R. mesaeum
(intermediate)

see *R. sanguineum* subsp. *mesaeum*.

R. mesopolium
(grey in the middle)

see *R. fulvastrum* subsp. *mesopolium*.

R. metternichii
(After Prince Metternich, Austrian Diplomat, 1773–1859)
H⁴ F²⁻³ L²⁻³ Pm.

April–May

s. Ponticum. s.s. Caucasicum.

Shrub up to 8 ft. Lvs. subverticillate, up to 6 in. long, 2 in. broad, oblong or oblong-oblanceolate, glossy above, with thin felty more or less agglutinate tawny or rust tomentum below. Fls in trusses of up to 15, 1½–2 in. long, campanulate, 7-lobed, rose, spotted deeper within. Japan.

The true form is very rare in Europe, plants growing under this name usually being *R. degronianum* or *R. makinoi*.

R. micranthum
(*small flowered*)
H⁴ F¹⁻² L¹⁻² Pm.s.

May–July

s. Micranthum.

Straggling shrub up to 6 ft. or more. Lvs. up to 1¾ in. long, ½ in. broad, oblanceolate, light brown-scaly below. Fls. many per truss, ¼–⅓ in. long, campanulate, milky-white, at a glance resembling a small spiraea rather than a rhododendron. Hupeh, Szechwan, Kansu, 6–8,000 ft. B.M. 8198.

R. microgynum
(*with small ovary*)
H⁴ F²⁻³ L²⁻³ Pd.

April

s. Taliense. s.s. Roxieanum.

Shrub up to 4 ft. with rigid branchlets clad with tawny indumentum when young. Lvs. up to 3 in. long and 1 in. broad, lanceolate or oblanceolate, opaque above, buff or dark fawn below. Fls. in truss of 5 or 6, about 1½ in. long, open campanulate, soft dull rose faintly crimson spotted or black-crimson. S.E. Tibet, 12,000 ft. Closely allied to *R. gymnocarpum*.

R. microleucum
(*small and white*)
H⁴ F³ L² Pd.

April

s. Lapponicum.

Small shrub up to 1½ ft. with branchlets densely leafy and covered with dark rusty-brown scales. Lvs. up to ⅔ in. long, narrowly oblanceolate, bright green above, sap-green and scaly below. Fls. in clusters of 2–3, up to ¾ in. across, widely funnel-shaped, pure white. Probably Yunnan. B.M. n.s. 171 A. A very attractive rock garden plant.

F.C.C. 1939 (L. de Rothschild, Exbury).

R. micromeres
(*with small parts*)
H³ F¹⁻² L¹⁻² Pm.s.

May–July

s. Glaucophyllum. s.s. Genestierianum.

Shrub, often straggly, up to 6 ft. Lvs. 1–3 in. long, oblong-elliptic, bright green above, glaucous grey and scaly below. Fls. in clusters of 3–8, up to ⅔ in. long, rotately campanulate, scaly outside, creamy-yellow or orange-yellow, rarely white. Tibet, Yunnan, Bhutan, Assam, Burma, 8–14,000 ft.

R. microphyton
(*small plant*)
H3 F1–2 L1–2 Pm.

April–May

s. Azalea. *s.s.* Obtusum.

Shrub up to 6 ft. with shoots clothed with appressed red-brown hairs. Lvs. persistent, up to $1\frac{1}{2}$ in. long, elliptic to lanceolate, dark green above paler below. Fls. in trusses of 3–6, and often with several trusses at the ends of the branchlets, $\frac{1}{2}$–$\frac{3}{4}$ in. across, funnel-form, rose to almost white, dotted carmine on the upper lobes. Yunnan, 6–10,000 ft.

R. mimetes
(*imitative*)
H4 F1–2 L1–2 Pm.

May

s. Taliense. *s.s.* Adenogynum.

Shrub up to 7 ft. with short thick branches. Lvs. up to 4 in. long and $1\frac{1}{2}$ in. broad, elliptic to oblong-oval, lower surface pale or deep buff. Fls. in lax truss of about 10, $1\frac{1}{2}$ in. long, widely funnel-campanulate, white, faintly flushed and margined with rose, with a few crimson markings. There is a form with broader leaves and with a splitting indumentum known as var. *simulans*. S.W. Szechwan, 11–12,000 ft.

R. minus
(*smaller*)
H4 F1–2 L1–2 Pm.

May–June

s. Carolinianum.

Shrub up to 12 ft. or more, usually less in cultivation. Lvs. up to $3\frac{1}{2}$ in. long, and $1\frac{1}{2}$ in. broad, ovate-elliptic to elliptic, rusty with scales below. Fls. in clusters of 6–12, about $1\frac{1}{2}$ in. long, funnel-shaped, densely scaly on the outside, pale pinkish-purple to rosy-pink, or white, with greenish or brown spots. S.E. United States. Taller growing and considerably later flowering than its near relative *R. carolinianum*. B.M. 2285.

R. mishmiense
from the Mishmi Hills, Assam)
H2 F2–3 L1–2 Pm.s.

April–May

s. and s.s. Boothii.

An epiphytic straggling shrub up to 4 ft. with shortly hirsute branchlets. Lvs. up to $3\frac{1}{2}$ in. long and 2 in. broad, elliptic to oblong-elliptic, ciliate on the margin, impressed-scaly below. Fls. in trusses of 3–8, about $1\frac{1}{4}$ in. long, broadly bell-shaped with spreading lobes, bright lemon-yellow, upper lobe usually heavily spotted with reddish-brown; calyx about $\frac{1}{2}$ in. long, deeply 5-lobed, fringed with golden-yellow or silvery-white hairs. Assam, S.E. Tibet, 7–10,000 ft.

Closely allied to *R. boothii* and, as with this species, best grown in a cool greenhouse.

A.M. 1940 (L. de Rothschild, Exbury) to form with an 8-flowered truss, the flowers of pale yellow (H.C.C. Aureolin 3/2) slightly spotted brownish-red on 3 upper lobes.

It is a parent of the A.M. clone 'Moth' (1955).

R. molle
(soft)

H4 F3-4 L1-2 Pm.

May

s. Azalea. s.s. Luteum.

Deciduous shrub up to 4 ft. with stout branche
villous and often setose when young. Lvs. up t
6 in. long, 2½ in. wide, ciliate and often revolut
at margin, grey-pubescent below. Fls. many to th
truss, expanding before the leaves, 2½ in. diam.
broad funnel-form, yellow or orange with larg
greenish blotch separated into dots. Long know
as *R. sinense* and a parent with *R. japonicum* o
the Mollis hybrids. E. and C. China in province
of Chekiang, Hupeh and Hunan.

R. mollicomum
(soft-haired)

H3-4 F2-3 L1-2 Pm.s.

April

s. Scabrifolium.

Shrub up to 6 ft. with softly pubescent branch
lets. Lvs. about 1¼ in. long and ⅓ in. broad
narrow-lanceolate, softly pubescent, scaly below
Fls. axillary, crowded near the apex of the shoo
single or in pairs, about ⅔ in. long, narrowl
tubular, rose or crimson. A more straggling form
with larger flowers is known as var. *rockii*. Yunnar
8–11,000 ft.

A.M. 1931 (Hon. H. D. McLaren, Bodnan
to form with bright rose flowers.

R. mollyanum
(After the late Duchess of
Montrose, known to her friends
as "Molly")

H3-4 F2-4 L3-4 Pm.-t.

April–May

s. Grande.

Small tree up to 30 ft. Lvs. up to over 12 i
long and 4 in. broad, narrowly oblong to oblancec
late, dark green above and with silvery-whit
plastered indumentum below. Fls. in larg
trusses of up to 20, up to 2½ in. long and as muc
across, campanulate, often frilled at the margir
pink with crimson blotch at base, or white staine
pink round the edge of the petals. S.E. Tibe

'Benmore' is an F.C.C. clone (Younger Botani
Garden, Benmore, by Dunoon, Argyle, 1957) t
form with loose truss of 20 flowers each a variabl
shade of Fuchsine Pink (H.C.C. 627/2) with som
deeper staining and a small deep crimson blotch o
the base of the throat.

R. monosematum
(with one blotch)

H4 F2-3 L2-3 Pm.

April

s. Barbatum. s.s. Maculiferum.

A rather compact shrub up to 10 ft. with youn
shoots greenish, or purple-tinted and with tawn
setose glands. Lvs. 3–5 in. long, 1–1½ in. broac
oblong, dark green above, pale green, glossy
below. Fls. in a round truss of up to 12, about 2 i
long, widely funnel-shaped, white or suffused rose
pink, or pink or deep rose. Szechwan. B.M. 867

R. morii
(After U. Mori, collector in
Formosa)

H4 F2-3 L1-2 Pm.-t.

April–May

s. Barbatum. s.s. Maculiferum.

Shrub up to 25 ft. Lvs. up to 5 in. long, 1½ i
broad, oblong-lanceolate, dark green above, pale
below. Fls. in a loose truss of up to 15, about 2 i
long, widely campanulate, white or white flushe

R. morii
(continued)

rose, with crimson spots, sometimes heavily blotched with red. Formosa, 6–10,000 ft.

Very beautiful when in full flower.

A.M. 1956 (Capt. Collingwood Ingram, The Grange, Benenden, Kent) to form with white flowers blotched and spotted with crimson.

R. moulmainense
from Moulmein,
Burma)
H^1 F^{1-2} L^{1-2} P^m.

March–April

s. Stamineum.

Shrub up to 6 ft. Lvs. $2\frac{1}{2}$–4 in. long and up to $1\frac{1}{2}$ in. broad, elliptic-lanceolate. Fls. in clusters of 1–4, axillary, $1\frac{1}{2}$ in. long, narrow funnel-shaped, white with yellow blotch on the upper side or rose-red. Burma, Siam, Malay Peninsula, 5,000 ft. B.M. 4904.

R. moupinense
from Moupin, i.e.
Paoksing-hsien, W.China)
H^4 F^{3-4} L^{1-2} $P^{d.–m.}$

Feb.–March

s. Moupinense.

Spreading shrub up to 4 ft. with bristly branchlets. Lvs. up to $1\frac{1}{2}$ in. long and 1 in. broad, elliptic to ovate-elliptic, shining above, densely scaly below, at first ciliate at margin. Fls. in clusters of 1–3, about $1\frac{1}{2}$ in. long and up to 2 in. across, funnel-shaped, white, pink or deep rose, with or without red or purple spots. Szechwan, 6,500–8,500 ft. B.M. 8598.

This beautiful species in spite of its coming from a comparatively low elevation in Szechwan is perfectly hardy although the flowers, opening so early in the year, are always liable to be frosted.

A.M. 1914 (Miss Willmott, Great Warley) to form with white flowers 2 in. across.

A.M. 1937 (Lord Aberconway, Bodnant) to form heavily suffused with rose-pink and freely spotted internally with crimson.

R. moupinense is a parent of the following A.M. clones: 'Bulbul' (1949), 'Cilpinense' (1927), 'Olive' (1942), 'Bo-Peep' (1937), 'Bric-à-Brac' (1945), 'Tessa' (1935), 'Tessa Roza' (1953), 'Seta' (1933), 'Golden Oriole Talavera' (1947), 'Golden Oriole Venetia' (1963), 'Ailsa Jean' (1946), 'Valpinense' (1943).

The following are F.C.C. clones: 'Golden Oriole Talavera' (1963), 'Seta' (1960).

R. mucronatum
pointed)
H^4 F^{2-3} L^{1-2} $P^{d.–m.}$

May

s. Azalea. s.s. Obtusum.

Wide-spreading shrub, up to 6 ft. with young shoots densely clothed with spreading grey to grey-brown indumentum. Lvs. partly persistent, up to $2\frac{1}{2}$ in. long and 1 in. broad, lanceolate to ovate-lanceolate. Fls. in clusters of 1–3, up to 2 in. long and broad, wide funnel-form, pure white, fragrant. Not known in the wild; cultivated in Japan and China. Commonly called *Azalea ledifolia*.

R. mucronatum
(*continued*)

A very attractive plant when in full flower.
B.M. 2901.

A form with larger white flowers, green at the
throat, has been called var. *noordtianum*.

A form with pale mauve flowers is known as var.
ripense and received the A.M. in 1933 (Hon.
H. D. McLaren, Bodnant).

R. mucronulatum
(*with a small point*)
H4 F2-3 L1-2 Pm.

Jan.–Feb.

s. Dauricum.

Shrub up to 8 ft. Lvs. deciduous, up to 3 in.
long, and 1¼ in. broad, elliptic-lanceolate or
lanceolate, scaly on both surfaces. Fls. single,
clustered at the ends of the shoots, precocious,
about 1¾ in. long, widely funnel-shaped, bright
rosy-purple. B.M. 8304.

A perfectly hardy rhododendron which can
present a most beautiful sight in the first week of
the year and one of the few early flowering
rhododendrons really worth growing in a cold
garden. Sometimes the young growth may be
injured by frost but the damage will be repaired
during the course of the summer.

A form which flowers a fortnight later is known
as var. *acuminatum*.

F.C.C. 1957 (Crown Estate Commissioners,
Windsor known as 'Winter Sunset') to form with
rich purplish-rose flowers.

A.M. 1924 (Royal Botanic Gardens, Kew) a
form with rich purplish-rose flowers.

A.M. 1935 (Royal Botanic Gardens, Kew) a
form with mauve-pink flowers, known as 'Roseum'.

R. myiagrum
(*the fly-catcher, alluding
to the sticky pedicels*)
H4 F1-3 L1-2 Pm.

May

s. Thomsonii. s.s. Campylocarpum.

Shrub up to 5 ft. Lvs. up to 3 in. long and 1½ in.
broad, orbicular to elliptic, dark green above,
glaucous below. Fls. in trusses of 4–5, 1–1½ in.
long, campanulate, white, with or without a
crimson blotch at the base, spotted or unspotted.
Yunnan, Burma, 10–13,000 ft. Possibly only a
form of *R. callimorphum*.

R. nakaharai
(After G. Nakahara, Japanese
collector)
H4 F2-3 L1-2 Pd.

June–July

s. Azalea. s.s. Obtusum.

Creeping shrub with shoots densely clothed
with appressed hairs. Lvs. persistent, up to ⅔ in.
long and ⅕ in. broad, oblanceolate, elliptic or
elliptic-obovate, dark green above, pale green
below. Fls. in clusters of 2–3, up to 1 in. long,
funnel-campanulate, dark brick-red. Formosa.

R. neriiflorum
*(with flowers like
Oleanders)*
H³⁻⁴ F³⁻⁴ L¹⁻² Pm.s.

April–May

s. and s.s. Neriiflorum.

Spreading shrub up to 9 ft. Lvs. up to 4 in. long and 1½ in. broad, oblong to oval, dark green above, white below. Fls. in trusses of 5–12, up to 2 in. long, tubular-campanulate, fleshy, bright scarlet, crimson, deep crimson or deep rose, free flowering; calyx large, coloured like the corolla. Yunnan, S.E. Tibet, Burma–Tibet frontier, 7–12,000 ft. B.M. 8727.

R. neriiflorum is a parent of the following F.C.C. and A.M. clones:

F.C.C. 'Little Ben' (1937), 'David' (1939), 'Aries' (1938).

A.M. 'F. C. Puddle' (1932), 'Daphne' (1933), 'Eithne' (1937).

R. neriiflorum is a valuable plant and certain forms have been named as follows:

Subsp. *euchaites* (H³⁻⁴ F³⁻⁴ Pm.) growing up to 15 ft. with very glaucous undersides to the leaves and with the flowers crimson-scarlet. Yunnan, Upper Burma, 9–11,000 ft.

A.M. 1929 (Lady Aberconway and Hon. H. D. McLaren, Bodnant).

Subsp. *phaedropum* (H³⁻⁴ F¹⁻² L¹⁻² Pm.); fls. in trusses of 4–8, varying in colour from straw-yellow, tawny-orange to scarlet. N.E. Upper Burma, Assam, 8–12,000 ft.

Subsp. *phoenicodum* (H³⁻⁴ F¹⁻² L¹⁻² Pm.); very similar to subsp. *euchaites* but with smaller leaves and flowers. Upper Burma, 10,000 ft. B.M. 9521.

R. nigropunctatum
(marked with black spots)
H⁴ F¹⁻² L¹⁻² Pd.

May–June

s. Lapponicum.

Shrub up to 1 ft. Lvs. about ¼ in. long, narrowly elliptic, densely scaly on both surfaces those below being pale greenish-yellow. Fls. solitary or in pairs, about ⅓ in. long, open funnel-shaped, pale purple. Szechwan, 10–15,000 ft. B.M. 8529.

R. nilagiricum
*from the Nilgiri,
Madras, India)*

see *R. arboreum* subsp. *nilagiricum*.

R. ningyuenense
*from Ningyuen,
Szechwan)*
H³ F¹⁻² L¹⁻² Pm.

May

s. and s.s. Irroratum.

Medium-sized shrub. Lvs. up to 4 in. long and 1½ in. broad, oblong-lanceolate. Fls. in trusses of 3–6, 1½–2 in. long, tubular-campanulate, pale rose, unspotted. Szechwan, 8–10,000 ft.

R. nipponicum
(*from Japan*)
H4 F1–2 L1–2 Pm.

May–June

s. Azalea. s.s. Nipponicum.
 Shrub up to 6 ft. with stiff red-brown branchlet
clothed when young with pilose and glandula
hairs, bark papery and peeling, cinnamon-brown
Lvs. deciduous, up to 7 in. long and 4 in. broad
obovate to obovate-oblong, turning orange t
crimson in autumn. Fls. in clusters of up to 1⁵
¾ in. long, ⅓ in. broad, tubular, white, expandin
with or after the leaves. C. Japan.

R. nitens
(*shining*)
H4 F1–2 L1–2 Pd.

June–July

s. Saluenense.
 Small erect shrub up to 1½ ft. Lvs. ¼–1 ir
long, oblong-elliptic, yellowish-brown scaly below
Fls. in clusters of 1–3, about 2 in. diamete
widely funnel-shaped or rotate, deep pinkish
purple or deep pink-magenta with crimson spots
Burma, 12,000 ft.
 It is near to R. *keleticum* but is of more erec
habit and is the latest of the Saluenense Series t
flower.

R. nitidulum
(*shining*)
H4 F1–2 L1–2 Pd.

April

s. Lapponicum.
 Shrub up to 4 ft. Lvs. about ½ in. long and ¼ ir
broad, broadly elliptic, densely scaly on both sur
faces. Fls. single or in pairs, ½ in. long, widely funnel
shaped, violet-purple. Szechwan, 10–12,000 ft.
 A dwarfer form with smaller leaves and usuall
with a coloured calyx, from higher elevations–
15,000 ft.—is known as var. *nubigenum*.

R. nivale
(*snowy*)
H4 F1 L1 Pd.

April–May

s. Lapponicum.
 Prostrate cushion-like shrub with densely scal
branches. Lvs. less than ¼ in. long, elliptic, densel
scaly on both surfaces. Fls. solitary or in pairs
about ½ in. long, widely funnel-shaped, purple
reddish-purple, bright mauve to violet. Sikkim
S. Tibet, Nepal, Bhutan, 15–18,000 ft. A ver
difficult plant to grow.

R. niveum
(*snowlike*)
H4 F2–4 L2–3 Pm.–t.

April–May

s. and s.s. Arboreum.
 Large shrub or small tree up to 15 ft. or mor
with young shoots clothed with dense white felt
indumentum. Lvs. up to 6 in. long and 2½ ir
broad, obovate-lanceolate, covered below with
at first a white felty indumentum, later greyish
brown. Fls. in a tight round truss of up to usuall
20, about 1½–2 in. long, tubular-campanulate, du
smokey-blue or purple-lilac. Sikkim, Bhutan
9–12,000 ft. B.M. 4730, 6827 (var. *fulvum*—wit
buff indumentum).
 A.M. 1951 (Mrs. R. M. Stevenson, Towe
Court, Ascot) to form with up to 30 Imperia
Purple (H.C.C. 33/3–33/2) flowers to the truss.

nudiflorum
(with naked flowers)
4 F1–2 L1–2 Pm.

May

s. Azalea. *s.s.* Luteum.

Shrub up to 9 ft. Lvs. up to 3½ in. long and 1¼ in. broad, elliptic to oblong or obovate, bright green and nearly glabrous beneath. Fls. in clusters of 6–12 expanding just before the leaves, 1–1½ in. wide, tubular-funnel-shaped, scented, near white, pale pink or pale to deeper violet-red with the tube medium to dark crimson; occasional plants have semi-double or frilled flowers with revolute petals, or with a yellow or orange blotch. E. North America. This species can be recognized in many of the Ghent hybrid azaleas.

nuttallii
after Thomas Nuttall, botanist and traveller, 1786–1859)
1–2 F4 L2–4 Pm.s.

April–May

s. Maddenii. *s.s.* Megacalyx.

Rather straggly shrub up to 30 ft. Lvs. up to 8 in. long and 4 in. broad, elliptic, bullate and reticulate above, densely scaly below, when young of a beautiful metallic purple. Fls. in trusses of 3–9, 5 in. or more long, tubular-funnel-shaped, fragrant, clear light yellow, or white flushed yellow within the tube, the lobes tinged with pink; calyx up to 1 in. long with large oblong-elliptic lobes. Bhutan, 4–5,000 ft. B.M. 5146. The largest flowered of rhododendron species in cultivation.

F.C.C. 1864.

A.M. 1936 (L. de Rothschild, Exbury) to form with smaller flowers and spreading calyx, which is said to be hardier than the type and which is known as var. *stellatum*.

R. nuttallii is a parent of the F.C.C. clones 'Tyermannii' (1925), 'William Wright Smith' (1960).

oblongifolium
(with oblong leaves)
3 F1–2 L1–2 Pm.

June–July

s. Azalea. *s.s.* Luteum.

Deciduous shrub up to 6 ft. Lvs. up to 4 in. long and 1½ in. broad, obovate or elliptic-obovate to oblong-oblanceolate, dark green above, light green below. Fls. expanding after the leaves have fully developed, in trusses of 7–12, tubular-funnel-shaped, usually white, sometimes pale or medium pink, with faint clove scent. S.E. North America, S.W. Arkansas to E. Texas and Oklahoma.

obtusum
(blunt)
4 F2–3 L1–2 Pd.–m.

May

s. Azalea. *s.s.* Obtusum.

Shrub, evergreen or semi-evergreen, rarely more than 3 ft. and sometimes nearly prostrate and with branchlets densely clothed with appressed brown hairs. Lvs. up to 1¼ in. long, oval to elliptic-oval, glossy green above, pale beneath. Fls. in clusters of 1–3, about 1 in. across, funnel-shaped, usually bright red, scarlet or crimson. N.W. Japan. A.M. 1898.

R. obtusum
(*continued*)

Important clones of *R. obtusum* have be
named as follows:

form *album* with white flowers.

var. *amoenum* with flowers usually hose-in-hos
rich magenta or rosy-purple. B.M. 4728.

'Amoenum Coccineum' is an unstable branch spe
of var. *amoenum* with light carmine-red hose-i
hose flowers.

R. occidentale
(*western*)
H⁴ F²⁻³ L¹⁻² Pm.

June

s. Azalea. s.s. Luteum.
Deciduous shrub up to 10 ft. Lvs. up to $3\frac{1}{2}$ i
long and $1\frac{1}{4}$ in. broad, elliptic to oblong-lanceolat
changing to yellow, scarlet and crimson in t
autumn. Fls. usually expanding with the leav
in trusses of 6–12, up to 3 in. across, bro
funnel-shaped with gradually flaring tube, cream
white to pale pink, often pinkish on the coro
reverse, with pale yellow to orange-yell
blotch, sweetly scented. N.W. America.
contributor to a beautiful race of hybrids—t
Occidentale hybrids. B.M. 5005.
A.M. 1944 (Royal Botanic Gardens, Kew)
form with white flowers with a yellow blot
heavily flushed with rose-pink.

R. odoriferum
(*fragrant*)
H² F²⁻³ L¹⁻² Pm.

May–June

s. and s.s. Maddenii.
Shrub up to 6 ft. with purple young shoo
Lvs. up to 4 in. long and $2\frac{1}{4}$ in. broad, elliptic
oblanceolate, densely brown-scaly below. Fls.
trusses of 6–7, about 2 in. long, tubular-funn
shaped, white, slightly flushed with rose on t
outside, tube tinged with green within.

R. oldhamii
(After Richard Oldham, collector
for Kew, 1837–64; died at Amoy)
H²⁻³ F²⁻³ L¹⁻² Pm.

May

s. Azalea. s.s. Obtusum.
Evergreen shrub up to 10 ft. with young shoo
densely clothed with red-brown glandular hai
Lvs. up to $3\frac{1}{2}$ in. long and $2\frac{1}{2}$ in. broad, elliptic
elliptic-oblong, covered with spreading red-brow
hairs, later more or less glabrous. Fls. in cluste
of 1–3, funnel-form, 2 in. across, bright brick-re
Formosa, from sea-level to 8,000 ft. B.M. 90

R. oleifolium
(*with olive-like foliage*)
H³ F²⁻³ L¹⁻² Pm.

April–May

s. Virgatum.
Shrub up to 6 ft. Lvs. up to 2 in. long and $\frac{1}{2}$ i
broad, narrow lanceolate, densely scaly belo
Fls. axillary, solitary or in pairs, about 1 in. lor
tubular-campanulate, rose, pink or whi
Yunnan, S.E. Tibet, 7–11,000 ft.
It is the Chinese and Tibetan counterpart of t
Himalayan *R. virgatum*, and is not to be confus
with *R. racemosum* var. *oleifolium*. B.M. 8802.

R. oporinum
(*autumn flowering*)
H4 F1–2 L1–2 Pm.

June–July

s. Heliolepis.
　　Shrub up to 10 ft. Lvs. about 3 in. long, 1½ in. broad, broadly lanceolate or oblong-lanceolate, pale rusty below, highly aromatic. Fls. in clusters of 5–10, about ¾ in. long, campanulate to tubular-campanulate, rose-pink or white, with or without a crimson blotch, spotted with crimson. Upper Burma, 11–12,000 ft.

R. orbiculare
(*circular, alluding to the leaves*)
H4 F2–3 L2–3 Pm.–t.

March–April

s. Fortunei. s.s. Orbiculare.
　　Rounded well-shaped shrub up to 10 ft. with bright green glaucous young shoots. Lvs. 2–4 in. long, up to 3 in. broad, broadly ovate to orbicular, cordate-auriculate at base, bright mat green above, very glaucous below. Fls. in loose trusses of 7–10, up to 2 in. long, campanulate, 7-lobed, rose-pink often with a bluish tinge. W. Szechwan, 8–10,000 ft. B.M. 8775.
　　A.M. 1922 (Hon. H. D. McLaren, Bodnant).
　　R. orbiculare is a parent of the A.M. clones 'Rosemary Chipp' (1928), 'Kenlis' (1948).

R. oreodoxa
(*glory of the mountains*)
H4 F1–3 L2–3 Pm.–t.

March–April

s. Fortunei. s.s. Oreodoxa.
　　Shrub or small tree up to 20 ft. or more. Lvs. 2–4 in. long, up to 1½ in. broad, narrow-elliptic or oblanceolate-elliptic, glaucous below. Fls. in truss of 10–12, about 1½–2 in. long, open campanulate, 7–8 lobed, pink, with or without purple spots. Very floriferous when it has reached a certain height but should be sheltered because of its early flowering habit; the flower buds are very frost-resistant. It includes the geographical forms *haematocheilum* (F1–2), B.M. 8518, *limprichtii* and *reginaldii* (F2–3).
　　A.M. 1937 (L. de Rothschild, Exbury) to form with flowers pale rose with darker stripe down centre of each petal.

R. oreotrephes
(*mountain bred*)
H4 F2–3 L1–2 Pm.–t.

April–May

s. Triflorum. s.s. Yunnanense.
　　Shrub up to 20 ft. or more with reddish branchlets. Lvs. ¾–4½ in. long, oblong-elliptic to elliptic to almost orbicular, scaly and glaucous below. Fls. in clusters of 4–10, terminal or terminal and axillary in uppermost leaves, up to 1¾ in. long, wide or narrow funnel-shaped, or sometimes funnel-campanulate, zygomorphic, mauve, mauve-pink, purple or rose, with or without crimson spots. Yunnan, Szechwan, Tibet, Burma, 9–16,000 ft.
　　With its free-flowering habit and glaucous leaves this is a most attractive plant. Sometimes it is semi-deciduous for in cold gardens it tends to lose its leaves. B.M. 8784.

R. oreotrephes
(*continued*)

With so wide a distribution, *R. oreotreph*
varies greatly and certain variations in the pas
have been given specific rank. *R. artosquameum*
R. exquisetum and *R. timeteum*, are such variant
and should be included here.

A.M. 1932 (as *R. timeteum*; L. de Rothschild
Exbury) to form with rosy-purple flowers.

A.M. 1935 (as *R. siderophylloides*; J. J. Crosfield
Embley Park, Hants) to form with bright pinkish
mauve flowers with darker spots.

A.M. 1937 (as *R. exquisetum*; L. de Rothschild
Exbury) to form with light mauvish-pink, red
spotted, flowers.

R. orthocladum
(*with straight twigs*)
H⁴ F¹⁻² L¹⁻² Pd.–m.

April

s. Lapponicum.

Shrub up to 4 ft. with densely scaly branchlet:
Lvs. about ½ in. long, oblanceolate, scaly an
rather greyish in colour. Fls. in clusters of 1–4
about ½ in. long, widely funnel-shaped, purplish
blue, pale mauve to deep lavender-blue. Yunnar
Szechwan, 11–14,000 ft.

R. oulotrichum
(*with curly hairs*)
H⁴ F¹⁻² L¹⁻² Pm.

April–May

s. Trichocladum.

Deciduous shrub, up to 6 ft. with nearl
glabrous branchlets. Lvs. about 1 in. long, obovat
to elliptic, pilose at margin when young. Fls
precocious, in clusters of about 3, about ¾ in. long
widely funnel-shaped and with long pilose pedicel
yellow. Yunnan, Tibet, Upper Burma, 9–10,50
ft.

R. ovatum
(*egg-shaped*)
H³ F¹⁻² L¹⁻² Pm.–t.

May–June

s. Ovatum.

Shrub up to 15 ft. with very pale bark. Lvs
about 2 in. long and up to 1 in. broad, broadl
ovate, with long mucro at the tip. Fls. solitar
from each of several buds near the end of th
branchlets, about 1 in. diam., rotate, white, pin
or purplish with purple spots. E. China. B.M
5064.

R. oxyphyllum
(*with pointed leaves*)
H¹ F¹⁻² L¹⁻² Pm.–t.

April

s. Stamineum.

Shrub or tree up to 20 ft. Lvs. 3½–5 in. long
1–2 in. broad, oblong-oblanceolate, sharpl
pointed. Fls. in axillary clusters of 3–5, about 2 in
long, tubular-funnel-shaped, white or whit
flushed rose, with a yellowish blotch. S. Yunnan
Burma, N. Siam, Kwangsi, 4–5,000 ft.

R. pachypodum
(*thick-footed*)
H² F²⁻⁴ L²⁻³ Pm.

March–April

s. Maddenii. s.s. Ciliicalyx.

Shrub up to 5 ft. Lvs. up to 4 in. long and 1½ in
broad, oblanceolate to elliptic-oblanceolate, densel
rusty, scaly and glaucous below. Fls. in trusses o
2–5, up to 4 in. long and 4 in. diam., tubular

R. pachypodum
(continued)

funnel-shaped, yellow or white. W. Yunnan, 7–11,000 ft. A very fine plant for the cool green-house.

F.C.C. 1936 (L. de Rothschild, Exbury) to form with white flowers with a pale yellow streak on the inside of the top lobe.

R. pachytrichum
(with thick hairs)
H4 F1–3 L2–3 Pm.–t.
March–April

s. Barbatum. s.s. Maculiferum.

Shrub up to 18 ft. with young shoots clothed with brownish shaggy hairs. Lvs. 2½–5 in. long, up to 2 in. broad, narrow oblong to oblanceolate or obovate, bright green above, pale green and shining below. Fls. in trusses of 7–10, 1½–2 in. long, campanulate, white to pale rose to deep rich pink and with a purple blotch. Some forms with the flowers of a purplish-magenta tint should be avoided. W. Szechwan, 7–11,000 ft. Closely allied to *R. monosematum*. Very handsome and floriferous when well grown.

A.M. 1963 'Sesame' (Lord Aberconway and Nat. Trust, Bodnant) form with white fls. tinged with varying shades of Solferino Purple.

R. × pallescens
(becoming paler in tint)
H4 F2–3 L1–2 Pm.
May

s. Triflorum. s.s. Yunnanense.

Sparse foliaged shrub up to 4 ft. Lvs. about 3 in. long, lanceolate or oblanceolate, glaucous and scaly below. Fls. terminal and axillary in the upper leaf axils, about 1½ in. long, widely funnel-shaped, pale pink, the margins of the lobes flushed with carmine, or white, slightly spotted. Regarded as a natural hybrid between *R. davidsoni-anum* and *R. racemosum*, raised from seeds of *Rock 59574 (R. eritimum)* from W. China. (See *Rhodo-dendron and Camellia Year Book*, 1963.)

A.M. 1933 (L. de Rothschild, Exbury) to form with flowers white, pink-flushed along the margin and dotted with pink inside the tube.

R. paludosum
(marshy)
H4 F1–2 L1–2 Pd.
April–May

s. Lapponicum.

Intricately branched shrub up to 2 ft. Lvs. about ½ in. long, elliptic, densely scaly on both surfaces, light brown below. Fls. usually solitary, about ⅓ in. long, shortly and openly tubular, bright violet. Yunnan, Tibet, 12–14,000 ft., usually growing in bogs.

R. pankimense
(from Pankim La, Assam)
H3–4 F1–3 L1–2 Pm.
April

s. and s.s. Irroratum.

Shrub up to 10 ft. Lvs. up to 4 in. long and 1 in. broad, lanceolate, dark green above, paler below. Fls. in trusses of 8–12, about 1¼ in. long, campanulate, crimson with numerous darker spots but without basal blotch. Assam, S.E. Tibet, 8–9,000 ft.

R. panteumorphum

H4 F1–2 L2–3 Pm.

April–May

s. Thomsonii. *s.s.* Campylocarpum.

Shrub up to 10 ft. Lvs. up to 4 in. long and 2 in. broad, oblong-elliptic, dark green above, paler below. Fls. in trusses of 4–8, about 1½ in. long, campanulate, pale yellow. S.E. Tibet, Yunnan, 11–14,000 ft.

R. paradoxum ·
(*unexpected*)

H4 F2–3 L2–3 Pm.

April–May

s. Taliense. *s.s.* Wasonii.

Shrub up to 7 ft. with young shoots covered with white scurfy indumentum. Lvs. 2–5 in. long, up to 2 in. broad, oblong, dark green and semi-bullate above, pale green below with loose patches of grey and brown indumentum. Fls. in a truss of about 8, 1½–2 in. long, campanulate, white with deep crimson blotch breaking into short lines of spots. Szechwan.

R. parishii
(After Rev. C. S. P. Parish, chaplain at Moulmein, d. 1897)

H1 F2–3 L2–3 Pm.–t.

· *Jan.*

s. Irroratum. *s.s.* Parishii.

Shrub or tree up to 20 ft. with young shoots tawny or rusty tomentose. Lvs. up to 5 in. long and 3 in. broad, broadly elliptic to obovate, dark mat green above, paler below. Fls. in trusses of up to 12, 1½–2 in. long, tubular-campanulate, red with deeper lines along the lobes. Burma, 6,200 ft. A fine species for the cool greenhouse.

R. parmulatum
(*with small shield*)

H4 F1–2 L1–2 Pm.

April–May

s. Neriiflorum. *s.s.* Sanguineum.

Shrub up to 4 ft. Lvs. up to 3 in. long and 1½ in. broad, ovate, dark olive-green above, glaucous below. Fls. in trusses of 3–5, up to 2 in. or rather more long, tubular-campanulate, pale creamy-white, creamy-yellow, white or white tinged pink, with crimson spots. S.E. Tibet, 10–14,000 ft. B.M. 9624.

R. parryae
(After Mrs. A. D. Parry, wife of an officer in the Assam Civil Service)

H1–2 F3–4 L2–3 Pm.s.

May

s. Maddenii. *s.s.* Ciliicalyx.

Shrub, rather straggling, or medium-sized tree up to 10 ft. with thin smooth pinkish-purple bark. Lvs. up to 6 in. long and 2½ in. broad, elliptic to oblong-elliptic, dark green above, glaucous-green and scaly below. Fls. in lax truss of up to 4, 3 in. long, up to 4½ in. across, shallow funnel-shaped, white with prominent yellow-orange blotch. Assam, 6,000 ft. In most gardens a plant for the cool house, though it can be grown out of doors in the south and west.

A.M. 1957 (Royal Botanic Garden, Edinburgh).

R. parvifolium
(*with small leaves*)

H4 F1–2 L1–2 Pd.

Jan.–March

s. Lapponicum.

Shrub up to 1½ ft. and with branchlets densely covered with flaky scales. Lvs. about ¾ in. long and ⅓ in. broad, oblong-lanceolate, scaly on both surfaces. Fls. in truss of up to 5, about ⅔ in. long,

R. parvifolium
(continued)

funnel-shaped, pale magenta-rose. N.E. Asia: Siberia and N. Korea. B.M. 9229. An albino form is known as var. *albiflorum*.

R. patulum
(spreading)
H4 F2–3 L1–2 Pd.–p.

May

s. Uniflorum.
 Dwarf or prostrate shrub up to 2 ft. Lvs. up to ¾ in. long, narrow, rather glaucous below. Fls. solitary or in pairs, up to 1¼ in. long, narrow or broad funnel-shaped, purple, the upper lobe spotted with crimson-purple. Assam Frontier, 11–12,000 ft. Very closely allied to *R. imperator*. Very often rather difficult in cultivation.

R. pectinatum
(toothed like a comb)
H1 F2–3 L1–2 Pm.–t.

April

s. Stamineum.
 Shrub or tree up to 20 ft. or more. Lvs. up to 8 in. long and 2 in. broad, oblong, long-acute, dark green above, pale below. Fls. in truss of 3–4 in each axillary inflorescence, 5 or 6 of which are clustered at the ends of last year's shoots, up to 2½ in. across, tubular-funnel-shaped, white with a pale yellow blotch, fragrant. Yunnan.
 A.M. 1935 (L. de Rothschild, Exbury).

R. pemakoense
(from the province of Pemako, E. Tibet)
H3–4 F2–3 L1–2 Pd.

March–April

s. Uniflorum.
 Dwarf erect or semi-erect shrub up to 1 ft., sometimes stoloniferous. Lvs. at most 1¼ in. long, obovate or oblong, obovate, dark green above, grey below. Fls. solitary or in pairs, up to 1½ in. long, funnel-shaped, pinkish-purple or purple. Tibet, 10,000 ft. There is a form which is stoloniferous and nearly all forms are very floriferous. Closely allied to *R. uniflorum*. The flower buds are liable to be frosted.
 A.M. 1933 (Sir John Ramsden, Gerrards Cross) to form with flowers white with a suffusion of mauve—under the number *K.W.* 6301.

R. pendulum
(hanging)
H2–3 F1–2 L1–2 Pd.–m.s.

April–May

s. Edgeworthii.
 Shrub, sometimes straggling and epiphytic up to 4 ft. and with densely woolly young shoots. Lvs. up to 2 in. long and 1¼ in. broad, elliptic or oblong-elliptic, impressed-reticulate above, dense woolly tomentose below. Fls in clusters of 2–3, about 1½ in. diameter, flat, white, tinged inside with yellow and sometimes touched with pink. Sikkim, Bhutan, Tibet, 7,500–12,000 ft.

R. pennivenium
(pinnately veined)
H4 F1–2 L1–2 Pm.–t.

April–May

s. *and* s.s. Irroratum.
 Shrub up to 20 ft. Lvs. 3–6 in. long and up to 2 in. broad, oblong-elliptic to broadly lanceolate, grey to fawn below, primary veins very prominent. Fls. in truss of up to 10, about ½ in. long, tubular-campanulate, fleshy, crimson with deeper spots within. Yunnan, 9–11,000 ft.

R. pentaphyllum
(*five-leaved*)
H⁴ F³ L²⁻³ Pm.

March–April

s. Azalea. *s.s.* Canadense.

Deciduous shrub or small tree up to 10 ft. or more. Lvs. in whorls of 5 at the ends of the branchlets, up to 2½ in. long and 1¼ in. broad, elliptic to elliptic-lanceolate, ciliate at margin, changing to orange and crimson in autumn. Fls. single or in pairs, opening before the leaves, up to 2¼ in. across, rotate-campanulate, bright rose-pink, unspotted. C. & S. Japan. A beautiful plant both for flower and foliage.

A.M. 1942 (Lord Aberconway, Bodnant) to form with flowers a warm pink, paler with age, H.C.C. 25/2–25/3.

R. peramabile
(*very lovely*)
H⁴ F²⁻³ L¹⁻² Pd.–m.

April–May

s. Lapponicum.

Erect shrub up to 2½ ft. Lvs. about ¾ in. long, elliptic, scaly below. Fls. in trusses of 7–10, about ⅓ in. long, funnel-shaped, deep violet-mauve. Closely allied to *R. intricatum* and probably nothing more than a luxuriant form of this species. Probably Yunnan.

R. peramoenum
(*very pleasing*)
H² F²⁻³ L²⁻³ Pm.

March–April

s. and s.s. Arboreum.

Shrub up to 12 ft. Lvs. up to 6 in. long and 1 in. broad, narrow-lanceolate, light green above with impressed veins, white or grey to fawn below. Fls. in rather tight truss of 15–20, about 2 in. long, campanulate, cherry-scarlet to deep rose-crimson. W. Yunnan, 8–11,000 ft.

R. peregrinum
(*foreign*)
H³ F²⁻³ L²⁻³ Pm.

March–May

s. Grande.

Small tree. Lvs. up to 7 in. long, 3½ in. broad, oblong-elliptic to broadly elliptic, light mat green above, greenish-grey to buff below. Fls. in lax truss of up to 20, about 2 in. long, broadly campanulate, soft pink in bud opening to white with a faint rose tinge on the outside and a blotch of bright red within. S.W. Szechwan. Appeared as a rogue amongst plants of *R. galactinum* grown from seeds of *Wilson* 4254.

R. phaedropum
(*of bright appearance*)

see *R. neriiflorum* subsp. *phaedropum*.

R. phaeochrysum
(*dark golden*)
H⁴ F¹⁻³ L¹⁻³ Pm.

April

s. and s.s. Lacteum.

Shrub up to 15 ft. Lvs. 2–5½ in. long, up to 2 in. broad, oblong-elliptic to oblong-lanceolate, with suède-like dark brown or fawn indumentum below. Fls. in truss of 8–15, about 2 in. long, funnel-campanulate, white, creamy-white, white flushed with rose, pinkish or purple, rarely yellow, with or without crimson spots, rarely with a red blotch. Yunnan, Szechwan, Tibet, 11–17,500 ft. Closely allied to *R. dryophyllum*.

R. phoenicodum
(with purple-red bell)

see *R. neriiflorum* subsp. *phoenicodon*.

R. pholidotum
(scaly)
H4 F1–2 L1–2 Pm.

June

s. Heliolepis.
Shrub up to 8 ft. with purplish scaly branchlets. Lvs. up to 2½ in. long and 1¼ in. broad, ovate-elliptic, impressed-reticulate above, scaly below. Fls. in a truss of about 5, about 1¼ in. long, widely funnel-shaped, rose to rose-purple, spotted. Yunnan, Tibet, Upper Burma, 10–12,000 ft.

R. planetum
(wandering; appeared in cultivation as a rogue)
H4 F2–3 L2–3 Pm.–t.

March–April

s. Fortunei. s.s. Davidii.
Shrub or small tree up to 15 ft. Lvs. up to 8 in. long and 2½ in. broad, oblong or elongate-oblong, bright green above, pale green below. Fls. in truss of up to 10, up to 2 in. long, funnel-campanulate, pink, usually without blotch and spots. Szechwan, 10–12,000 ft. B.M. 8953.

R. pocophorum
(fleece-bearing)
H3–4 F2–3 L2–3 Pm.

March–April

s. Neriiflorum. s.s. Haematodes.
Shrub up to 10 ft. Lvs. up to 6 in. long and 3 in. broad, oblong to oblong-obovate, covered below with thick brown woolly indumentum. Fls. in compact truss of 15–20, about 2 in. long, tubular-campanulate, deep crimson or crimson-scarlet. S.E. Tibet, 12–15,000 ft.
R. pocophorum is a parent of the A.M. clone 'Ibex' (1948).

R. pogonostylum
(with bearded style)
H2 F1–2 L1–2 Pm.–t.

April–June

s. and s.s. Irroratum.
Tree up to 15 ft. Lvs. up to 5 in. long and 2 in. broad, rigid, oblong-lanceolate to oblong-ovate. Fls. in truss of about 8, about 1½ in. long, tubular-campanulate, pink, spotted dark red. S.E. Yunnan, 7–10,000 ft. A form with much less spotting has been named *R. adenostemonum*.

R. polifolium
(many-leaved)
H4 F1–2 L1–2 Pd.

April–May

s. Lapponicum.
Shrub up to 2 ft. Lvs. nearly ½ in. long, oblong-oblanceolate, densely scaly, yellowish-brown below. Fls. in clusters of 1–3, about ⅓ in. long, widely funnel-shaped, mauve or deep purplish-blue. Szechwan.

R. polyandrum
(with many stamens)
H2–3 F2–4 L2–3 Pm.s.

May–June

s. and s.s. Maddenii.
Somewhat straggling shrub up to 10 ft. Lvs. up to 4 in. long and 1½ in. broad, oblong or oblong-lanceolate, glossy-reticulate above, densely cinnamon-scaly below. Fls. in trusses of 3–6, about 3 in. long, tubular-funnel-shaped, white, deepening to yellow in the throat, or white flushed with pink or pale yellow, fragrant. Bhutan, Assam,

R. polyandrum
(*continued*)

7–8,500 ft. Some forms are among the hardiest of the Maddenii rhododendrons.

A.M. 1933 (Lt.-Col. L. C. R. Messel, Handcross, Sussex) to form with white flowers, yellow in the throat.

A.M. 1938 (Lt.-Col. L. C. R. Messel) to form with rose-pink flowers.

R. polyandrum is a parent of the A.M. clone 'Cinnandrum Tangerine' (1937).

R. polylepis
(*with many scales*)
H⁴ F¹⁻² L¹⁻² Pm.

April

s. Triflorum. s.s. Yunnanense.

Thin shrub up to 12 ft. Lvs. up to 4 in. long and 1½ in. broad, oblong-lanceolate, lanceolate or oblanceolate, covered with dry flaky scales below. Fls. in clusters of 3–5, about 1½ in. long, widely funnel-shaped, zygomorphic, pale or dark purple or violet-purple, with or without yellow spots. S.W. Szechwan, 7,200–11,500 ft. B.M. 8309 (as *R. harrovianum*).

R. ponticum
(*from Pontus,
Asia Minor*)
H⁴ F¹⁻³ L¹⁻² Pm.–t.

June

s. and s.s. Ponticum.

A plant needing no description. Introduced about 1763 and naturalized in so many of our woods, it can be a splendid sight when in full flower. Many plants in stands of *ponticum* are from natural crosses with other rhododendrons. It makes an effective windbreak and serves as stock for grafting. Asia Minor, the Caucasus, Armenia. B.M. 650. *R. baeticum* is a form of *R. ponticum* growing wild in the Iberian Peninsula, whilst 'Cheiranthifolium' is a garden form with very narrow wavy leaves. A white form has also been found in Pontic Range of E. Turkey.

R. pothinum
(*much desired*)

see *R. temenium* subsp. *pothinum*.

R. poukhanense
(*from Mt. Poukhan,
Korea*)
H⁴ F¹⁻² L¹⁻² Pd.–m.

May

s. Azalea. s.s. Obtusum.

Compact shrub up to 6 ft. Lvs. usually completely deciduous, up to 3½ in. long and 1 in. broad, oblanceolate to lanceolate or ovate-lanceolate, dark green and with veins impressed above, pale below, turning to orange and crimson in the autumn. Fls. in clusters of 2 or more opening with or before the leaves, 2 in. across, very fragrant, rose to pale lilac-purple. C. & S. Korea. See *R. yedoense*.

R. praestans
(*excellent*)
H³⁻⁴ F²⁻³ L³⁻⁴ Pm.–t.

April–May

s. Grande.

Shrub or tree up to 30 ft. Lvs. up to 18 in. long and 8 in. broad, oblong-oblanceolate or oblong-obovate, dark green and with impressed veins above, lower surface with grey-white to fawn

R. praestans
(continued)

plastered indumentum, petiole short, broad and flat. Fls. in trusses of 15–20, nearly 2 in. long, obliquely bell-shaped, deep magenta-rose or pink, with a crimson blotch, 8-lobed. Yunnan, W. Burma, S.E. Tibet, 9–13,000 ft.

R. praeteritum
(passed over)
H4 F2–3 L2–3 Pm.

March–April

s. Fortunei. *s.s.* Oreodoxa.

Shrub up to 15 ft. with bright green young branches and reddish-brown older ones. Lvs. up to 4 in. long and 1½ in. broad, oval-oblong or oblong-elliptic, dark green above, pale below. Fls. in truss of 7–10, up to 1½ in. long, widely campanulate, 5-lobed, pink. Very close to *R. oreodoxa* but with 5-lobed corolla.

R. praevernum
(before the Spring)
H4 F2–3 L2–3 Pm.–t.

Feb.–March–April

s. Fortunei. *s.s.* Davidii.

Medium-sized shrub or small tree up to 12 ft. or more. Lvs. up to 7 in. long and 2½ in. broad, elliptic to oblanceolate, dark green above, pale grey-green below. Fls. in trusses of 8–10, up to 2½ in. long, bell-shaped, white or white flushed with rose with a wine-red blotch at the base. Closely allied to *R. sutchuenense*. Hupeh, 5–7,000 ft.

R. praevernum is a parent of the A.M. cultivar 'Springtime' (1945).

R. prattii
(After A. E. Pratt, explorer in China during 1887–90)
H4 F1–3 L1–3 Pm.

April–May

s. Taliense. *s.s.* Adenogynum.

Shrub up to 10 ft. Lvs. up to 6 in. long and 3 in. broad, broadly ovate to elongate-elliptic, round or even slightly cordate at base, with fawn to brown indumentum below. Fls. in truss of 12–20, nearly 2 in. long, broadly bell-shaped, white spotted with deep pink, 5-lobed; calyx leafy, nearly ½ in. long. Szechwan, 9–13,000 ft. B.M. 9414.

R. preptum
(distinguished)
H3–4 F2–3 L2–3 Pm.

April–May

s. Falconeri.

Shrub or tree up to 8 ft. Lvs. up to 7 in. long and 3 in. broad, elongate-obovate, olive-green above, pale buff indumentum below. Fls. in truss of up to 20, up to 1½ in. long, oblique campanulate, creamy white with a crimson blotch. Upper Burma, and Yunnan, 11–12,000 ft.

R. primulaeflorum
(primrose-flowered)
H4 F2–3 L1–2 Pd.–m.

April–May

s. Anthopogon.

Highly aromatic shrub up to 6 ft. with deciduous leaf-bud scales. Lvs. up to 1⅓ in. long, oblong to oblong-elliptic or ovate-oblong, densely scaly and white below. Fls. in small more or less capitate trusses, up to ¾ in. long, narrowly tubular, yellow or white or pale rose. Yunnan, Szechwan, Kansu, 11–15,000 ft.

R. primulaeflorum
(*continued*)

There is a form with the corolla-tube densely puberulous outside, known as var. *cephalanthoides* and another with densely scaly corolla-lobes known as var. *lepidanthum*. Mostly closely allied to *R. cephalanthum* but with deciduous leaf-bud scales.

R. pronum
(*prostrate*)
H4 F1-2 L1-2 Pd.p.

April–May

s. Taliense. s.s. Roxieanum.

Low, slow growing prostrate shrub up to 1 ft. with bud scales persisting for many years and with gnarled rooting branchlets. Lvs. up to nearly 3 in. long and 1 in. broad, oblong-elliptic to oblanceolate, dull-grey to fawn below. Fls. in trusses of 8–12, about 1½ in. long, campanulate, creamy-yellow copiously marked with deep crimson. Yunnan. S.E. Tibet, Szechwan, 12–15,000 ft.

R. prostratum
(*low growing*)
H4 F1-2 L1-2 Pd.p.

April–May

s. Saluenense.

Prostrate spreading shrub up to 1½ ft. with bristly branchlets. Lvs. up to ¾ in. long, elliptic to ovate-elliptic, glossy and reticulate above, densely brown-scaly below. Fls. in clusters of 1–3, about ¾ in. long, widely funnel-shaped, crimson or deep purple-rose with crimson spots. Yunnan, Szechwan, Tibet, 15–16,000 ft., often almost at the limit of vegetation. B.M. 8747.

R. proteoides
(*resembling Protea*)
H4 F1-2 L2-3 Pd.

April

s. Taliense. s.s. Roxieanum.

Slow growing shrub up to 3 ft. with bud-scales persisting for several years. Lvs. up to 1½ in. long and ½ in. broad, oblong, margin revolute, with thick wooly rufous indumentum below. Fls. in compact trusses of 8–10, up to 1½ in. long, bell-shaped, creamy-yellow, or white, sometimes flushed rose, with copious crimson spots. Yunnan, Szechwan, S.E. Tibet, 12–14,000 ft.

R. protistum
(*first of the first*)
H2-3 F2-4 L2-3 Pm.-t.

Feb.–March

s. Grande.

Shrub or tree up to 30 ft. Lvs. up to 18 in. long and 9 in. broad, lanceolate to oblanceolate, dark and rugulose and with the main veins impressed above, with thin greyish-green indumentum below. Fls. in trusses of 20–30, about 2 in. long, tubular-campanulate, creamy-white flushed rose. N.W. Yunnan, Upper Burma, 9–13,000 ft. A fine species very near to *R. giganteum*.

R. prunifolium
(*with plum-like leaves*)
H4 F2-3 L1-2 Pm.

July–Aug.

s. Azalea. s.s. Luteum.

Shrub up to 12 ft. or more becoming round-topped at maturity with young shoots usually dark purplish-red later becoming grey. Lvs. up to 5 in. long and 1½ in. broad, elliptic to obovate,

R. prunifolium
(continued)

dark green above, paler below. Fls. opening after the leaves are fully developed, in trusses of 4–5, up to 2 in. across, tubular-funnel-shaped, usually reddish-orange to orange-red or red, but also varying to orange and yellow. Very valuable for its late-flowering habit. S.E. North America along the Southern Georgia–Alabama border.

'Summer Sunset' is an A.M. clone (Crown Estate Commissioners, Windsor, 1950) to form with flowers of Vermilion, H.C.C. 18/1.

R. przewalskii
After N. M. Przewalski, 1839–88, Russian traveller and geographer)
H⁴ F¹⁻² L¹⁻² Pm.

April–May

s. Lacteum.

Shrub up to 9 ft. Lvs. up to 4½ in. long and 1½ in. broad, elliptic to oblong-elliptic to oblong, lower surfaces with thin fawn, brown or white indumentum or sometimes with a few scattered hairs. Fls. in trusses of 10–15, 1–1½ in. long, funnel-campanulate or campanulate, white or rose-pink, with or without spots. Kansu, Tibet, Szechwan, 10–14,000 ft.

R.pseudochrysanthum
(like R. chrysanthum)
H⁴ F³⁻⁴ L²⁻³ Pm.

April

s. Barbatum. s.s. Maculiferum.

Compact shrub, up to 9 ft. Lvs. rather crowded, up to 3 in. long and 1½ in. broad, ovate to elliptic to oblong-lanceolate, recurved at margin, dark green and glossy above, paler green below, when young covered with woolly indumentum. Fls. in truss of 9 or more, up to 2 in. long, campanulate, dark pink in bud opening pale pink or even white, with deeper rose lines outside, spotted crimson inside. Formosa, 6–13,000 ft.

A.M. 1956 (E. de Rothschild, Exbury) to form with flowers white flushed with varying shades of pink and throat spotted crimson.

R. pseudoyanthinum
(like R. yanthinum)

see *R. concinnum* var. *pseudoyanthinum*.

R. pubescens
(downy)
H⁴ F²⁻³ L¹⁻² Pm.

April–May

s. Scabrifolium.

Shrub up to 6 ft. with bristly and pubescent branchlets. Lvs. about ¾ in. long, narrowly lanceolate, densely hairy on both surfaces. Fls. in clusters of 1–4, about ½ in. long, ¾ in. broad, funnel-shaped, rose or pinkish-white. Szechwan, Yunnan, 10,000 ft. Now generally merged with *R. spiciferum*. B.M. 9319.

'Fine Bristles' is an A.M. clone (Crown Estate Commissioners, Windsor, 1955) to form with flowers white suffused with shades of Persian Rose (H.C.C. 628/1); buds a deep shade of pink.

R. puderosum
(*very bashful*)
H3-4 F2-3 L2-3 Pt.

April–May

s. Grande.

Tree up to 25 ft. with young branches densely clothed with persisting bud-scales. Lvs. up to 9 in. long and 3 in. broad, oblanceolate or oblong pale green above, silver-grey below. Fls. in trusses of up to 24, 1½ in. long, ventricose-campanulate, mauve-pink with magenta patch at base S. Tibet, 11–12,500 ft.

R. pulchrum
(*beautiful*)
H3 F2-3 L1-2 Pm.

May

s. Azalea. s.s. Obtusum.

Shrub up to 6 ft. with young shoots clothed with grey-brown hairs. Lvs. persistent, up to 2½ in. long and ¾ in. broad, elliptic to elliptic-lanceolate. Fls. in clusters of 1–4, about 2½ in. broad, funnel-shaped, usually rose-purple, with dark purple spots. Not known in the wild but introduced, in various forms from China, Japan and possibly is a hybrid between *R. scabrum* and *R. mucronatum*. B.M. 2667. Sometimes known as *R. phoeniceum* var. *smithii*.

Several forms have been named as follows:
'Maxwellii': fls. bright rose-red of large size with darker blotch. A.M. 1960 (Wisley Trials).

'Tebotan': fls. double, purple, with tiny bunch of green undeveloped leaves showing at the centre B.M. 3239, as var. *phoeniceum*. 'Violet Cloud' is an A.M. clone (Crown Estate Commissioners 1962); fls. of Mallow Purple (H.C.C. 630) with some crimson spotting. 'Omurasaki': also known as var. *calycinum*, has rosy-purple flowers with crimson spots. A.M. (Royal Botanic Gardens, Kew), 1962.

R. pumilum
(*dwarfish*)
H4 F1-3 L1-2 Pd.

May–June

s. Uniflorum.

Dwarf shrub up to 1 ft. Lvs. at most ¾ in. long elliptic to obovate-elliptic, scaly and usually glaucous below. Fls. in clusters of 1–3, at most ¾ in. long, campanulate, pink or rose. Sikkim, Tibet, 11–14,000 ft.

A.M. 1935 (Lord Swaythling, Townhill Park, Southampton) to form with pinkish-mauve flowers with dark red calyx.

R. puralbum
(*very white*)
H4 F2-3 L2-3 Pm.

May

s. Thomsonii. s.s. Souliei.

Shrub up to 15 ft. Lvs. 2–5 in. long, up to 2 in. broad, oblong or oblong-elliptic, apex round, base round or cordulate, dark green above, bright glaucous-green below. Fls. in trusses of about 8, about 1½ in. long, open cup- or saucer-shaped, pure white; calyx up to nearly ½ in. deep. Yunnan, 11–14,000 ft. Closely allied to *R. wardii* and *R. souliei*, differing in the pure white flowers.

R. pyrrhoanthum
(*with fiery-red flowers*)
H3 F1–2 L1–2 Pd.p.

April

s. Neriiflorum (?). *s.s.* Forrestii (?).

Prostrate shrub. Lvs. up to 3 in. long and $1\frac{1}{2}$ in. broad, oblong-oval, dark green above, pale yellow-green below. Fls. in truss of about 5, about $1\frac{1}{4}$ in. long, campanulate, blood-red, unspotted. Yunnan (?). Of very doubtful origin and possibly a hybrid.

R. quinquefolium
(*leaves in fives*)
H4 F2–3 L3 Pm.–t.

April–May

s. Azalea. *s.s.* Schlippenbachii.

Deciduous shrub or small tree up to 25 ft., in cultivation usually smaller, with branchlets partly verticillate, partly alternate. Lvs. in fours or fives at the ends of the branchlets, about 2 in. long and up to $1\frac{1}{4}$ in. broad, broadly elliptic to obovate, ciliate and often margined with red-purple, colouring in the autumn. Fls. expanding after the leaves, in trusses of 1–3, up to 2 in. diameter, rotate-campanulate, pendulous, pure white with green spots. C. Japan.

Very attractive both in foliage—especially in autumn foliage—and in flower though rather shy to bloom when young.

A.M. 1931 (Dowager Countess Cawdor, Haslemere).

R. racemosum
(*flowers in racemes*)
H4 F1–3 L1–2 Pd.–m.

March–April

s. Scabrifolium.

Shrub up to 6 ft., occasionally more, with rather leggy branches sometimes coloured red. Lvs. up to 2 in. long and 1 in. broad, oblong-elliptic, very glaucous below and densely scaly. Fls. axillary, sometimes forming a raceme along the branchlets, in clusters of 3–6, about 1 in. long, funnel-shaped, pink, white or white tinged pink or pale or deep rose. Yunnan, Szechwan, 9–14,000 ft. B.M. 7301.

Various forms are grown in gardens including that under number *Forrest* 19404, which is a good dwarf form with bright pink flowers and red branchlets.

F.C.C. 1892 (J. Veitch & Son, Chelsea).

A.G.M. 1930.

R. racemosum is a parent of the A.M. clones 'Racil' (1957), 'Fittra' (1949), 'Spinulosum' (1944), 'Exbury Spinulosum' (1948).

R. radicans
(*rooting*)
H4 F2–3 L1–2 Pd.p.

May–June

s. Saluenense.

Prostrate shrub or forming a small mound up to 6 in. with persistent leaf-bud scales and rooting branches. Lvs. up to $\frac{3}{4}$ in. long, linear to narrow-oblong, densely scaly below. Fls. usually solitary, about $\frac{3}{4}$ in. long, widely tubular, purple, pubescent and scaly on the outside. An attractive rock garden plant. S.E. Tibet, 14–15,000 ft.

R. radicans
(continued)

A.M. 1926 (J. B. Stevenson, Tower Court, Ascot), completely prostrate form with rosy-purple flowers about 1 in. across under number *Forrest* 19919.

R. ramosissimum
(very branched)
H4 F1–2 L1–2 Pd.

April–May

s. Lapponicum.
Shrub up to 3 ft. with short scaly branchlets. Lvs. about ¼ in. long, broadly elliptic, densely rusty-red scaly below. Fls. in clusters of 1–3, about ⅓ in. long, widely funnel-shaped, dark purple, purplish-red or dark purplish-blue. Szechwan, 11–14,500 ft.

R. ramsdenianum
(After Sir John Ramsden)
H3 F1–2 L1–2 Pm.–t.

April

s. and s.s. Irroratum.
Bushy tree up to 40 ft. Lvs. up to 4 in. long, 1½ in. broad, broadly lanceolate to oblong-lanceolate. Fls. in truss of 12–15, about 1½ in. long, tubular-campanulate, fleshy, scarlet-crimson, crimson or deep rose, unspotted, with or without a dark crimson blotch. S.E. Tibet, 8,000 ft.

R. ravum
(grey)
H4 F2–3 L1–2 Pd.–m.

May

s. Lapponicum.
Shrub up to 4 ft. with densely scaly branchlets. Lvs. about ¾ in. long, ¼ in. broad, obovate to oblanceolate, densely scaly on both surfaces. Fls. in clusters of 3–5, about ¾ in. long, narrow or wide funnel-shaped, deep rose or purple. Yunnan, Szechwan, 10–11,000 ft. B.M. 9561.
Closely allied to *R. cuneatum*.

R. recurvoides
(resembling R. recurvum)
H4 F2–3 L2–3 Pd.–m.c.

April–May

s. Taliense. s.s. Roxieanum.
Small compact shrub up to 5 ft. with vegetative bud scales persisting for many years and with young shoots densely strigose. Lvs. up to 3 in. long and 1 in. broad, lanceolate, oblanceolate or oval, rugulose above and with primary nerves impressed, tawny-tomentose below, margin recurved. Fls. in compact truss of 4–7, about 2½ in. wide and 1½ in. long, funnel-campanulate, white or rose, spotted. Upper Burma, 11,000 ft.
A.M. 1941 (Col. E. H. Bolitho, Trengwainton, Heamoor, Cornwall) to form with flowers of pale Rose Bengal (H.C.C. 25/3), 2¾ in. wide and 1½ in. deep.

R. repens
(creeping)

see *R. forrestii* var. *repens*.

R. reticulatum
(net-like)
H4 F2–3 L1–2 Pm.–t.

April–May

s. Azalea. s.s. Schlippenbachii.
Deciduous shrub up to 15 ft. or more with yellow-brown young shoots. Lvs. in twos or threes at the end of the branchlets, up to 2½ in. long and 2¼ in. broad, broad-ovate or rhombic,

R. reticulatum
(continued)

occasionally oval, main veins impressed above, markedly reticulate beneath, changing colour in autumn to vinous or blackish-purple. Fls. expanding before the leaves, solitary or in pairs, rarely in groups of up to 4, up to 2 in. across, rotate-funnel-shaped, bright purple or rose-purple, with or without spots. Japan. B.M. 6972, 7681 (var. *pentandrum*).

R. retusum
(blunt, alluding to the leaves)
I1 F2–3 L1–2 Pd.–m.

May

Sect. Vireya. *Subsect.* Pseudovireya of Sleumer.
Shrub up to 4 ft. Lvs. up to 2½ in. long, oblong or elliptic-obovate, almost sessile, margins recurved, dark green above, pale below and with reddish scales. Fls. in lax truss of up to 9, up to 1½ in. long, tubular-funnel-form, bright scarlet. W. Java, about 3,000 ft.

R. rex
(King)
I4 F3–4 L3–4 Pm.–t.

April–May

s. Falconeri.
Tree up to 45 ft. with grey-white tomentose young shoots. Lvs. 12 in. or more long and 4 in. or more broad, oblanceolate, dark green and shining above, grey to pale buff indumentum below. Fls. in large trusses of up to 30, up to 2½ in. long, tubular-campanulate, rose or white with crimson blotch and spots. Szechwan, 10–11,000 ft. A very beautiful and rather variable rhododendron, closely allied to *R. fictolacteum* but much finer.
F.C.C. 1935 (as *R. fictolacteum*, Ward's var. (*K.W.* 4509); J. J. Crosfield, Embley Park, Romsey, Hants) to form with flowers over 2½ in. across and over 2 in. long, with suberect or spreading lobes, white with a deep crimson blotch at the base.
A.M. 1946 (as *R. fictolacteum* var. *roseum* (*K.W.* 4509); Lord Aberconway, Bodnant) to form with flowers 3 in. wide and 2½ in. long, pale Amaranth Rose (H.C.C. 530/3), with a small basal crimson blotch, opening from rose coloured buds.
'Quartz' is an A.M. clone (1955) raised from *Rock* 03800, with flowers 3 in. diam., white with a faint pinkish-blue tinge, a deep crimson blotch at the base of the throat and with scattered crimson spots on the upper lobes (Crown Estate Commissioners, Windsor).

R. rhabdotum
(striped)
I1–2 F3–4 L2 Pm.–s.

May–July

s. Maddenii. s.s. Megacalyx.
Straggling shrub or small tree up to 12 ft. with densely scaly and bristly young branchlets. Lvs. up to 6 in. long and 2 in. broad, obovate to oblong to elliptic, glaucous-green below and scaly. Fls. 4–6 per truss, up to 4 in. long, widely funnel-shaped, creamy-white, deeply suffused with

R. rhabdotum
(*continued*)

yellow within and marked externally with five re[d] stripes. S.E. Tibet, Bhutan, Assam, 5–8,500 f[t] B.M. 9447. Too tender for outdoor cultivation i[n] most gardens.

F.C.C. 1934 (L. de Rothschild, Exbury).

A.M. 1931 (Lady Aberconway and Hon. H. [D] McLaren, Bodnant).

R. rigidum
(*stiff*)
H4 F1–3 L1–2 Pm.

March–May

s. Triflorum. s.s. Yunnanense.

Shrub up to 7 ft. Lvs. 1–2½ in. long, elliptic [t] oblong-elliptic to oblanceolate, pale glaucous-gree[n] below. Fls. terminal or terminal and axillary i[n] the uppermost leaves, in trusses of 2–6, abou[t] ¾ in. long, widely funnel-shaped, zygomorphi[c] pink, deep rose-lavender or white, often spotte[d] Yunnan, Szechwan, 2,600–11,000 ft. The plant[s] widely grown as *R. caeruleum*, and less wide[ly] grown as *R. hesperium* and as *R. sycnanthu[m]* belong here.

A.M. 1939 (as *R. caeruleum*; L. de Rothschil[d] Exbury) to form with flowers white, reddish on to[p] of the tube without and speckled red withi[n] *Rock* 59207.

R. rigidum (under the name *R. caeruleum* va[r] *album*) is a parent of the A.M. clone 'Peac[e]' (1946).

R. ririei
(After Rev. B. Ririe, of the Chinese Inland Missions; friend of E. H. Wilson)
H4 F2–3 L2–3 Pm.–t.

Feb.–March

s. Arboreum. s.s. Argyrophyllum.

Shrub up to 18 ft. Lvs. up to 6 in. long and 2 i[n] broad, oblong-elliptic, lanceolate or oblanceolat[e] bright mat green above, silvery-white or greyis[h] green below. Fls. in trusses of up to 10, up to 2 i[n] long, campanulate, dull purple to smoke-blu[e] with dark conspicuous nectaries at the bas[e] Szechwan. This rhododendron is most attracti[ve] when well grown and well flowered, but the ear[ly] flowers are liable to be frosted.

A.M. 1931 (Hon. H. D. McLaren, Bodna[nt]) to form with light magenta-purple flowers.

R. ririei is a parent of the A.M. clone 'May[a]' (1940).

R. roseotinctum
(*tinged with rose*)

see *R. sanguineum* subsp. *roseotinctum*.

R. roseum
(*rosy*)
H4 F2–3 L1–2 Pm.

May

s. Azalea. s.s. Luteum.

Deciduous shrub up to 12 ft. Lvs. up to 3 i[n] long and 2½ in. broad, unfolding more or less [at] the same time as the flowers, elliptic or obova[te] to obovate-oblong, hairy and bluish-green or du[ll] green below. Fls. in trusses of 5–9, about 1¾ i[n] across, tubular-funnel-shaped with flaring pointe[d] petals, clear deep pink to violet-red, occasional[ly]

142

R. roseum
(continued)

paler, usually with darker brown-red blotch, with distinctive clove scent. Very hardy and very attractive in its best colour forms. E. North America.

A.M. 1955 (Mrs. R. M. Stevenson, Tower Court, Ascot) to form with flowers of Phlox Pink (H.C.C. 635/2), with the tube and unopened buds a slightly darker shade.

R. roxieanum
After Mrs. Roxie Hanna, of Tali-fu, China, friend of G. Forrest)
H4 F2–3 L2–3 Pd.–m.

April–May

s. Taliense. s.s. Roxieanum.

Very slow-growing shrub up to 9 ft. with densely woolly branches and leaf-bud scales persisting for several years. Lvs. up to 4 in. long and ¾ in. broad, linear, narrow-lanceolate or oblanceolate, covered below with fawn or rusty indumentum. Fls. in compact truss of up to 15, up to 1¼ in. long, campanulate, creamy-white or white faintly flushed with rose, with or without crimson markings. Yunnan, S.E. Tibet, Szechwan, 11–14,000 ft. B.M. 9383.

A dwarf alpine form with very narrow leaves is known as var. *oreonastes*.

A very variable species in size of plant, size and shape of leaf, and in size of truss and in size and colour of flower. All forms are good but it takes many of them a long time to reach flowering size.

R. rubiginosum
(reddish-brown)
H4 F2–3 L1–2 Pm.–t.

April–May

s. Heliolepis.

Shrub or tree up to 30 ft. with purplish branchlets. Lvs. up to 2½ in. long and 1 in. broad, elliptic-lanceolate, densely covered below with rust-coloured scales. Fls. usually in trusses of 4–8, sometimes more, usually about 1¼ in. long, funnel-shaped, scaly on the lobes outside, rosy-lilac, pink, or rose, spotted with brown. Szechwan. Yunnan, S.E. Tibet, 7,500–14,000 ft. B.M. 7621.

Some forms have much bigger flowers and trusses than others; but all forms are usually very floriferous and fine garden plants.

'Wakehurst' A.M. 1960 (Sir Henry Price, Bt., Wakehurst Place, Sussex), clone with mallow purple (H.C.C. 630/2) fls. with prominent crimson spots on upper lobe.

R. rubrolineatum
(lined with red)
H4 F1–2 L1–2 Pm.

May

s. Trichocladum.

Deciduous or partly evergreen shrub up to 5 ft. Lvs. about 1¼ in. long and ⅝ in. broad, obovate-elliptic, scaly below. Fls. in trusses of about 3, about ¾ in. long, widely funnel-shaped, yellow, lined and flushed with rose on the outside. N.W. Yunnan, S.E. Tibet, 11–14,000 ft.

R. rubropilosum
(*red-haired*)
H3 F1-2 L1-2 Pm.

May

s. Azalea. s.s. Obtusum.

Shrub up to 10 ft. with young shoots densel
covered with grey to red-brown appressed hair
Lvs. crowded at ends of branchlets, up to $1\frac{3}{4}$ in
long and $\frac{3}{4}$ in. wide, oblong-lanceolate to elliptic
lanceolate, dark green above, pale green below
Fls. in trusses of 2–4, about 1 in. across, funnel
form, pink, spotted with mauve. Formosa.

R. rude
(*rough*)
H4 F2-3 L2-3 Pm.

April–May

s. Barbatum. s.s. Glischrum.

Shrub up to 9 ft. with bristly young shoots an
with bud scales persisting for a year or two. Lvs
up to 8 in. long and 3 in. broad, broadly oblance
olate to oblong-obovate, dark green, hispid an
with impressed main veins above, paler below
and covered with long crisped hairs, man
with glandular tips. Fls. in truss of up to 10
up to $1\frac{1}{2}$ in. long, open campanulate purplish
crimson with darker lines; calyx at least $\frac{1}{2}$ in. long
Yunnan, 11–12,000 ft.

R. rufum
(*red*)
H4 F1-2 L1-3 Pm.

April

s. Taliense. s.s. Wasonii.

Shrub or small tree up to 15 ft. Lvs. up t
5 in. long and 2 in. broad, elliptic, oblong o
oblong-obovate, tawny to rust-brown below. Fls
in truss of up to 10, up to $1\frac{1}{4}$ in. long, funnel
campanulate, white or pinkish-purple, spotte
crimson. Szechwan, Kansu, 10–12,000 ft. Som
forms have particularly good foliage.

R. rupicola
(*dweller in stony places*)
H4 F2-3 L1-2 Pd.

April–May

s. Lapponicum.

Small shrub up to 2 ft. with densely scal
branchlets. Lvs. about $\frac{1}{2}$ in. long, broadly elliptic
densely scaly. Fls. in clusters of 2–5, about $\frac{1}{2}$ in
long, widely funnel-shaped, deep plum-crimson
Yunnan, Szechwan, 10–14,000 ft.

R. russatum
(*reddened*)
H4 F3-4 L1-2 Pd.

April–May

s. Lapponicum.

Shrub up to 4 ft. with scaly branchlets. Lvs
about 1 in. long and $\frac{1}{2}$ in. broad, oblong-lanceolate
densely rusty-scaly below. Fls. in clusters of 4–6
up to $\frac{3}{4}$ in. long, open funnel-shaped, bright dee
blue-purple and a white throat. N.W. Yunnan
Szechwan, 11–14,000 ft. B.M. 8963.

One of the most striking and beautiful of th
dwarf alpine species which should be in ever
collection. The plant formerly known as R
cantabile is now included in this species.

F.C.C. 1933 (L. de Rothschild, Exbury) to form
with intense purple flowers, white-pubescent i
the throat.

R. russatum
(*continued*)

A.M. 1927 (A. M. Williams, Launceston) to form with intense violet-blue flowers.

A.G.M. 1938.

R. russatum is a parent of the A.M. clone 'Song Bird' (1957).

R. russotinctum
(*tinged with red*)
H4 F1–2 L1–2 Pm.

April–May

s. Taliense. s.s. Roxieanum.

Shrub up to 8 ft. with glandular young branchlets and leaf-buds scales persisting for a year or two. Lvs. up to 4 in. long and 1 in. broad, narrowly oblong, with rusty-red indumentum below. Fls. in truss of up to 8, about 1½ in. long, campanulate, white flushed rose and with a few crimson spots. S.E. Tibet, N.W. Yunnan, 9–14,000 ft.

R. saluenense
(*from the Salwin River*)
H4 F2–3 L1–2 Pd.

April–May

s. Saluenense.

Shrub up to 4 ft. sometimes creeping, sometimes upright, with bristly branchlets. Lvs. up to 1½ in. long and 1 in. broad, elliptic to ovate-elliptic, densely scaly below, aromatic. Fls. in clusters of 1–7, about 1 in. long and up to 2 in. broad, widely funnel-shaped, deep pinkish-purple or deep purplish-crimson with crimson spots. S.E. Tibet, Yunnan, Szechwan, 11–14,500 ft. B.M. 9095.

Very variable in habit and in size and shape of flowers of which there is often a second flush.

A.M. 1945 (E. de Rothschild, Exbury) to form with flowers a dark mauve-purple (H.C.C. 29/1).

R. sanguineoides

see *R. sanguineum* subsp. *sanguineoides*.

R. sanguineum
(*blood red*)
H4 F1–3 L1–2 Pd.

May

s. Neriiflorum. s.s. Sanguineum.

Shrub up to 3 ft. Lvs. up to 2½ in. long and 1 in. broad, obovate or narrow oblong, dark green above, grey-white below. Fls. in trusses of 3–6, about 1½ in. long, tubular-campanulate, bright crimson. Yunnan, S.E. Tibet, 13–14,000 ft. B.M. 9263. Tends to be a very shy flowerer.

An exceedingly variable species and certain forms have been named as follows:

Subsp. *atrorubrum* (H4 F1–2 L1–2 Pd.); flowers black-crimson. S.E. Tibet, Yunnan.

Subsp. *cloiophorum* (H4 F1–2 L1–2 Pd.); flowers yellowish-rose or rose with darker margin. Yunnan, S.E. Tibet, 11–14,000 ft.

Subsp. *consanguineum* (H4 F1–2 L1–2 Pm.); flowers dark crimson or carmine. Yunnan, S.E. Tibet, 14,000 ft.

Subsp. *didymum* (H4 F2 L1–2 Pd.–m.); flowers black-crimson, S.E. Tibet, 14–15,000 ft. B.M. 9217.

R. sanguineum
(*continued*)

A parent of the A. M. clones 'Townhill Red Cap' (1945), 'Arthur Osborn' (1933), 'Impi' (1945).

Subsp. *haemaleum* (H^4 F$^{2-3}$ L$^{1-2}$ P^d.); flowers deep black-crimson. S.E. Tibet, Yunnan, 11–13,000 ft.

Subsp. *himertum* (H^4 F$^{1-2}$ L$^{1-2}$ P^d.); flowers yellow. S.E. Tibet, 12–15,000 ft.

Subsp. *leucopetalum* (H^3 F$^{1-2}$ L$^{1-2}$ P^m.); flowers white. Yunnan, 12–13,000 ft.

Subsp. *mesaeum* (H^4 F$^{1-2}$ L$^{1-2}$ P^m.); flowers black-crimson. S.E. Tibet, 12–15,000 ft.

Subsp. *roseotinctum* (H^4 F$^{1-2}$ L$^{1-2}$ P^m.); flowers rose or yellowish-red. Yunnan, S.E. Tibet, Upper Burma, 11–16,000 ft.

Subsp. *sanguineoides* (H^4 F$^{1-2}$ L$^{1-2}$ P^d.); flowers crimson. S.E. Tibet, 13–14,000 ft.

R. sargentianum
(After C. S. Sargent, Director of the Arnold Arboretum, Mass., d. 1927)
H^4 F$^{2-3}$ L$^{1-2}$ P^d.

April–May

s. Anthopogon.

Dwarf compact shrub up to 1 ft. with short twiggy branchlets and persistent leaf-bud scales. Lvs. up to $\frac{3}{4}$ in. long, broadly elliptic, reticulate and shining above, scaly below. Fls. few to the truss, $\frac{1}{2}$–$\frac{2}{3}$ in. long, about $\frac{1}{2}$ in. diameter, densely scaly outside, lemon-yellow or white. Szechwan, 9–11,000 ft. B.M. 8871. The yellow-flowered forms are the more desirable.

A.M. 1923 (Lady Aberconway and the Hon. H. D. McLaren, Bodnant) to form with pale yellow flowers.

R. scabrifolium
(*with rough leaves*)
H^3 F$^{2-3}$ L$^{1-2}$ P$^{m.s.}$

March–April

s. Scabrifolium.

Shrub often of ungainly habit, up to 10 ft., with bristly and pubescent branchlets. Lvs. up to 2 in. long and $\frac{3}{4}$ in. broad, broadly oblanceolate, scabrid and bullate above, softly tomentose and reticulate below. Fls. in clusters of 2–3, axillary in the upper leaves, about $\frac{3}{4}$ in. long, tubular-funnel-shaped, white, pink or deep rose. Yunnan, 5–10,000 ft. B.M. 7159.

R. scabrum
(*rough*)
H^2 F$^{2-3}$ L$^{1-2}$ P^m.

April–May

s. Azalea. s.s. Obtusum.

Evergreen shrub up to 6 ft. Lvs. up to 4 in. long and $1\frac{1}{2}$ in. broad, elliptic-lanceolate to lanceolate, subcrenulate and slightly revolute at the margin. Fls. in trusses of 2–6, $2\frac{1}{2}$ in. across, broad funnel-form, rose-red to brilliant scarlet, with dark dots on upper lobes; calyx large and green, sometimes as much as $\frac{1}{2}$ in. long. Liu Kiu Islands. B.M. 8478.

R. schistocalyx
(*with split calyx*)
3 F2–3 L1–2 Pm.–t.

April

s. Irroratum. s.s. Parishii.
  Shrub up to 20 ft. Lvs. up to 8 in. long and 3 in. broad, oblong-oblanceolate to oblong-lanceolate, dark green and mat above, pale green below. Fls. in trusses of 8–10, up to 2 in. long, tubular-campanulate, bright rose or deep crimson with a reddish calyx about ¾ in. long, split on one side almost to the base, elsewhere unequally 5-lobed. Yunnan, 9–11,000 ft.

R. schizopeplum
(*with split covering*)
4 F1–2 L1–2 Pm.

April–May

s. and s.s. Taliense.
  Shrub up to 6 ft. Lvs. about 3 in. long and 1½ in. broad, elliptic, oblong-elliptic to oblong, covered below with white, later buff or brown, irregularly splitting indumentum. Fls. in trusses of 8–10, up to 1½ in. long, campanulate, rose with deep crimson spots. Yunnan, 12–14,000 ft.

R. schlippenbachii
(after Baron von Schlippenbach, naval officer and traveller)
4 F3–4 L2–3 Pm.

April–May

s. Azalea. s.s. Schlippenbachii.
  Deciduous shrub up to 15 ft. Lvs. in whorls of 5 at ends of branchlets, up to 3½ in. long and 3 in. broad, obovate, round or emarginate at apex, dark green above, paler below, changing in the autumn to yellow, orange and crimson. Fls. precocious, in trusses of 3–6, up to 3½ in. wide, flat or saucer-shaped, pale pink to rose-pink with reddish spots on the upper lobes. C. Japan, Korea and Manchuria. B.M. 7373. A most beautiful species.
  F.C.C. 1944 (Lord Aberconway, Bodant) to form with flowers 3 in. across and coloured Rhodamine Pink (H.C.C. 527/2).
  A.M. 1896 (Messrs. J. Veitch and Sons) to form with soft pink flowers, spotted on upper segments with crimson.

R. scintillans
(*sparkling*)
4 F2–4 L1–2 Pd.

April–May

s. Lapponicum.
  Small shrub with twiggy scaly branchlets. Lvs. about ½ in. long and ⅙ in. broad, oblanceolate, densely scaly on both surfaces. Fls. in trusses of 3, about ½ in. long, 1¾ in. broad, open funnel-shaped, lavender-blue or purplish-rose with best forms almost a royal-blue. Yunnan, 10–14,500 ft.
  F.C.C. 1934 (L. de Rothschild, Exbury) to form with lavender-blue flowers.
  A.M. 1924 (Lady Aberconway and the Hon. H. D. McLaren, Bodnant) to form with flowers of purplish-rose.

147

R. scopulorum
(*of the crags*)
H¹ F²⁻³ L¹⁻² Pm.

April–May

s. Maddenii. *s.s.* Ciliicalyx.
Shrub or tree up to 15 ft. Lvs. crowded, up to 2½ in. long and 1¼ in. broad, obovate-oblanceolate light glaucous-green above. Fls. fragrant, in trusses of 3–7, up to 3 in. wide and 2 in. deep widely funnel-shaped, white or white tinged pink with a yellowish blotch. E. Tibet, 6,000 ft B.M. 9399. Essentially a plant for the cool greenhouse.
A.M. 1936 (L. de Rothschild, Exbury) to form with pale pink flowers.

R. scottianum
(After Munro B. Scott, a Kew botanist, killed at Arras; 1889–1917)
H¹ F²⁻³ L¹⁻² Pm.

May–June

s. Maddenii. *s.s.* Ciliicalyx.
Shrub up to 12 ft. with densely scaly branchlets Lvs. up to 4 in. long and 1½ in. broad, obovate densely scaly below. Fls. in truss of 2–4, up to 4 in. long and as much across the mouth, wide funnel-shaped, white, occasionally flushed with rose, and with a yellow blotch, very sweetly scented; calyx from almost obsolete to nearly ½ in long. Yunnan, 6–8,000 ft. B.M. 9238.

R. scyphocalyx
(*cup-shaped calyx*)

see *R. dichroanthum* subsp. *scyphocalyx*.

R. searsiae
(After Sarah G. Sears, an American artist)
H⁴ F¹⁻² L¹⁻² Pm.

April–May

s. Triflorum. *s.s.* Yunnanense.
Shrub up to 12 ft. Lvs. 1–3 in. long, lanceolate oblong-lanceolate or oblanceolate, densely scaly and bluish-glaucous below. Fls. in trusses of 3–8 up to 1½ in. long, widely funnel-shaped, zygomorphic, white, or pale rose, or purplish-mauve with light green spots. Szechwan, 7,500–9,800 ft Closely allied to *R. concinnum*. B.M. 8993.

R. seinghkuense
(*from the Seinghku Valley, Upper Burma*)
H¹ F²⁻³ L¹⁻² Pd.s.

April

s. Edgeworthii.
Epiphytic undershrub up to 3 ft. with woolly villous branchlets. Lvs. up to 3 in. long and 1½ in broad, ovate to oblong-elliptic, bullate above rufous-tomentose below. Fls. solitary or in pairs up to 1½ in. across, 1 in. long, broadly bell-shaped bright sulphur-yellow with red-brown anthers Burma, 6–10,000 ft.
A.M. 1953 (Commissioners of Crown Lands Windsor).

R. selense
(*from the Sie-La, W. Yunnan*)
H⁴ F¹⁻³ L²⁻³ Pm.

April–May

s. Thomsonii. *s.s.* Selense.
Shrub up to 9 ft. Lvs. 1–3½ in. long, oblong to elliptic to obovate, dark green above, pale below Fls. in trusses of 3–8, up to 1½ in. long, funnel campanulate, pink or rose, with or without crimson blotch at the base, usually unspotted but not necessarily so. Tibet, Yunnan, Szechwan 10–14,500 ft.

R. selense
(*continued*)

R. selense is often very slow to flower and often tends to hide the flowers beneath the foliage. A form with oblong-lanceolate leaves and tomentose ovary, from S.E. Tibet, at 12,000 ft., has been called var. *duseimatum*; a form with small leaves and small flowers, often dark rose to crimson in colour, from the Yunnan–Tibet border at 12–14,000 ft., has been called var. *pagophilum*; and a form with white, unmarked, flowers, from Yunnan and S.E. Tibet, at 11–13,000 ft. has been called var. *probum*.

R. semibarbatum
(*partially bearded*)
H4 F1 L1–2 Pm.
June

s. Semibarbatum.
Deciduous shrub up to 10 ft. Lvs. up to 2 in. long and 1 in. broad, elliptic to elliptic-oblong, dark green above, lighter green below, minutely crenulate, in the autumn turning to yellow, orange and crimson. Fls. small, solitary, partly hidden by the foliage, up to ¾ in. across, rotate-funnel-shaped, white or yellowish-white, flushed pink, spotted with red. Japan. B.M. 9147.

R. semilunatum
(*half-crescent-shaped*)
H3 F1–2 L1–2 Pd.–m.
May

s. Trichocladum.
Deciduous shrub up to 3 ft. Lvs. about ¾ in. long and ⅓ in. broad, oblong-oblanceolate, ciliate at margin, densely scaly below. Fls. in truss of 3, about ¾ in. long, widely tubular, deep yellow. S.E. Tibet.

R. semnoides
(*resembling R. semnum*)
H3 F2–3 L2–3 Pm.–t.
March–April

s. Grande.
Small tree up to 20 ft., with young shoots clothed with buff or greyish tomentum. Lvs. up to nearly 12 in. long and 5 in. broad, oblanceolate, covered below with loose felty light brown indumentum. Fls. in truss of up to 20, up to 2 in. long, campanulate, white, flushed rose and with a crimson blotch. S.E. Tibet, 12–13,000 ft. B.M. n.s. 18.

R. septentrionale
(*belonging to the North*)

see *R. dichroanthum* subsp. *septentrionale*.

R. serotinum
(*late, i.e. autumnal*)
H4 F2–3 L2–3 P m.–t.s.
Aug.–Sept.

s. and s.s. Fortunei.
Shrub up to 15 ft. often of rather lax straggling growth. Lvs. up to 6 in. long and nearly 3 in. broad, dull green above, pale glaucous-green below. Fls. in trusses of up to 8, about 2 in. long, funnel-campanulate, white, slightly flushed rose outside, blotched and tinged with red within. China. B.M. 8841. Very closely allied to *R. decorum*, but flowering in August and September, and well worth growing for this particular reason.
A.M. 1925 (Royal Botanic Gardens, Kew) to form with white fls., slightly flushed with rose on outside, blotched and tinged with red inside tube.

R. serpyllifolium
(*with leaves like thyme*)
H⁴ F¹ L¹⁻² Pd.

April–May

s. Azalea. s.s. Obtusum.

Deciduous shrub up to 4 ft. Lvs. crowded at ends of branchlets, obovate or elliptic, up to ½ in. long, but usually smaller. Probably the smallest in fact in the genus. Fls. solitary or in pairs, usually less than ½ in. across, short funnelform, rosy-pink. C. &. S. Japan. B.M. 7503. There is an albino form known as var. *albiflorum*.

R. serrulatum
(*with small teeth*)
H³⁻⁴ F¹⁻² L¹⁻² Pm.–t.

July–Sept.

s. Azalea. s.s. Luteum.

Deciduous shrub up to 18 ft. with reddish-brown branchlets. Lvs. up to 3½ in. long and 1½ in. wide, usually smaller, elliptic to obovate-oblong, serrulate at the margin. Fls. in clusters of 6–10, unfolding after the leaves, about 1½ in. long, funnel-form, white, sometimes flushed pale violet-red, tube glandular-sticky. S.E. North America. Less showy than its near relative *R. viscosum*, but notable for its late flowering habit.

R. setiferum
(*bristle-bearing*)
H⁴ F²⁻³ L¹⁻² Pm.

April–May

s. Thomsonii. s.s. Selense.

Shrub up to 9 ft. with young branchlets more or less densely clad with glandular setae. Lvs. up to 3½ in. long and 1½ in. broad, oblong. Fls. in truss of about 10, about 1½ in. long, funnel-campanulate, creamy-white, lined with crimson at the base. Yunnan, 12–13,000 ft.

R. setosum
(*bristly*)
H⁴ F¹⁻² L¹⁻² Pd.

May

s. Lapponicum.

Shrub up to 4 ft. with densely bristly branchlets. Lvs. up to ½ in. long and ¼ in. broad, oblong-elliptic, densely setose and scaly. Fls. in clusters of 3–8, up to 1 in. long, widely funnel-shaped, bright purplish-pink or rose-purple. Sikkim, S.E. Tibet, 11–16,000 ft. B.M. 8523.

R. shepherdii
(After H. Shepherd, Curator, Liverpool Botanic Garden; 1780–1854)
H²⁻³ F²⁻³ L¹⁻² Pm.

March–April

s. and s.s. Irroratum.

Shrub or small tree up to 12 ft. Lvs. up to 4 in. long and 1 in. broad, oblong-elliptic, deep green above, pale below. Fls. in truss of 10–12, 1½–2 in. long, tubular-campanulate, deep scarlet with dark red spots. Bhutan. B.M. 5125.

R. sherriffii
(After Major G. Sherriff)
H⁴ F¹⁻³ L¹⁻² Pm.

April

s. Campanulatum.

Shrub up to 12 ft. Lvs. up to 3 in. long and 1½ in. broad, oblong-elliptic to oblong-oval, covered below with thick, soft, dark-brown indumentum. Fls. in trusses of 4–6, about 1½ in. long, funnel-campanulate, deep rich carmine; calyx crimson with fine glaucous bloom. S. Tibet, 11,500–12,500 ft. B.M. n.s. 337.

Rather shy flowering usually. Tentatively placed in Campanulatum series near to *R. fulgens* but it does not fit well into any recognized series.

R. shweliense
(*from the Shweli River*)
H⁴ F¹⁻² L¹⁻² Pᵈ.

May

s. and s.s. Glaucophyllum.
Small shrub up to 2½ ft. with densely scaly branchlets. Lvs. very aromatic, up to 2 in. long, oblong-obovate or obovate, very scaly below. Fls. in clusters of 2–4, ½–¾ in. long, campanulate, densely scaly on the outside, pink, tinged yellow, with purple spots. Yunnan, 10–11,000 ft. Closely akin to *R. brachyanthum* but with different coloured and very scaly flowers.

R. sidereum
(*excellent*)
H²⁻³ F²⁻³ L²⁻³ Pᵐ.⁻ᵗ.

April

s. Grande.
Large shrub or tree up to 30 ft. Lvs. up to 10 in. long and 2 in. broad, oblong-elliptic to oblong-oblanceolate, dark mat green above, silvery-grey to fawn below. Fls. in truss of up to 20, 1½–2 in. long, campanulate, 8-lobed, creamy-white to clear yellow with a crimson blotch. N.E. Upper Burma, Yunnan, 9–10,000 ft.

R. siderophyllum
(*rusty coated leaves*)
H⁴ F²⁻³ L¹⁻² Pᵐ.

May

s. Triflorum. *s.s.* Yunnanense.
Shrub up to 12 ft. Lvs. up to 3½ in. long and 1¼ in. broad, oblong-lanceolate, elliptic or lanceolate, dark brown, scaly below. Fls. terminal and axillary in uppermost leaves, in clusters of 3–8, about ½ in. long, widely funnel-shaped, zygomorphic, white, pink, rose, violet-purple or lavender-blue, with or without crimson or dark brown spots. Yunnan, Szechwan, Kweichow, 6–10,500 ft. B.M. 8759 under this name is *R. davidsonianum*.
A.M. 1945 (E. de Rothschild, Exbury).

R. simiarum
(*of the monkeys*)
H⁴ F¹⁻² L¹⁻² Pᵐ.

April–May

s. Arboreum. *s.s.* Argyrophyllum.
Shrub up to 8 ft. Lvs. up to 4 in. long and 1½ in. broad, oblanceolate to obovate, round at apex, nerves impressed above, with grey to fawn or buff indumentum below. Fls. in truss of 4–6, 1½ in. long, funnel-campanulate, pink, pale within and with a few rose-pink dots. S.E. China, 3,200 ft. B.M. 8111. In cultivation under the name of *R. fordii*.

R. simsii
(After John Sims, Editor of *Botanical Magazine*, vols. 14–53, 1800–26)
H² F²⁻³ L¹⁻² Pᵐ.

May

s. Azalea. *s.s.* Obtusum.
Spreading evergreen or semi-evergreen much branched shrub up to 6 ft. Lvs. up to 2 in. long and ¾ in. broad, elliptic to oblong-elliptic, dull green above, paler below, strigose. Fls. in clusters of 2–6, about 2½ in. diameter, broad funnel-form, rose-red to bright or dark red, with deeper spots. China, Formosa. B.M. 1480. Formerly known as *R. indicum* and parent of greenhouse hybrid azaleas.
F.C.C. 1933 (G. W. E. Loder, Wakehurst Place, Sussex) to form with bright rose flowers.

R. sinogrande
(*Chinese R. grande*)
H³⁻⁴ F³⁻⁴ L⁴ Pm.–t.

April

s. Grande.

Tree up to 30 ft. Lvs. beautiful and silvery when young, when mature up to 36 in. long and 12 in. broad, oblong-oblanceolate or oblong-elliptic, shining and with nerves impressed above, lower surface with silvery-grey or fawn skin-like indumentum. Fls. up to 20 or more, in a truss up to 12 in. or more high, 2½–3 in. long, ventricose campanulate, 8–10 lobed, dull creamy-white with crimson blotch. The northern form, known as var. *boreale*, has flowers of a soft yellow throughout or pale yellow with a crimson blotch. A magnificent foliage plant, the largest leaved of all rhododendrons which requires wind protection. Yunnan, Upper Burma, S.E. Tibet, 10–14,000 ft. B.M. 8973.

F.C.C. 1926 (G. H. Johnstone, Probus) to form with ivory-white flowers with a big crimson blotch.

A.M. 1922 (Dame Alice Godman, Horsham) to form with creamy-white flowers, crimson blotched at base.

R. sinonuttallii
(*Chinese R. nuttallii*)
H¹ F⁴ L²⁻³ Pm.s.

April–May

s. Maddenii. s.s. Megacalyx.

Straggling shrub up to 15 ft. Lvs. when young of a beautiful metallic purple colour, when mature up to 8 in. or more long and 4 in. broad, elliptic, bullate-reticulate above, scaly below. Fls. in trusses of 3–6, fragrant, 4 in. or more long, and as much across the reflexed waved lobes, white or white flushed yellow at base, with sparse crimson markings; calyx as much as an inch long. S.E. Tibet. Very closely allied to *R. nuttallii* and no doubt only a geographical form.

A.M. 1955 (Messrs. The Sunningdale Nurseries, Windlesham, Surrey).

R. smirnowii
(After M. Smirnov, friend of Baron Ungern-Sternberg, its discoverer)
H⁴ F²⁻³ L²⁻³ Pm.

May–June

s. Ponticum. s.s. Caucasicum.

Shrub or tree up to 10 ft. with young shoots covered with white felty tomentum. Lvs. up to 6 in. long and 1½ in. broad, oblong, obovate or oblanceolate, margin recurved, when young covered with white woolly tomentum, when mature glabrous above and with pale brown tomentum below. Fls. in loose trusses of 10–12, about 1½ in. long, funnel-campanulate, pale or deep rose-purple. Caucasus and N.E. Asia Minor. B.M. 7495.

R. smithii
(After Sir James E. Smith, 1759–1828, English botanist and founder of the Linnean Society)
H⁴ F²⁻³ L²⁻³ Pm.–t.

March–April

s. and s.s. Barbatum.

Shrub or tree up to 20 ft., with bristly young shoots, very sticky bud scales and smooth bark with a plum-coloured bloom. Lvs. up to 6 in. long and 2 in. broad, oblong-lanceolate, margin

R. smithii
(continued)

reflexed, upper surface rich green and glossy with impressed main veins, loose patchy tomentum below. Fls. in compact trusses of up to 16, about 2 in. long, tubular-campanulate, scarlet-crimson. E. Sikkim, Bhutan, 8–10,000 ft. B.M. 5120. Closely allied to *R. barbatum* but distinguished by indumentum on under-surface of leaves.

R. souliei
After Père J. A. Soulié, 1858–905, of the French Foreign Missions in Tibet)

H4 F2–4 L2–3 Pm.

May

s. Thomsonii. *s.s.* Souliei.

Shrub up to 12 ft. with light glaucous-green or purple young shoots. Lvs. up to 3 in. long, almost round, of metallic-green lustre, light glaucous-green below. Fls. in truss of 5–8, 2 in. or more in diameter, open saucer-shaped, white to a soft or deeper rose. Szechwan, Tibet, 9–14,000 ft. B.M. 8622.

Allied to *R. wardii* and *R. puralbum* and one of the few rhododendrons which does better in the eastern parts of Britain.

F.C.C. 1909 (Messrs. J. Veitch, Chelsea) to form with flowers pale rose, deeper towards the edge and on the back of the petals.

F.C.C. 1936 (L. de Rothschild, Exbury) to form called "var. Exbury Pink" with flowers a deeper shade of pink than in the Veitch form.

F.C.C. 1951 (Crown Estate Commissioners, Windsor) to form called "Windsor Park var." with flowers white with a pink flush deepening to Phlox Pink (H.C.C. 625/1) at the margins, whilst base of the 3 upper lobes is stained with small crimson blotch.

R. souliei is a parent of the A.M. clones 'Decsoul' (1937), 'Perdita' (1948), 'Rosy Morn' (1931), 'Thomasine' (1931).

R. speciosum
good-looking)

H4 F2–3 L1–2 Pm.

May

s. Azalea. *s.s.* Luteum.

Deciduous shrub up to 6 ft. Lvs. up to $3\frac{1}{2}$ in. long and $1\frac{1}{2}$ in. broad, ovate or elliptic to oblong, serrulate-ciliate. Fls. in clusters of 6–15, 2 in. across, tubular-funnel-shaped with flat-flaring petals, scarlet, bright red to orange and apricot, with or without an orange blotch. E. North America. B.M. 180 (as *R. nudiflorum coccineum*). Known also as *R. flammeum* and in its best forms a very attractive plant.

R. sperabile
to be hoped for)

H3–4 F2–3 L1–2 Pm.

April–May

s. and *s.s.* Neriiflorum.

Shrub up to 6 ft. Lvs. up to 4 in. long and $1\frac{1}{2}$ in. broad, elliptic or lanceolate, margin often recurved, dark green above, with thick tawny to pale cinnamon woolly indumentum below. Fls. in

R. sperabile
(continued)

trusses of 3–5, about $1\frac{1}{2}$ in. long, tubular-campanulate, scarlet or deep crimson, fleshy. N.E Upper Burma, 10–12,000 ft. Often flowers twic in one year. B.M. 9301.

A.M. 1925 (L. de Rothschild, Exbury) from *Farrer* 888—form with scarlet flowers.

A form with long leaves and a less dense pale indumentum which is white to pale fawn is know as var. *weihsiense*.

R. sperabiloides
(like R. sperabile)
H3–4 F2–3 L1–2 Pd.–m.
March–April

s. and s.s Neriiflorum.

Shrub up to 4 ft. making a neat bush. Lvs up to 3 in. long and $1\frac{1}{2}$ in. broad, oblong-ellipti to oblanceolate, semi-bullate above, with inter rupted scurfy tomentum below. Fls. in truss o 6–8, about 1 in. long, tubular-campanulate, dee to light crimson. S.E. Tibet, 12–13,000 ft.

R. sphaeroblastum
(with rounded buds)
H4 F1–2 L1–2 Pm.
April

s. and s.s. Taliense.

Shrub up to 6 ft. with greenish or purple youn shoots. Lvs. up to 6 in. long and 3 in. broad, ova to oblong-oval, thick cinnamon to rusty-tomentos below. Fls. in truss of up to 12, about $\frac{1}{2}$ in. long funnel-campanulate, white (flushed rose in bud with crimson spots. Szechwan, 11–14,000 ft.

R. spiciferum
(breaking spikes)
H3 F2–3 L1–2 Pm.
April–May

s. Scabrifolium.

Shrub up to 3 ft. with bristly and pubescen branchlets. Lvs. about 1 in. long, narrowl oblanceolate, bristly and pubescent. Fls. i clusters of 1–4, about $\frac{1}{2}$ in. long, funnel-shaped pale or deep rose or pinkish-white, axillar towards the apex of the shoots. Yunnan.

R. spilanthum
(with spotted flowers)
H4 F1–2 L1–2 Pd.
May

s. Lapponicum.

Shrub up to 3 ft. with grey splitting bark twiggy-scaly branchlets and leaves very similar t those of *R. hippophaeoides*. Fls. solitary, widel funnel-shaped, purplish-blue or pale mauve Szechwan.

R. spilotum
(stained)
H3–4 F2–3 L1–2 Pm.
April–May

s. Barbatum. *s.s.* Glischrum.

Shrub or small tree with densely setose glandular young shoots. Lvs. up to 5 in. long an $1\frac{1}{2}$ in. broad, oblong-lanceolate to oblong-ellipti upper surface with veins impressed, pale gree below. Fls. in trusses of 6–8, about $1\frac{1}{2}$ in. long bell-shaped, pink or white tinged pink, with crimson blotch. N.E. Upper Burma.

R. spinuliferum
(*bearing spines*)
H²⁻³ F²⁻³ L¹⁻² Pᵐ·

April

s. Scabrifolium.

Thin shrub up to 8 ft. or more with softly pubescent branchlets. Lvs. up to 3 in. long and 1½ in. broad, oblanceolate to obovate, bullate above, reticulate below, pubescent. Fls. axillary towards the apex of the shoots, about 1 in. long, narrow, curiously tubular, upright, crimson to brick-red, with anthers and stamens protruding from the corolla. Yunnan, 6–8,000 ft. B.M. 8408.

R. spinuliferum is a parent of the A.M. clones 'Spinbur' (1957), 'Spinulosum' (1944), 'Exbury Spinulosum' (1948) and of the F.C.C. clone 'Seta' (1962).

R. stamineum
(*with many stamens*)
H² F²⁻³ L¹⁻² Pᵐ·

April–May

s. Stamineum.

Shrub up to 6 ft. Lvs. 3–4 in. long, up to 1½ in. broad, whorled, obovate to oblanceolate, long-acuminate. Fls. axillary, about 1 in. long, narrowly-tubular, lobes narrow, white with a yellow blotch. Yunnan, Szechwan, Hupeh, Kweichow. B.M. 8601.

R. stenaulum
(*narrow-grooved*)
H¹ F²⁻³ L¹⁻² Pᵐ·⁻ᵗ·

April

s. Stamineum.

Shrub up to 15 ft. Lvs. up to 5 in. long and 1½ in. broad, oblong-lanceolate, long-acuminate, glabrous. Fls. in loose trusses of up to 10, about 2 in. long, narrow funnel-shaped, pale lilac, tinged pale violet within, darker towards margins of lobes, tube narrow, pale crimson outside. W. Yunnan, 9,000 ft.

A.M. 1937 (L. de Rothschild, Exbury) to form with flowers of silvery-lilac with faint violet tinge within, darker towards margin of lobes, tube spotted pale brown at base.

R. stewartianum
(After L. B. Stewart, 1876–1934, Curator, Royal Botanic Garden, Edinburgh)
H⁴ F¹⁻³ L¹⁻³ Pᵐ·

Feb.–March–April

s. and s.s. Thomsonii.

Small bush up to 10 ft. Lvs. 2–5 in. long, obovate or obovate-elliptic or oblong-obovate, bright green above, somewhat grey-green below. Fls. in truss of 3–7, 1½–2 in. long, tubular-campanulate, very variable in colour: Farrer describes a hillside covered with this species with fls. ranging from pure white to shades of soft primrose-yellow and others flushed with rose and even deep crimson—no two bushes of the same colour; calyx almost obsolete to over ½ in. long. S.E. Tibet, Upper Burma, Assam, 10–14,000 ft.

A form with a large calyx and large leaves is known as var. *aiolosalpinx* and one with minute calyx and small leaves as var. *tantulum*.

A.M. 1934 (L. de Rothschild, Exbury).

R. stictophyllum
(*with spotted leaves*)
H⁴ F¹⁻² L¹⁻² Pd.

April

s. Lapponicum.
Intricately branched shrub up to 2 ft. Lvs. about ¼ in. long, narrowly elliptic, densely scaly on both surfaces. Fls. in clusters of 1–4, ⅓ in. long, open funnel-shaped, rose, purple to mauve. W. Szechwan.

R. strigillosum
(*beset with bristles*)
H³⁻⁴ F¹⁻⁴ L¹⁻³ Pm.–t.

March–April

s. Barbatum. s.s. Maculiferum.
Shrub up to 20 ft. which has been called the Chinese *R. barbatum* and which has the young shoots beset with long stiff bristles. Lvs. up to 7 in. long and 2 in. broad, oblong-lanceolate or oblanceolate, margin recurved, bright green above and with veins impressed, clothed below with isolated bristles. Fls. in trusses of up to 12, up to 2½ in. long, tubular-campanulate, brilliant crimson-scarlet. Szechwan, 7–10,000 ft. B.M. 8864.
A.M. 1923 (Lady Aberconway and Hon. H. D. McLaren, Bodnant) to form with flowers of rich blood-red.
R. strigillosum is a parent of the following clones: 'Portia' (F.C.C. 1947), 'Matador' (F.C.C. 1946), 'Lady Digby' (A.M. 1946), 'Rocket' (A.M. 1954).

R. sulfureum
(*sulphur-coloured*)
H²⁻³ F²⁻³ L¹⁻² Pd.–m.

April

s. and s.s. Boothii.
Shrub up to 4 ft. with smooth brown bark. Lvs. 1–3½ in. long, oblanceolate to ovate, glaucous and scaly below. Fls. in clusters of 4–8, about 1¼ in. across, ¾-in. deep, bell-shaped, bright or deep sulphur-yellow, rarely greenish-orange. Yunnan, Burma, 7–13,000 ft. B.M. 8946. Some forms are more hardy than others.
A.M. 1937 (as *R. commodum*—Earl of Stair, Stranraer, Wigtownshire).
R. sulfureum is a parent of the A.M. clones 'Sulfmeg' (1940), 'Golden Oriole Venetia' (1963) and F.C.C. clone 'Golden Oriole Talavera' (1963).

R. supranubium
(*above the clouds*)
H² F²⁻³ L¹⁻² Pm.

April–May

s. Maddenii. s.s. Ciliicalyx.
Shrub up to 12 ft. with densely scaly young branchlets. Lvs. up to 3½ in. long and 1¼ in. broad, oblanceolate or obovate, glaucous and scaly below. Fls. 1–3 per truss, 1½–2 in. long, widely funnel-shaped, white, flushed with rose, fragrant. Yunnan, 10–12,000 ft. Usually grows at a higher elevation in the Chinese Alps than any other of its Series.

R. surasianum
(After C. P. Surasi, Siam)
H¹⁻² F²⁻³ L¹⁻² Pm.

June

s. Maddenii. s.s. Ciliicalyx.
Shrub up to 12 ft. Lvs. up to 4 in. long, 1½ in. broad, elliptic, obovate to oblong, densely scaly below. Fls. in clusters of 2–3, about 3 in. long,

R. surasianum
(*continued*)

widely funnel-shaped, pale pink. N. Siam, 4,500 ft.

R. sutchuenense
(*from Szechwan*)
H4 F2–4 L2–3 P m.–t.

Feb.–March

s. Fortunei. s.s. Davidii.

Shrub or tree up to 20 ft. or more. Lvs. up to 12 in. long and 3 in. broad, oblong-oblanceolate or narrowly oblong-oval, dark mat green above, paler below. Fls. many per truss, up to 3 in. long, widely bell-shaped, rosy-lilac, or rosy-pink or white stained faintly with pink, with purple spots and without a blotch. Szechwan, Hupeh, 5–8,000 ft. B.M. 8362.

So-called var. *geraldii* with a deep purplish blotch (A.M. 1945—The Misses Godman, Horsham) has been stated to be a hybrid between *R. sutchuenense* and *R. praevernum*.

R. sutchuenense is a parent of the A.M. clones 'Seagull' (1938), 'Seamew' (1940), 'Maya' (1940).

R. taggianum
(After H. F. Tagg, 1874–1933, botanist at Edinburgh Botanic Garden)
H1–2 F4 L1–2 Pm.–s.

April–May

s. Maddenii. s.s. Megacalyx.

Loose growing rather straggly shrub up to 8 ft. with densely glandular-scaly branchlets. Lvs. up to 5 in. long and 2½ in. broad, oblong-lanceolate fairly densely scaly below. Fls. in trusses of 3–4, about 3 in. long and even 4 in. or more across the rather reflexed lobes, broadly tubular-funnel-shaped, white with pale yellow basal blotch, beautifully fragrant. Yunnan, Burma, Burma-Tibet frontier, 7–11,000 ft. B.M. 9612.

F.C.C. 1943 (Murray Adams-Acton, 37 Palace Gate, W.8) to form with buds tinged with salmon-pink.

A.M. 1932 (Marquess of Headfort, Kells).

R. taggianum is a parent of the A.M. clone 'Lord Stair' (1952).

R. taliense
(*from Tali Range, Yunnan*)
H4 F1–2 L1–2 Pm.

April–May

s. and s.s. Taliense.

Shrub up to 10 ft. with woolly tomentose young shoots. Lvs. up to 4 in. long and 1½ in. broad, oblong-ovate to broadly lanceolate, dark green above, with tawny felt-like indumentum below. Fls. in tight truss of 10–15, about 1½ in. long, funnel-campanulate, on densely hairy pedicels, creamy-yellow or cream flushed with rose, with deep crimson markings. Yunnan, 10–12,000 ft.

R. tanastylum
(*with long style*)
H3 F1–2 L1–2 Pm.–t.s.

April

s. and s.s. Irroratum.

Shrub or tree up to 20 ft. often of rather straggly habit. Lvs. up to 5 in. long and 2 in. broad, broadly lanceolate or oblanceolate, margin undulate, mat green above, paler green below. Fls.

R. tanastylum
(*continued*)

about 8 to the truss, about 2 in. long, tubular
campanulate, deep crimson, crimson-scarlet, some
times rose-purple, with few or many deeper spot
S.E. Tibet, Upper Burma, W. Yunnan, 8–11,000 f

R. tapetiforme
(*carpet-like*)
H4 F1–2 L1–2 Pd.

April

s. Lapponicum.
Shrub up to 2 ft., usually forming a carpet an
with scaly branchlets. Lvs. about ½ in. lon,
broadly elliptic, tawny-scaly below. Fls. in cluste
of 2–4, about ½ in. long, widely funnel-shape
pink, pale rose-purple, or deep blue-purpl
Szechwan, Yunnan, 11–15,000 ft.

R. taronense
(*from the Taron Gorge,
Yunnan*)
H1 F3–4 L1–2 Pm.s.

April

s. Maddenii. s.s. Ciliicalyx.
Straggling epiphytic shrub up to 15 ft., wit
thin brown peeling bark. Lvs. up to 6 in. lon
and 2½ in. broad, elliptic to elliptic-lanceolat
laxly scaly above and below. Fls. in truss of up
about 7, about 2½ in. long, broad funnel-shape
white with a yellow blotch, sometimes flushe
pink, fragrant. Upper Burma, Yunnan, 4–11,00
ft. B.M. n.s. 1. A beautiful plant for cultivatio
under glass.
F.C.C. 1935 (L. de Rothschild, Exbury) to for
with flowers white, flushed pink, darker outsid
especially along the middle line of the lobes

R. tatsienense
(*from Tatsienlu, now
Kang-ting, W. China*)
H3–4 F1–2 L1–2 Pd.–m.

April–May

s. Triflorum. s.s. Yunnanense.
Shrub up to 6 ft. Lvs. ½–2½ in. long, elliptic
obovate, ovate to oblong-lanceolate, scal
especially below. Fls. terminal, or terminal an
axillary in the uppermost leaves in clusters of 1–(
about ⅔ in. long, widely funnel-shaped, zygo
morphic, purple, rose, pale rose, rose-lavende
rose-pink, with or without red spots. Szechwa
Yunnan, 7–12,000 ft.
R. leilungense and R. stereophyllum belong her

R. telmateium
(*from the marshes*)
H4 F1–2 L1–2 Pd.

April–May

s. Lapponicum.
Shrub up to 3 ft. with densely scaly branchlet:
Lvs. about ⅓ in. long, oblanceolate, reddish
brown scaly below. Fls. in clusters of 2–3, abou
½ in. long, openly funnel-shaped, deep rose-purpl
with white throat. Yunnan, Szechwan, 10–13,000 f

R. telopeum
(*conspicuous*)
H4 F1–2 L1–2 Pm.

May

s. Thomsonii. s.s. Campylocarpum.
Shrub up to 10 ft. Lvs. up to 1½ in. long
orbicular to elliptic, glaucous below. Fls. i
trusses of 4–5, up to 1½ in. long, campanulate
bright yellow with or without a faint crimso:
blotch. S.E. Tibet, Yunnan, 12–14,000 f
Closely akin to R. caloxanthum.

R. temenium
(from a sacred place near the Doker La, Tsarong, n E. Tibet)
H4 F1–2 L1–2 Pd.–m.

May–June

s. Neriiflorum. s.s. Sanguineum.

Shrub up to 5 ft. Lvs. up to 3 in. long and up to 1 in. broad, oblong or oblong-oval. Fls. in trusses of about 6, 1–1½ in. long, tubular-campanulate, fleshy, deep crimson or purplish-crimson. S.E. Tibet, Yunnan, 13–14,500 ft.

R. temenium is a variable species and certain forms have been named as follows:

Subsp. *chrysanthemum*; flowers yellow. S.E. Tibet, 13–14,000 ft.

A.M. 1958 (Mrs. Kenneth).

Subsp. *gilvum*; flowers yellow. S.E. Tibet, 13,000 ft.

Subsp. *glaphyrum*; flowers white, white flushed rose, deep rose or pale yellow faintly flushed rose. S.E. Tibet, 13–15,000 ft.

Subsp. *pothinum*; flowers deep crimson, crimson, purplish-crimson or carmine. S.E. Tibet, 13–14,000 ft.

R. tephropeplum
(with ash-grey covering)
H3–4 F2–3 L1–2 Pd.–m.

April–May

s. Boothii. s.s. Tephropeplum.

Shrub up to 6 ft. Lvs. 1¼–5 in. long, lanceolate to oblong-obovate, black-scaly and glaucous below. Fls. in clusters of 3–9, ¾–1¼ in. long, tubular-campanulate, pink, rose, carmine-rose, purplish, rarely white. Burma, Yunnan, S.E. Tibet, Assam, 8–14,000 ft. A very variable species; Kingdon-Ward forms have larger leaves and flowers than those collected by Forrest and Rock.

A.M. 1929 (Lady Aberconway and the Hon. H. D. McLaren, Bodnant) to form with pale, rather transparent pink flowers.

R. thayerianum
After a well-known New England family, patrons of botany and horticulture)
H4 F2–3 L2–3 Pm.–t.

June–July

s. Arboreum. s.s. Argyrophyllum.

Shrub up to 15 ft. Lvs. closely clustered around the flower trusses, 5–6 in. long, about 1½ in. broad, light green above, with thin skin-like pale brown indumentum below. Fls. in compact trusses of up to 20, up to 1½ in. long, funnel-campanulate, white, tinged pink, or deeply flushed on the outside. W. Szechwan, 9,000 ft.

A fine rhododendron especially valuable for its late flowering habit. B.M. 8983.

R. thomsonii
After Thomas Thomson, 1817–8, Supt., Calcutta Botanic Garden, 1845–61)
H4 F3–4 L2–3 Pm.–t.

April

s. and s.s. Thomsonii.

Shrub or small tree up to 20 ft. with attractive smooth peeling bark and with the young green shoots having an evanescent waxy bloom. Lvs. 1½–3½ in. long, up to about 2½ in. broad, ovate or broadly elliptic or orbicular, dark green and at

R. thomsonii
(*continued*)

first glaucous above, whitish to pale green and glaucous below. Fls. in loose trusses of up to 12 usually fewer, 1½–2½ in. long, campanulate, deep blood red; calyx up to ¾ in. long, cup-shaped green or red. Sikkim, Nepal, Bhutan, Tibet, 10–14,000 ft. B.M. 4997.

This well-known rhododendron, one of the finest of species, often does not flower until it has reached a certain size and then flowers with great profusion. It is by no means uniform and certain forms have been named as follows:

var. *candelabrum* (F¹⁻²) has paler coloured flowers and a small calyx. Sikkim, E. Himalaya, 10–13,000 ft.

var. *pallidum* (F¹⁻²) has flowers of rose-pink or rose-orange with magenta patches at the base. Tibet, 11,000 ft.

R. thomsonii received the A.G.M. in 1925 and is a parent of many A.M. clones: 'Adelaide' (1935), 'Shilsonii' (1900), 'Exminster' (1923), 'Embley Pink' (1930), 'Embley Park' (1936), 'Sir John Ramsden' (1926, and A.M. 1948 and F.C.C. 1955, after trial at Wisley), 'Faltho' (1954), 'Rosalind' (1938), 'Betty' (1937), 'Barclayi Robert Fox' (1921), 'Exbury Cornish Cross' (1935), 'Pengaer' (1911), 'Aurora' (1922), 'Thomasine' (1931), 'Bodnant Thomwilliams' (1935), 'Anne' (1928), 'Aries' (1932, F.C.C. 1938).

R. thymifolium
(*with leaves like thyme*)
H⁴ F¹⁻² L¹⁻² Pd.–m.

April

s. Lapponicum.

Shrub up to 4 ft. with densely scaly branchlets. Lvs. about ⅓ in. long, narrowly oblanceolate, densely yellowish-brown-scaly below. Fls. solitary or in pairs, about ⅓ in. long, widely funnel-shaped, purple, lavender-blue or mauve. Szechwan, Kansu, 10–14,000 ft.

R. tosaense
(*from Tosa, Japan*)
H²⁻³ F¹⁻² L¹⁻² Pm.

April–May

s. Azalea. s.s. Obtusum.

Much branched evergreen or semi-evergreen shrub up to 7 ft. Lvs. crowded at ends of branchlets, up to 1½ in. long and ⅖ in. broad, lanceolate, elliptic-lanceolate or oblanceolate, grey-pubescent, changing in autumn to purplish-crimson. Fls. in clusters of 1–6, funnel-shaped, about 1¼ in. across, lilac-purple. S. Japan. B.M. n.s. 52.

R. traillianum
(After G. W. Trail, 1836–97, well-known botanist and father-in-law of G. Forrest)
H⁴ F¹⁻³ L²⁻³ Pm.–t.

April–May

s. Lacteum.

Shrub or tree up to 30 ft. Lvs. 2–7 in. long, up to 1½ in. broad, oblong to oblong-lanceolate, main nerves impressed above, covered below with brown, fawn, rust or cinnamon indumentum. Fls. in trusses of up to 15, 1–1¾ in. long, funnel-campanulate or

R. traillianum
(continued)

campanulate, white, white flushed rose, pink or rose, with or without crimson spots. Yunnan, Szechwan, 11–14,500 ft. B.M. 8900.

R. trichanthum
(with hairy flowers)
H4 F1-2 L1-2 Pm.-t.
May–June

s. Triflorum. s.s. Augustinii.
   Shrub up to 20 ft. with densely bristly branchlets. Lvs. up to 4½ in. long, oblong-lanceolate or ovate-lanceolate or lanceolate, laxly scaly below and setose-pubescent along the mid-rib. Fls. in clusters of 3–5, about 1½ in. long, widely funnel-shaped, zygomorphic, light or dark purple, or rose, bristly on the lower part. Szechwan, 5–11,000 ft. B.M. 8880, as *R. villosum*. This is the plant for so long known as *R. villosum*. Although hardy it needs shade and protection from wind.

R. trichocladum
(with hairy twigs)
H4 F1-2 L1-2 Pm.
April–May

s. Trichocladum.
   Deciduous shrub up to 4 ft. Lvs. about 1½ in. long and ¾ in. broad, oblong, finely reticulate above, minutely scaly below, fringed with hairs. Fls. in trusses of 3–5, about 1 in. long, widely funnel-shaped, greenish-yellow, spotted with dark green, on pilose pedicels. N.E. Upper Burma. B.M. 9073. There is a form in which the upper leaf surface is covered with very long hairs known as var. *longipilosum*.
   R. trichocladum is a parent of the A.M. clone 'Chink' (1961).

R. trichophorum
(bearing hairs)
H4 F1-2 L1-2 Pm.
May–June

s. Triflorum. s.s. Augustinii.
   Shrub up to 10 ft. with bristly branchlets as in *R. trichanthum* and lvs. as in *R. augustinii*, and with pinkish-mauve flowers. It is possibly a natural hybrid between *R. trichanthum* and possibly *R. augustinii*, and was raised from seeds of *Wilson* 4242 from Szechwan, in which province both species are common.

R. trichostomum
(hairy-mouthed)
H3-4 F2-3 L1-2 Pd.
May–June

s. Anthopogon.
   Small shrub up to 4 ft. with twiggy branchlets. Lvs. up to 1⅓ in. long, linear-lanceolate to narrow oblanceolate, or ovate, covered below with loose flaky scales. Fls. in capitate truss, up to ¾ in. long, tubular, rose or white, villous within the throat. Yunnan, Szechwan, 8–12,000 ft.
   A form with a longer corolla-tube is known as var. *hedyosmum* (F2). B.M. 9202.
   A form with a glabrous corolla is known as var. *ledoides* (F3). B.M. 8831.
   A form with the corolla densely scaly on the outside is known as var. *radinum* (F3).
   'Sweet Bay' (A.M. 1960) is a seedling of *R.*

R. trichostomum
(*continued*)

trichostomum var. *radinum* with flowers of Tyrian Rose (H.C.C. 24/3), suffused with white (Crown Estate Commissioners, Windsor).

R. triflorum
(*three-flowered*)
H⁴ F¹⁻² L¹⁻² Pm.

May–June

s. and s.s. Triflorum.

Shrub up to 10 ft. with smooth peeling dark red bark most beautiful when seen against the sunlight. Lvs. up to 3 in. long, ovate-lanceolate, oblong-lanceolate, elliptic, densely scaly glandular below. Fls. in trusses of 2–4, about 1½ in. long, widely funnel-shaped, zygomorphic, lemon-yellow, spotted with green or yellow tinged pink. Assam, Tibet, Burma–Tibet frontier, 7–13,000 ft.

The form known as var. *mahogani*, or "Ward's Mahogany Triflorum", from 9–12,500 ft. in S.E. Tibet, has flowers with a mahogany-coloured blotch and spots or suffused with mahogany in varying degree.

R. triplonaevium
(*with triple moles*)
H⁴ F¹⁻² L²⁻³ Pd.–m.

April–May

s. Taliense. *s.s.* Roxieanum.

Shrub up to 6 ft. with rufous-tomentose young shoots. Lvs. up to 6 in. long and 1½ in. broad, lanceolate or oblanceolate, slightly recurved at the margin, rust-coloured below. Fls. in tight truss of up to 12, about 1½ in. long, campanulate, white or white flushed with rose with a tri-radiate crimson blotch. N.W. Yunnan, 11–12,000 ft.

R. tritifolium
(*with polished leaves*)
H⁴ F¹⁻² L²⁻³ Pm.

April–May

s. Taliense. *s.s.* Roxieanum.

Shrub up to 6 ft. with young shoots rusty-tomentose. Lvs. 4–6 in. long, 1–1½ in. broad, elongate-lanceolate or oblanceolate, covered below with cinnamon to rusty indumentum. Fls. in compact truss of up to 15, about 1½ in. long, funnel-campanulate, white, suffused with rose with a crimson blotch and a few spots. N.W. Yunnan, 11–12,000 ft.

R. tsangpoense
(*from the Tsangpo River*)
H⁴ F²⁻³ L¹⁻² Pd.

May–June

s. and s.s. Glaucophyllum.

Shrub up to 3 ft. Lvs. up to 2 in. long, obovate to oblong-elliptic, very glaucous-scaly below. Fls. in groups of 2–6, nearly 1 in. long, broadly tubular-campanulate, pink, pinkish-purple or deep crimson or violet; calyx large, nearly ¼ in. long. Tibet, Burma, Assam, 12–13,000 ft.

A very variable and very free-flowering species. A form in which the flowers are small and narrowly tubular-campanulate is known as var. *curvistylum* and one in which the lower leaf surface is very densely scaly is known as var. *pruniflorum*.

R. tsariense
from Tsari, S.E. Tibet)
H4 F1-2 L2-3 Pd.–m.
April–May

s. Campanulatum.
 Shrub up to 5 ft. with young branchlets densely yellow-tomentose. Lvs. up to $2\frac{1}{2}$ in. long and $1\frac{1}{4}$ in. broad, obovate to elliptic-obovate, lower surface with dense fawn or woolly indumentum. Fls. in loose truss of 3–4, up to $1\frac{1}{2}$ in. long, campanulate, pale blush-pink, cream or white, often sprinkled with red spots. S.E. Tibet, Bhutan, 11,500–14,500 ft. Closely akin to *R. lanatum* but with smaller leaves and white or pink flowers.

R. tschonoskii
After Tschonoski, a Japanese collector)
H4 F1 L1-2 Pm.
May

s. Azalea. s.s. Obtusum.
 Deciduous shrub up to 8 ft. Lvs. crowded at the ends of the branchlets, at most 1 in. long and $\frac{1}{4}$ in. broad, narrow lanceolate to elliptic-lanceolate, clothed on both sides with appressed red-brown hairs, changing in the autumn to orange-red and crimson. Fls. in clusters of 3–6, only about $\frac{1}{3}$ in. across, funnel-form, white. Japan and Korea.

R. ungernii
After Baron Ungern-Sternberg, ι. 1868, Professor at Dorpat)
H4 F1-2 L2-3 Pm.–t.
July

s. Ponticum. s.s. Caucasicum.
 Shrub up to 20 ft. with white tomentose young shoots. Lvs. up to 8 in. long and 3 in. broad, oblong-oblanceolate, dark green above, covered below with dense grey to fawn woolly indumentum. Fls. in lax truss of 20–30, about $1\frac{1}{2}$ in. long, funnel-campanulate, pale rose or pinky-white with faint spotting. Caucasus, and N.E. Asia Minor, 5,000–7,000 ft. B.M. 8332. This very hardy rhododendron is worth growing for its foliage alone. Although it is of value as a late flowerer the flowers frequently are rather hidden by the new growths.

R. uniflorum
one-flowered)
H4 F2-3 L1 Pd.
April–May

s. Uniflorum.
 Dwarf shrub up to 1 ft. with subprocumbent branches. Lvs at most 1 in. long, obovate or oblong-obovate, glaucous below. Fls. solitary or in pairs, about 1 in. long, broadly funnel-shaped, purple. S.E. Tibet, 11–12,000 ft. Closely allied to *R. pemakoense*.

R. uvarifolium
with Uvaria-like leaves)
H4 F1-3 L2-3 Pm.–t.
March–April

s. Fulvum.
 Shrub or small tree up to 30 ft. with beautiful silvery young growths. Lvs. 3–10 in. long, and up to $2\frac{1}{2}$ in. broad, oblanceolate to obovate, dark green and with nerves impressed above, covered below with white or ash-grey, sometimes fawn, indumentum. Fls. in fairly tight truss of up to 18, $1\frac{1}{4}$–2 in. long, campanulate or funnel-campanulate, white, white flushed rose, or pale rose, spotted crimson or unspotted and with or without a

R. uvarifolium
(*continued*)

crimson blotch at the base. Yunnan, Szechwan, S.E. Tibet, 7–14,000 ft. Formerly known as *R. niphargum* and as such figured in B.M. 9480. There is a form in which the leaves are oblong-oval, broader and thicker in texture and with the indumentum whitish and silky below, known as var. *griseum*.

R. vaccinioides
(*like Vaccinium*)
H³ F¹⁻² L¹⁻² Pd.–s.

April–May

s. Vaccinioides.

Small straggly epiphytic shrub with densely rugose branchlets and with leaf-bud scales persisting for at least a year. Lvs. about $\frac{3}{4}$ in. long, spathulate-oblanceolate, without visible lateral nerves. Fls. single or in pairs, $\frac{1}{3}$ in. long, campanulate, lilac-pink, or white tinged with pink. Sikkim, S.E. Tibet, 6–12,000 ft. B.M. 9407 B.

R. valentinianum
(After Père S. P. Valentin, Tsedjong Mission, China)
H³⁻⁴ F²⁻³ L¹⁻² Pd.

April

s. Maddenii. *s.s.* Ciliicalyx.

Small shrub up to 3 ft. with densely setose young shoots. Lvs. in rosettes of 4–5 at the end of the shoots, $1\frac{1}{2}$ in. long, $\frac{3}{4}$ in. broad, elliptic or oblong-elliptic, setose-ciliate at margin and above, densely scaly below. Fls. in truss of 2–6, about $1\frac{1}{2}$ in. long, bright butter-yellow, pubescent and scaly outside. N.W. Yunnan, 11–12,000 ft. Much hardier than is usually supposed. Plants grown under this name (Rock 22302) are *R. fletcherianum*.
A.M. 1936 (Hon. H. D. McLaren, Bodnant).
R. valentinianum is a parent of the A.M. cultivars. 'Valaspis' (1935), 'Valpinense' (1943).

R. vaseyi
(After G. S. Vasey, 1822–93, who discovered the species in North Carolina in 1878)
H⁴ F²⁻⁴ L¹⁻² Pm.

April–May

s. Azalea. *s.s.* Canadense.

Deciduous shrub up to 15 ft. Lvs. up to 5 in. long and 2 in. broad, elliptic to elliptic-oblong, undulate at margin, dark green above, paler below. Fls. opening before the leaves in clusters of 4–8, up to 2 in. across, widely funnel-shaped or rotate-campanulate, 2-lipped, pale pink or rose-pink, or white, with orange-red or red spots. E. North America. The best forms are very beautiful when in flower. B.M. 8081.
A.G.M. 1927.

R. veitchianum
(After the famous family of Nurserymen)
H¹ F³⁻⁴ L²⁻³ Pm.s.

May–June–July

s. Maddenii. *s.s.* Ciliicalyx.

Rather straggling shrub up to 8 ft. Lvs. up to 5 in. long, and $1\frac{1}{2}$ in. broad, obovate-oblanceolate or elliptic-obovate, scaly both above and below. Fls. in trusses of up to 5, about 3 in. long, widely funnel-shaped, deeply 5-cleft, white, slightly tinged with green, the petal-margins crinkled. Burma, Tenasserim, Siam, 3–6,000 ft. B.M. 4992

R. vellereum
(*fleecy*)
H4 F2-3 L1-2 Pm.

April

s. and s.s. Taliense.

Shrub or small tree up to 15 ft. Lvs. up to 5 in. long and 2 in. broad, oblong-elliptic to oblong-oblanceolate, nerves impressed above, silvery-white to fawn indumentum below. Fls. in rather tight truss of 15–20, about 1½ in. long, funnel-campanulate, white or rose with purple or carmine spots. S.E. Tibet, 9–15,000 ft. B.M. n.s. 147.

R. venator
(*hunter, alluding to the scarlet flowers*)
H3-4 F2-3 L1-2 Pm.

May–June

s. Irroratum. s.s. Parishii.

Shrub up to 8 ft., of bushy habit and with the young shoots clad with long stalked, gland-tipped setae and white hairs. Lvs. up to 6 in. long and 1 in. broad, oblong-lanceolate to oblance-olate, bright green and rugulose above, glaucous-green below. Fls. in trusses of 4–11, 1½ in. long, tubular-campanulate, scarlet or reddish-orange on fawn to rusty-tomentose pedicels. S.E. Tibet, 8–8,500 ft.

A.M. 1933 (Hon. H. D. McLaren, Bodnant) to form with reddish-orange flowers.

R. vernicosum
(*shiny*)
H4 F1-3 L2-3 Pm.-t.

April–May

s. and s.s. Fortunei.

Shrub or tree up to 20 ft. Lvs. up to 5 in. long and 2½ in. broad, oblong-oval to oblong-elliptic, round at apex, mat and wax covered above becoming glossy when rubbed or heated, pale glaucous-green below. Fls. in trusses of 6–12, 1½–2 in. long, funnel-campanulate, white, pink, bright rose or rose-lavender with or without crimson markings, 7-lobed. Yunnan, Szechwan, 9–14,000 ft. B.M. 8834, 8904–5. Allied to *R. decorum*, *R. vernicosum* is a very variable species and several geographical forms have been given the names *euanthum* (F2), *rhantum* (F1-2) and *sheltonae* (F1-2). All forms are attractive plants.

R. verruculosum
(*with small warts*)
H4 F1-2 L1-2 Pd.

May

s. Lapponicum.

Compact shrub up to 3 ft. with short densely scaly branchlets. Lvs. about ½ in. long and ¼ in. broad, broadly elliptic, scales on upper surface thick and fleshy, those below thin. Fls. usually solitary, about ½ in. long, widely funnel-shaped, purple or pink. W. Szechwan, 10,000 ft.

A.M. 1932 (Col. Stephenson R. Clarke, Hay-wards Heath) to form with purple flowers.

R. vesiculiferum
(*vesicle-bearing*)
H4 F2-3 L2-3 Pm.

April–May

s. Barbatum. s.s. Glischrum.

Shrub or tree up to 10 ft. with densely bristly shoots. Lvs. 3–6 in. long and up to 2 in. broad, oblong-lanceolate to oblanceolate, dark green and almost bullate above, with bladder-like hairs

R. vesiculiferum
(*continued*)

on the veins on the lower surface. Fls. in trusses of 10–15, about 1½ in. long, campanulate, purplish-rose with a crimson or purple blotch. Yunnan, Burma–Tibet frontier, 9–11,000 ft.

R. vestitum
(*clothed*)
H⁴ F¹⁻² L²⁻³ Pm.

June

s. Thomsonii. s.s. Selense.

Shrub up to 5 ft. with shoots at first bristly-glandular. Lvs. up to 2½ in. long and 1 in. broad, oblong, elliptic or oval, under surface with patchy scurfy indumentum. Fls. in truss of about 6, about 1½ in. long, funnel-campanulate, white, flushed rose (deep rose in bud) with a few crimson markings and a crimson blotch. S.E. Tibet, 14,000 ft. Because of the indumentum on the lower leaf surface, *R. vestitum* is rather anomalous in s.s. Selense. It is doubtful if any of the plants in cultivation under this name, are correctly named.

R. vilmorinianum
(After the famous French seeds-men)
H⁴ F¹⁻² L¹⁻² Pm.

May

s. Triflorum. s.s. Yunnanense.

Shrub up to 6 ft. Lvs. up to 2½ in. long, oblong to lanceolate, scaly below. Fls in clusters of 2–4, about 1½ in. long, funnel-shaped, zygomorphic, white, or white tinged pink, with ochre-coloured spots. Szechwan. Strongly reminiscent of a white-flowered *R. augustinii*.

R. violaceum
(*violet-coloured*)
H⁴ F¹⁻² L¹⁻² Pd.

April–May

s. Lapponicum.

Shrub up to 4 ft. with short scaly branchlets. Lvs. ⅓ in. long, narrowly oblong-elliptic, very scaly. Fls. in clusters of 1–3, nearly ½ in. long, openly funnel-shaped, violet-purple. W. Szechwan, 12–13,000 ft.

R. virgatum
(*with willowy twigs*)
H²⁻³ F²⁻³ L¹⁻² Pm.

April–May

s. Virgatum.

Shrub up to 6 ft. with rather leggy branches. Lvs. up to 2½ in. long and ¾ in. broad, broadly lanceolate, very scaly below. Fls. solitary or in pairs, about 1 in. long, tubular-campanulate, purple, lilac, rose, pink, or pale pink or white. Sikkim, Bhutan, 9,000 ft. B.M. 5060.

R. viridescens
(*becoming green*)
H⁴ F¹⁻² L¹⁻² Pm.

June

s. Trichocladum.

Shrub up to 4 ft. with bristly branchlets. Lvs. persisting only on one-year-old shoots, up to 1½ in. long and 1 in. broad, oblong-elliptic, bright green above, glaucous and scaly below, at first pilose-bristly at margin. Fls. in clusters of 4–5, about ¾ in. long, widely funnel-shaped, pale yellowish-green with green spots. S.E. Tibet, 10–11,000 ft.

R. viscosum
(sticky)
H4 F2–3 L1–2 Pm.

June–July

s. Azalea. *s.s.* Luteum.

Much branched deciduous shrub, variable in habit, up to 15 ft. with hairy young shoots. Lvs. up to 1½ in. long, oblong-oblanceolate, ovate, elliptic or obovate, dark green above, usually glaucous-green below. Fls. appearing after the lvs. are fully developed, in clusters of 4–12, about 1½ in. across and nearly 2 in. long, narrow tubular-funnel-shaped, fragrant, glandular-sticky, white, occasionally suffused with pink. E. North America.

The so-called "Swamp Honeysuckle" is valuable for its late flowering and fragrance.

A.M. 1921 (F. G. Strover, South Northwood) to form with white flowers.

A.G.M. 1937.

R. wallichii
(After Nathaniel Wallich, one-time Superintendent, Calcutta Botanic Garden, credited with first introducing *R. arboreum* by some authorities; 1786–1854)
H4 F1–3 L1–2 Pm.

April

s. Campanulatum.

Shrub up to 10 ft. with dark brown bark. Lvs. 2–5 in. long, up to 2 in. broad, elliptic, obovate or oblong, dark green above, pale green below and covered with powdery reddish-brown tufts of hair. Fls. in trusses of 6–10, 1–2 in. long, broadly campanulate, lilac, spotted with rose. Sikkim, Nepal, Bhutan, Assam, 10–14,000 ft. B.M. 4928. Closely allied to *R. campanulatum* and really only separable by microscopic details of indumentum.

R. wardii
(After F. Kingdon Ward, collector and explorer; 1885–1958)
H4 F2–4 L2–3 Pm.–t.

May

s. Thomsonii. *s.s.* Souliei.

Shrub up to 20 ft. Lvs. up to nearly 4 in. long, usually shorter, and up to 2 in. broad, oblong-elliptic or semi-orbicular, dark green above, pale glaucous-green below. Fls. in loose truss of up to 2 in. across, openly cup or saucer-shaped, bright yellow or clear lemon-yellow, sometimes flushed with green and sometimes with a crimson blotch at the base. Yunnan, Szechwan, S.E. Tibet. 10–14,000 ft.

A.M. 1926 (as *R. croceum*; A. M. Williams, Launceston) to form with flowers bright yellow and with a touch of crimson on the interior.

A.M. 1926 (as *R. astrocalyx*; A. M. Williams, Launceston) to form with flat clear-lemon flowers.

A.M. 1931 (L. de Rothschild, Exbury) to form with flowers bright yellow, flushed green, grown from seeds of *K.W.* 4170.

'Ellesstee' is a seedling of *R. wardii* of *Ludlow, Sherriff* and *Taylor* collecting, with the flowers having a deep crimson blotch in the throat. A.M. 1959 (Capt. Collingwood Ingram, Benenden, Kent) and 'Meadow Pond'. A.M. 1963 (Comm. of Crown Lands).

R. wardii
(*continued*)

R. *wardii* is a parent of the A.M. clones 'Inamorata' (1950), 'Prelude' (1951), 'Hawk' (1949), 'Exbury Hawk' (1947), 'Jervis Bay' (1951), 'Idealist' (1945), 'Cowslip' (1937), as well as of the F.C.C. cultivar 'Crest' (1953).

R. wasonii
(After Rear-Adm. Cathcart Romer Wason, R.N., 1874–1941, friend of E. H. Wilson)
H⁴ F¹⁻³ L²⁻³ Pm.

May

s. Taliense. s.s. Wasonii.

Shrub up to 6 ft. with foliage buds densely clad with white to pale fawn tomentum. Lvs. up to 4 in. long and 2 in. broad, oval or broadly lanceolate, dark glossy green above, white below when young, brown or rusty-red later. Fls. in loose truss of up to 10, 1½ in. long, bell-shaped, white, creamy-white, pink, rose or yellow, with crimson spots. W. Szechwan, 9–11,000 ft. B.M. 9190. A variable plant, one form of which, with pinkish fls. has been named var. *rhododactylum* (F³).

R. watsonii
(After W. C. Haines-Watson, Chinese Customs)
H³⁻⁴ F¹⁻² L²⁻³ Pm.

April

s. Grande.

Shrub or tree up to 20 ft. Lvs. up to 9 in. long and 6 in. broad, subsessile, obovate, elliptic or oblanceolate, dark green and shining above, covered with silvery-fawn indumentum below. Fls. in loose trusses of up to 15, 1½ in. long, bell-shaped, white or white tinged pink, with crimson blotch. W. Szechwan, 9–11,000 ft.

R. websterianum
(After F. G. Webster, of Boston, U.S.A.)
H⁴ F¹⁻² L¹⁻² Pd.

April

s. Lapponicum.

Shrub up to 3 ft. with scaly branchlets. Lvs. about ⅓ in. long, narrow-elliptic, yellowish-grey-scaly below. Fls. usually solitary, about ¾ in. long, funnel-shaped, rosy-purple. W. Szechwan, 10–14,000 ft.

R. weldianum
(After Gen. Stephen Minot Weld, former President of Mass. Hort. Soc.)
H⁴ F¹⁻² L²⁻³ Pm.

April–May

s. Taliense. s.s. Wasonii.

Shrub up to 10 ft. Lvs. up to 5 in. long and 2 in. broad, oblong-elliptic, densely tomentose below. At first white, later rusty-brown. Fls. in rather loose truss of up to 12, about 1 in. long, funnel-campanulate, white or pinkish-purple, spotted crimson. W. Szechwan, 9–10,000 ft.

R. weyrichii
(After Dr. Weyrich, Russian naval surgeon, 1828–63)
H⁴ F²⁻³ L¹⁻² Pm.

April–May

s. Azalea. s.s. Schlippenbachii.

Deciduous shrub up to 15 ft. Lvs. in twos or threes at ends of branchlets, up to 3½ in. long and 2½ in. broad, broad-ovate or suborbicular, covered at first with reddish-brown hairs. Fls. in clusters of 2–4, expanding before or with the leaves, up to 2½ in. across, rotate-funnel-form, bright brick-red with purple blotch. Japan and Quelpaert. B.M. 9475.

R. wightii
(After Robt. Wight, M.D., Supt., Madras Botanic Garden; 1796–1872)

H3–4 F2–3 L2–3 Pm.–t.s.

s. Lacteum.

Shrub sometimes rather straggly, or small tree, up to 15 ft. Lvs. up to 8 in. long and 3 in. broad, oblong-elliptic, oblong-obovate or oblanceolate, bright green above, covered below with fawn or rust suede-like indumentum. Fls. in lax rather one-sided truss of up to 20, up to 2 in. long, bell-shaped, pale yellow or lemon-yellow, rarely white tinged pink, spotted crimson, with or without a crimson blotch. Sikkim, Bhutan, 11–14,000 ft. B.M. 8492.

A.M. 1913 (Miss Clara Mangles, Littleworth, Seal, Surrey) to form with flowers of pale sulphur yellow marked with crimson at base.

R. wightii is a parent of the A.M. clones 'China' (1948) and 'Tittenhurst' (1933).

R. williamsianum
(After J. C. Williams, 1861–1939, of Caerhays, Cornwall)

H3–4 F2–3 L2–3 Pd.–m.

April

s. Thomsonii. *s.s.* Williamsianum.

Small spreading shrub up to 5 ft. with bronze young shoots and leaves. Lvs. up to 1¾ in. long and almost as broad, broadly elliptic to rounded, ovate or cordate, bright green above, glaucous below. Fls. usually in loose truss of 2–3, 1½–2 in. long, campanulate, clear shell-pink, 5-lobed. Szechwan, 8–10,000 ft. B.M. 8935. A most attractive species and rather reminiscent of *R. orbiculare* in spite of the latter's 7-lobed corolla. Rather anomalous in the Thomsonii Series in its dwarf spreading habit.

A.M. 1938 (Lord Aberconway, Bodnant).

R. williamsianum is a parent of the A.M. clones 'Bow Bells' (1935), 'Arthus J. Ivens' (1944), 'Bodnant Thomwilliams' (1935), 'Cowslip' (1937).

R. wilsonae
(After Mrs. Wilson, wife of E. H. Wilson, d. 1931)

H1–2 F1–2 L1–2 Pm.

April

s. Stamineum.

Shrub up to 6 ft. Lvs. whorled, up to 4 in. long and 2 in. broad, narrow-elliptic, lateral nerves impressed above. Fls. usually solitary, axillary and terminal, about 1½ in. long, widely funnel-shaped, flesh-pink, W. Hupeh, 5–6,000 ft.

R. wiltonii
(After E. C. Wilton, of the Chinese Consular Service)

H4 F2–3 L2–3 Pm.

April–May

s. Taliense. *s.s.* Wasonii.

Shrub up to 10 ft. with young shoots clad with greenish-white felt. Lvs. up to 5 in. long and 1½ in. broad, oblong-obovate to oblanceolate, bullate above, at first white, later cinnamon-brown below. Fls. in trusses of up to 10, up to 1½ in. long, funnel-campanulate to campanulate, white or flesh-pink with red spots and a small blotch. W. Szechwan, 7–9,000 ft. B.M. 9388.

A.M. 1957 (E. de Rothschild, Exbury) to form with flowers white with dark crimson blotch in throat, irregularly flushed outside with pink.

R. xanthocodon
(*yellow bell*)
H4 F2–3 L2–3 Pm.

May

s. Cinnabarinum.

Shrub or small tree up to 15 ft. with young shoots golden-scaly and young foliage very glaucous. Lvs. up to nearly 3 in. long and nearly 2 in. broad, elliptic or oblong-elliptic, dull green and densely scaly above, glaucous-green and densely scaly below, aromatic. Fls. in truss of 5 –10, up to 1½ in. long, campanulate to funnel-shaped, fleshy, rich cream-yellow, or yellow, without spots. Bhutan, S.E. Tibet, 11–12,000 ft. Closely allied to *R. cinnabarinum*.

A.M. 1935 (L. de Rothschild, Exbury) to form with yellow flowers.

R. xanthostephanum
(*yellow garland*)
H3 F2–3 L1–2 Pm.

April–May

s. Boothii. s.s. Tephropeplum.

Shrub up to 9 ft. Lvs. 2–4 in. long, lanceolate to oblanceolate, scaly, silvery below. Fls. 4–8 to the truss, about 1 in. diam., campanulate scaly without, bright yellow or sometimes pale or even greeny-yellow; calyx lobes erect. Yunnan Tibet, Burma, 7–13,500 ft. B.M. 8882, as *R aureum*. Allied to *R. auritum* but the calyx lobe are not reflexed and the flowers usually are of a better colour.

'Yellow Garland', A.M. 1961, a seedling of *R xanthostephanum*, grown from seeds of *Forres* 21707 with the flowers Aureolin (H.C.C. 3/1 (Crown Estate Commissioners, Windsor).

R. xanthostephanum is a parent of the A.M. clone 'Saffron Queen' (1948).

R. yakusimanum
(*from Yakusima*)
H4 F3–4 L2–3 Pd.–m.

May

s. Ponticum. s.s. Caucasicum.

Rounded shrub of about 4 ft. Lvs. about 3½ in long and up to 1½ in. broad, recurved at the margin, when young entirely fuscous-tomentose later dark green and glossy above, thick heavy fuscous-tomentose below. Fls. in compact truss of up to 10, up to 8 in. wide, campanulate, when in bud deep rose, a delicate pink when partially opened, white when fully expanded. Japan, the Island of Yakusima.

F.C.C. 1947 (Royal Horticultural Society Gardens, Wisly).

Parent of A.M. clones 'Lady Bowes Lyon (1962) and 'Renoir' (1961).

R. yedoense
(*from Yedo, now Tokyo*)
H4 F2–3 L1–2 Pm.

May

s. Azalea. s.s. Obtusum.

An azalea, cultivated in Japan and Korea, with rosy-purple double flowers and regarded as the cultivated form of what frequently is called *R yedoense* var. *poukhanense*. Probably it should have no more than clonal status and has in fact been

170

R. yedoense
(*continued*)

called 'Yodogawa'. See *R. poukhanense*. A.M. 1961 (Capt. Collingwood Ingram, Benenden, Kent).

R. yungningense
(*from Yungning, Szechwan*)
H4 F1–2 L1–2 Pd.

April–May

s. Lapponicum.

Shrub up to 3 ft. with short, densely scaly branchlets. Lvs. about ⅓ in. long, oblong-oblanceolate, densely rusty-scaly below. Fls. solitary or in pairs, about ⅓ in. long, widely funnel-shaped, deep purple, pale rose-purple or deep purplish-blue. Szechwan, 13–14,000 ft.

R. yunnanense
(*from Yunnan*)
H4 F2–4 L1–2 Pm.

May

s. Triflorum. s.s. Yunnanense.

Very free flowering shrub up to 12 ft. Lvs. sometimes semi-deciduous, 1–4 in. long, oblance-olate or lanceolate, setose-pilose above and at the margin when young, scaly on both surfaces. Fls. terminal or terminal and axillary in the upper leaves, in trusses of 3–5, wide funnel-shaped, zygomorphic, pink, white, pale rose-lavender or lavender, with or rarely without spots. Yunnan, Szechwan, Burma, S.E. Tibet, Kweichou, 6,500–14,000 ft. B.M. 7614. This species, which is worth a place in every garden is extremely variable and several forms have been given specific names such as *aechmophyllum*, *chartophyllum*, *pleistanthum*, *suberosum*. They should all be regarded as synonyms of *R. yunnanense*.

A.M. 1903 (F. W. Moore, Glasnevin, Dublin). A.G.M. 1934.

R. yunnanense is a parent of the A.M. clones 'Alison Johnstone' (1945) and 'Youthful Sin', A.M. 1960.

R. zaleucum
(*very white*)
H3–4 F2–3 L1–2 Pm.–t.

April

s. Triflorum. s.s. Yunnanense.

Shrub up to 20 ft. Lvs. up to 3½ in. long, lanceolate to obovate to elliptic, white and glau-cous below. Fls. terminal or terminal and axillary in upper leaves, in trusses of 3–5, wide funnel-shaped, zygomorphic, white or pale rose, pale purple or yellow, with or without crimson spots. Very distinct by virtue of the white lower surface to the leaf. Burma, Yunnan, 6–13,000 ft.

A.M. 1932 (Col. R. Stephenson Clarke, Hay-wards Heath) to form with mauve-pink, slightly spotted flowers.

R. zeylanicum
(*from Ceylon*)
H2–3 F2–3 L2–3 Pm.–t.

April–May

s. and s.s. Arboreum.

Tree up to 30 ft. or more. Lvs. up to 5 in. long and 2 in. broad, elliptic to elliptic-oblong, dark green and bullate and convex above, clothed below with dense fawn to tawny indumentum. Fls. in dense truss, 1½–2 in. long, campanulate,

171

R. zeylanicum
(continued)

red to scarlet-red or occasionally pink. Ceylon, 3–8,000 ft. B.M. 7696, as *R. arboreum* var. *kingianum*.

R. zeylanicum is a parent of the following clones: F.C.C. 'Coreta' (1935); A.M. 'Gwilt King' (1952), 'Saint Keverne' (1922).

List of Synonyms

acraium	=	primulaeflorum.
acuminatum	=	mucronulatum var. acuminatum.
adamsii	=	primulaeflorum.
adenostemonum	=	a form of pogonostylum.
adoxum	=	vernicosum.
aechmophyllum	=	yunnanense.
aemulorum	=	mallotum.
aeruginosum	=	campanulatum var. aeruginosum.
aiolopeplum	=	dryophyllum.
aiolosalpinx	=	stewartianum var. aiolosalpinx.
aischropeplum	=	roxieanum.
albicaule	=	decorum.
allipetalum	=	temenium var. allipetalum.
album	=	a form of arboreum.
algarvense	=	ponticum ?
amaurophyllum	=	saluenense.
amoenum	=	obtusum var. amoenum.
angustifolium	=	hirsutum.
araliaeforme	=	a form of vernicosum.
argenteum	=	grande.
argyi	=	mucronatum ?
aristatum	=	barbatum.
aromaticum	=	anthopogon.
artosquameum	=	oreotrephes.
ashleyi	=	maximum ?
asmenistum	=	cloiophorum.
assamicum	=	formosum.
asteium	=	mesopolium.
astrocalyx	=	wardii.
atentsiense	=	ciliicalyx.
atroviride	=	concinnum.
aucklandii	=	griffithianum.
augustinii var. azureus	=	augustinii.
augustinii f. grandifolia	=	augustinii var. chasmanthum.
augustinii f. subglabra	=	augustinii var. chasmanthum.
augustinii var. yui	=	augustinii.
aureum *Franch*.	=	xanthostephanum
aureum *Georgi*	=	chrysanthum.
australe	=	leptothrium.
axium	=	selense.
baeticum	=	ponticum.
batangense	=	stictophyllum.
batemanii	=	campanulatum.
beimäense	=	erythrocalyx.
benthamianum	=	concinnum var. benthamianum.

bicolor	=	canescens.
blandfordiaeflorum	=	cinnabarinum var. blandfordiae- florum.
blandulum	=	jucundum.
blinii	=	lutescens.
blumei	=	niveum.
brachyandrum	=	eclecteum var. brachyandrum.
brachystylum	=	trichocladum.
brettii	=	longesquamatum.
breynii	=	indicum.
buergeri	=	obtusum forma.
bureavioicles	=	burearii.
burmannii	=	mucronatum.
burriflorum	=	diphrocalyx.
butyricum	=	chrysodoron.
caeruleo-glaucum	=	campylogynum var. charopoeum.
caeruleum	=	rigidum.
calcicola	=	cuneatum.
calciphilum	=	calostrotum var. calciphilum.
californica (Azalea)	=	occidentale.
californicum	=	macrophyllum.
calleryi	=	simsii.
candelabrum	=	thomsonii var. candelabrum.
cantabile	=	russatum.
cardioeides	=	oreotrephes.
caryophyllum	=	rubropilosum.
catapastum	=	desquamatum.
catesbaeum	=	ponticum hybrid ?
caucaseum	=	caucasicum.
cephalanthoides	=	primulaeflorum var. cephalanthoides.
cerasiflorum, nomen	=	campylogynum.
cerinum	=	sulfureum.
chaffanjonii	=	stamineum.
chalarocladum	=	selense.
chamaecistus	=	Rhodothamnus chamaecistus.
chamaetortum	=	cephalanthum.
charianthum	=	davidsonianum.
charidotes	=	chameunum.
charitostreptum	=	brachyanthum var. hypolepidotum.
charopoeum	=	campylogynum var. charopoeum.
chartophyllum	=	yunnanense.
chartophyllum var. praecox	=	hormophorum.
chasmanthoides	=	augustinii var. chasmanthum.
chasmanthum	=	augustinii var. chasmanthum.
cheilanthum	=	ravum.
chengshienianum	=	ambiguum
chionophyllum	=	hypoglaucum.
chlanidotum	=	citriniflorum.
cinereum	=	ravum.
clivicola	=	primulaeflorum.
coccinopeplum	=	roxieanum.

174

colletum	=	beesianum.
colobodes, nomen	=	chameunum.
commodum	=	sulfureum.
concinnum f.		
laetevirens	=	concinnum.
concinnum var.		
lepidanthum	=	concinnum.
confertissimum	=	parvifolium.
coombense	=	concinnum.
cooperi	=	camelliaeflorum.
cordatum	=	souliei.
coreanum	=	yedoense var. poukhanense.
coronarium	=	luteum.
cosmetum	=	chameunum.
costulatum	=	lutescens.
crebreflorum	=	cephalanthum var. crebreflorum.
cremastum	=	campylogynum var. cremastum.
cremnastes	=	lepidotum.
cremnophilum	=	primulaeflorum.
crenatum	=	racemosum.
crispiflora (Azalea)	=	a form of indicum.
croceum	=	wardii.
cucullatum	=	roxieanum.
cumberlandense	=	bakeri
cuthbertii	=	minus.
cyclium	=	callimorphum.
cymbomorphum	=	erythrocalyx.
dahuricum	=	dauricum.
damascenum	=	campylogynum.
danielsianum	=	indicum.
daphniflorum	=	rufescens.
davuricum	=	dauricum.
decandrum	=	reticulatum.
decumbens	=	indicum.
deleiense	=	tephropeplum.
dendritrichum	=	uvarifolium.
depile	=	oreotrephes.
dianthiflora (Azalea)	=	a double form of linearifolium var. macrosepalum.
dichropeplum	=	phaeochrysum.
dilatatum	=	reticulatum.
docimum, nomen	=	erythrocalyx.
dolerum	=	selense.
duclouxii	=	spinuliferum.
dunnii	=	henryi.
duseimatum	=	selense var. duseimatum.
edgarii	=	campanulatum.
elaeagnoides	=	lepidotum.
emaculatum	=	beesianum.
eriandrum	=	rigidum.
erileucum	=	zaleucum.
eriocarpum	=	a variety of simsii.

175

eriphyllum, nomen	=	cyanocarpum var. eriphyllum.
erythrocalyx		
subsp. beimäense	=	erythrocalyx.
erythrocalyx		
subsp. docimum	=	erythrocalyx.
erythrocalyx		
subsp. eucallum	=	erythrocalyx.
erythrocalyx		
subsp. truncatulum	=	erythrocalyx.
euanthum	=	vernicosum.
eucallum	=	erythrocalyx.
exquisetum	=	oreotrephes.
fissotectum	=	schizopeplum.
fittianum	=	dauricum.
flammea (Azalea)	=	calendulaceum.
flavum	=	chrysanthum.
fordii	=	simiarum.
foveolatum	=	coriaceum.
fragrans *Maxim.*	=	primulaeflorum.
franchetianum	=	decorum.
fuchsiaeflorum	=	spinuliferum.
fulva (Azalea)	=	speciosum.
fulvoides	=	fulvum.
gibsonii	=	formosum.
giraudiasii	=	decorum.
glabrius	=	japonicum.
glauco-aureum	=	campylogynum.
glaucum	=	glaucophyllum.
gloeoblastum	=	wardii.
gnaphalocarpum	=	mariesii.
gracilipes	=	hypoglaucum.
gymnomiscum	=	primulaeflorum.
haemonium	=	anthopogon var. haemonium.
hagnoense	=	indicum.
hallaisanense	=	yedoense var. poukhanense.
hannoense	=	indicum.
harrovianum	=	polylepis.
hedyosmum	=	trichostomum var. hedyosmum.
hedythamnum	=	callimorphum.
hedythamnum		
var. eglandulosum	=	cyanocarpum.
heishuiense	=	tatsienense.
helvolum	=	dryophyllum.
hesperium	=	rigidum.
hexamerum	=	decorum.
hispidum	=	a variety of viscosum.
horaeum	=	citriniflorum subsp. horaeum.
hortense	=	a form of linearifolium var. macro-sepalum.
humicola, nomen	=	saluenense.
humifusum, nomen	=	chameunum.
hutchinsonianum	=	concinnum.

hyacinthiflorum	=	ponticum.
hymenanthes	=	degronianum and metternichii, each in part.
hypolepidotum	=	brachyanthum var. hypolepidotum.
hypotrichotum	=	oreotrephes.
intortum	=	dryophyllum.
ioanthum	=	siderophyllum.
ixeuticum	=	crinigerum.
jahandiezii	=	siderophyllum.
jangtzowense	=	apodectum.
japonicum *Schneider*	=	metternichii.
jenkinsii	=	maddenii.
kamtschaticum	=	camtschaticum.
kansuense	=	imperfectly known species, *s.* Taliense ?
kialense	=	przewalskii.
kingianum	=	zeylanicum.
kirkii	=	discolor.
klossii	=	moulmainense.
komiyamae	=	tosaense.
laetevirens	=	concinnum.
lagopus	=	reticulatum.
lamprophyllum	=	ovatum.
lancifolium *Hook. f.*	=	barbatum (*Moench* = ponticum).
lateritium	=	indicum.
latifolium	=	hirsutum.
ledifolium	=	mucronatum.
ledifolium var. purpureum	=	pulchrum var. calycinum.
ledoides	=	trichostomum var. ledoides.
leilungense	=	tatsienense.
lemeei	=	lutescens.
lepidanthum	=	primulaeflorum var. lepidanthum.
lepidotum var. chloranthum	=	lepidotum.
leptanthum	=	leiopodum.
leptosanthum	=	leiopodum.
leucandrum	=	siderophyllum.
leucanthum	=	mucronatum.
leucolasium	=	hunnewellianum.
levistratum	=	dryophyllum.
liratum	=	apodectum.
liukiuense	=	scabrum.
longifolium	=	grande.
lophophorum	=	phaeochrysum.
lusidusculum	=	obtusum forma.
mackenzianum	=	stenaulum
macrantha (Azalea)	=	indicum.
macrosepalum	=	linearifolium var. macrosepalum.
macrostemon	=	obtusum forma.
mairei	=	lacteum.
malindangense	=	quadrasianum.

mandarinorum	=	discolor.
mannophorum	=	roseotinctum.
manopeplum	=	esetulosum.
matsumurai	=	yedoense.
maximowiczianum	=	non-existent.
maxwellii	=	pulchrum var. maxwellii.
megaphyllum	=	basilicum.
mesembrinum	=	a variety of simsii.
messatum	=	xanthostephanum.
metrium	=	selense.
microterum, nomen	=	beesianum.
mirabile, nomen	=	genestierianum.
modestum	=	ciliatum ?
monbeigii	=	uvarifolium.
morsheadianum	=	imperfectly known ? Arboreum Series.
motsouense	=	racemosum.
muliense	=	chryseum.
mussoti, nomen	=	wardii.
mutabile	=	campanulatum.
myrtifolia (Azalea)	=	hongkongense.
myrtifolium *Schott*		
et Kotschy	=	kotschyi. (*Lodd.* = ponticum.)
myrtilloides	=	campylogynum var. myrtilloides.
nagasakianum	=	reticulatum.
nakaii	=	degronianum var.
nanothamnum	=	selense.
nanum	=	polycladum.
narcissiflorum	=	double white flowered form of mucronatum.
nebrites	=	himertum.
nepalense	=	arboreum.
nikoense	=	pentaphyllum.
niko-montanum	=	chrysanthum var. niko-montanum.
niphargum	=	uvarifolium.
niphobolum	=	stewartianum.
nitidum	=	viscosum.
nmaiense	=	cephalanthum var. nmaiense.
nobile	=	possibly a hybrid of campanulatum.
nudiflora (Azalea)	=	calendulaceum or speciosum.
nudipes	=	reticulatum.
nwaiense	=	nmaiense.
oblongum	=	griffithianum.
obovatum	=	lepidotum.
obscurum	=	siderophyllum.
officinale	=	chrysanthum.
oomurasaki	=	pulchrum forma.
oreinum	=	alpicola.
oreotrephoides	=	oreotrephes.
oresbium	=	edgarianum.
oresterum	=	wardii.
osakazuki	=	pulchrum var.
osmerum	=	russatum.

pachysanthum	=	morii.
pagophilum	=	selense var. pagophilum.
pamprotum, nomen	=	chameunum.
pentamerum	=	degronianum.
periclymena (Azalea) } periclymenoides }	=	nudiflorum.
phaeochlorum	=	oreotrephes.
phoeniceum	=	pulchrum.
pilovittatum	=	delavayi.
pittosporaefolium	=	stamineum.
planifolium	=	wallichii.
pleistanthum	=	yunnanense.
plebeium	=	heliolepis.
poecilodermum	=	roxieanum.
poliopeplum	=	himertum.
pontica (Azalea)	=	luteum.
porphyroblastum	=	globigerum.
porrosquameum	=	brevistylum.
poukhanense	=	yedoense var. poukhanense
praeclarum	=	primulaeflorum.
prasinocalyx	=	wardii.
primulinum	=	flavidum.
prinophyllum	=	roseum.
pritzelianium	=	micranthum.
probum	=	selense var. probum.
procerum	=	maximum.
prophantum	=	kyawi.
propinquum	=	achroanthum.
pruniflorum	=	tsangpoense var. pruniflorum.
pseudoyanthinum	=	concinnum var. pseudoyanthinum.
pubigerum	=	oreotrephes.
punctatum *Ker*	=	carolinianum. (*Andr.* = minus.)
puniceum	=	pulchrum.
purpureum	=	maximum.
purshii	=	maximum.
pycnocladum	=	diacritum.
radinum	=	trichostomum var. radinum.
randaiense	=	rubropilosum.
rarosquameum	=	rigidum.
rasile	=	diaprepes.
rawsonii	=	pulchrum forma.
recurvum	=	roxieanum.
recurvum var. oreonastes	=	roxieanum var. oreonastes.
regale	=	basilicum.
repens	=	forrestii var. repens.
repens var. chamaedoron	=	chamae-thomsonii var. chamae- thauma.
repens var. chamaethauma	=	chamae-thomsonii var. chamae- thauma.

repens var.
    chamae-thomsonii = chamae-thomsonii.
rhaibocarpum = dasycladum.
rhantum = vernicosum.
rhododactylum = wasonii var. rhododactylum.
rhodora = canadense.
rhombicum = reticulatum.
riparium = calostrotum.
ripense = mucronatum var. ripense.
rivulare = calostrotum.
rollissonii = zeylanicum.
rosaeflora (Azalea) = indicum var. balsaminaeflorum.
rosthornii = micranthum.
rotundifolium = orbiculare.
roylei = cinnabarinum var. roylei.
rubriflorum, nomen = campylogynum.
rubropunctatum
         Hayata = hyperythrum.
rubro-punctatum
    Lévl. et Vant = siderophyllum.
salignum = lepidotum.
scabrifolium var.
    pauciflora = spinuliferum.
sciaphilum = edgeworthii.
sclerocladum = ravum.
seguini = yunnanense.
selense subsp. axium = selense.
selense
 subsp. chalarocladum = selense.
selense subsp. dolerum= selense.
selense
    subsp. duseimatum = selense var. duseimatum.
selense subsp. metrium= selense.
selense
    subsp. nanothamnum= selense.
selense
    subsp. pagophilum = selense var. pagophilum.
selense subsp. probum = selense var. probum.
semanteum = impeditum.
semnum = coryphaeum.
sericocalyx, nomen = chameunum.
sheltonae = vernicosum.
shikokianum = weyrichii.
shojoense = mariesii.
siamense = moulmainense.
siderophylloides = oreotrephes.
sieboldii = kaempferi ?
sigillatum = dryophyllum.
silvaticum = lanigerum.
sinense *Maxim.* = japonicum. (*Sweet* = molle.)
sinolepidotum = lepidotum.
sinovaccinioides = vaccinioides.

sinovirgatum	=	oleifolium.
sonomense	=	occidentale var. sonomense.
sordidum	=	tsangpoense var. pruniflorum.
sparsiflorum	=	camelliaeflorum.
sphaeranthum	=	trichostomum.
spodopeplum	=	tephropeplum.
spooneri	=	decorum.
squamata (Azalea)	=	farrerae.
squarrosum	=	desquamatum.
stenophyllum	=	makinoi.
stenoplastum	=	desquamatum.
stereophyllum	=	tatsienense.
strictum	=	yunnanense.
subcoombense	=	concinnum.
suberosum	=	yunnanense.
sublanceolatum		
sublateritium	=	scabrum.
sycnanthum	=	rigidum.
syncollum	=	phaeochrysum.
tanakai	=	Stamineum series.
tapeinum	=	megeratum.
tapelouense	=	tatsienense.
taquetii	=	mucronulatum.
tebotan	=	pulchrum var. tebotan
tectum	=	obtusum forma.
telopeum		
forma telopeoides	=	panteumorphum.
theiochroum	=	sulfureum.
theiophyllum	=	dryophyllum.
thomsonii		
var. album	=	thomsonii.
thomsonii		
var. flocculosa	=	thomsonii.
thomsonii		
var. grandiflorum	=	thomsonii.
thomsonii		
var. cyanocarpum	=	cyanocarpum.
thunbergii	=	obtusum.
thyodocum	=	baileyi.
timeteum	=	oreotrephes.
torquatum	=	roseotinctum.
transiens	=	obtusum forma.
trichopodum	=	oreotrephes.
trinerve	=	tschonoskii.
truncatulum	=	erythrocalyx.
tsarongense	=	primulaeflorum.
vaniotii	=	esquirolii.
venosum	=	falconeri.
venustum	=	nudiflorum.
verticillata (Azalea)	=	arborescens.
vicarium	=	telmateium.
vicinum	=	dryophyllum.

villosum	=	trichanthum.
vittatum	=	simsii var. vittatum.
wadanum	=	reticulatum.
wallaceanum	=	imperfectly known, series Taliense.
warrenii	=	albiflorum var.
xanthinum	=	trichocladum.
xanthoneuron	=	denudatum.
xenosporum	=	detonsum forma.
yakumontanum	=	reticulatum.
yanthinum	=	concinnum.
yanthinum var.		
lepidanthum	=	concinnum.
yaragongense	=	ramosissimum.
yodogawa	=	yedoense.

Rhododendrons not in General Cultivation

Rhododendrons formerly included in the List of Rhododendrons in their Series but now omitted as they are not known to be in cultivation.

R. aberrans
R. admirabile
R. afganicum
R. agetum
R. aizoides
R. albiflorum
R. amandum
R. amundsenianum
R. annamense
R. anthopogonoides
R. argipeplum
R. asperulum
R. asterochnoum
R. atrorubrum
R. atrovirens
R. aureolum
R. bachii
R. bivelatum
R. boninense
R. bonvalotii
R. breviperulatum
R. bulu
R. calophyllum
R. calvescens
R. cardiobasis
R. cavaleriei
R. cerochitum
R. chawchiense
R. chengianum
R. chienianum
R. chunii
R. ciliipes
R. circinnatum
R. codonanthum
R. coeloneurum
R. comisteum
R. cruentum
R. dasycladoides
R. dealbatum
R. dekatanum

R. dendrocharis
R. denudatum
R. didymoides
R. dignabile
R. elegantulum
R. emarginatum
R. epapillatum
R. epipastum
R. erastum
R. esquirolii
R. euchroum
R. euonymifolium
R. excellens
R. faberoides
R. faithae
R. feddei
R. fokienense
R. formosanum
R. glanduliferum
R. glandulosum
R. hainanense
R. hancockii
R. henryi
R. hirsuticostatum
R. hongkongense
R. huianum
R. igneum
R. insculptum
R. invictum
R. kanehirai
R. kawakamii
R. kiyosumense
R. kwangtungense
R. lampropeplum
R. lasiostylum
R. latoucheae
R. leclerei
R. leiopodum
R. leptopeplum
R. leucobotrys

R. levinei
R. liliiflorum
R. lithophilum
R. longiperulatum
R. longipes
R. lucidum
R. ludwigianum
R. macrogemmum
R. magorianum
R. mayebarae
R. melleum
R. mengtszense
R. miniatum
R. minutiflorum
R. missionarum
R. monanthum
R. naamkwanense
R. nakotiltum
R. nankotaisanense
R. noriakianum
R. notatum
R. ochraceum
R. ombrochares
R. openshawianum
R. ovatosepalum
R. papillatum
R. persicinum
R. perulatum
R. petrocharis
R. pilicalyx
R. pingianum
R. platyphyllum
R. platypodum
R. pogonophyllum
R. polycladum
R. pomense
R. populare
R. porphyrophyllum
R. potanini
R. principis

R. pseudociliicalyx
R. purdomii
R. quadrasianum
R. radendum
R. redowskianum
R. rhodanthum
R. rockii
R. roseatum
R. rosmarinifolium
R. rubens
R. rufescens
R. rufohirtum
R. rufosquamosum
R. saisiuense

R. sanctum
R. sasakii
R. seniavinii
R. serpens
R. shimidzuanum
R. sino-falconeri
R. smilesii
R. spanotrichum
R. subnikomontanum
R. subsessile
R. taiense
R. tamurai
R. tashiroi

R. trichophlebium
R. trilectorum
R. tsaii
R. tsoi
R. tutcherae
R. vialii
R. vidalii
R. viscistylum
R. wattii
R. westlandii
R. windsori
R. wongii
R. youngae

COLLECTORS' NUMBERS

Rhododendrons in Cultivation in Great Britain and Ireland, collected by Forrest, Farrer, Kingdon-Ward, Yu on Professor Hu's expedition and the McLaren Rhododendrons; Rock, Ludlow and Sherriff; Ludlow, Sherriff and Taylor; Ludlow, Sherriff and Elliot; Ludlow, Sherriff and Hicks, Polunin; Lowndes; Polunin, Sykes and Williams; Stainton, Sykes and Williams.

Forrest Rhododendrons

1910 EXPEDITION

Burma-Yunnan, Teng-yueh, Shweli-Salween divide, Tali-Lichiang range

1912–14 EXPEDITION

Upper Burma and Yunnan, Chungtien plateau, Tali, Atuntze, Mekong-Salween divide

FORREST

12731	wardii
12845	leptothrium
12889	gymnogynum
12893	floccigerum
12899	ceraceum aff.
12901	glischrum
12934	saluenense
12942	megeratum
12944	crinigerum
12947	roxieanum
12948	fictolacteum
12950	dasycladum
12968	chameunum
12969	litiense
12982	dasycladum
13005	roxieanum
13023	praestans
10323	beesianum
13143	beesianum
13244	crinigerum
13258	chameunum
13259	forrestii var. repens

13299	floccigerum
13301	martinianum
13302	brachyanthum var. hypo-lepidotum
13303	campylogynum
13304	sanguineum
13315	wardii
13348	proteoides
13380	adroserum
13383	chameunum
13387	heptamerum
13438	heptamerum
13439	martinianum
13440	floccigerum
13508	eriogynum
13512	pachypodum. In cult. sulfereum
13518	campylogynum
13526	platyphyllum
13550	brachyanthum var. hypolepidotum
13568	beesianum

1917–19 EXPEDITION
N.E. Upper Burma, Yunnan/Szechwan/Tibet Frontiers

13768	drumonium
13789	detonsum
13791	hippophaeoides
13792	hippophaeoides
13793	hippophaeoides
13794	hippophaeoides
13798	racemosum. Pure white
13799	hippophaeoides
13800	hippophaeoides. Bright rose
13803	racemosum
13804	racemosum
13841	primulaeflorum
13842	hippophaeoides
13847	diacritum
13852	hylothreptum
13852	irroratum
13864	irroratum. Creamy-yellow, faintly flushed rose
13881	leptothrium
13896	lukiangense

13897	dasycladum
13899	scintillans
13900	chloranthum
13904	chameunum
13905	dasypetalum. In cult. at Headfort compactum
13915	russatum
13923	uvarifolium
13931	oreotrephes
13933	selense
13935	floccigerum
13936	erythrocalyx
13938	erythrocalyx
13947	chryseum
13949	martinianum. In cult. selense forma
13951a	erythrocalyx
13965	edgarianum. Deep purple-blue
13990	uvarifolium
13996	glischrum
14000	chryseum

FORREST NO.	
14911	crinigerum
14987	chaetomallum
14988	fulvum
15002	yunnanense
15004	augustinii var. chasmanthum
15018	dasycladum
15023	floccigerum
15035	lepidostylum
15038	aganniphum
15039	iodes
15043	tritifolium
15070	adenogynum
15071	brevistylum
15072	adenogynum
15076	impeditum
15077	primulaeflorum
15079	primulaeflorum
15080	primulaeflorum
15085	diacritum
15086	primulaeflorum
15087	trichostomum var. radinum
15088	primulaeflorum var. cephalanthoides
15091	polycladum
15092	primulaeflorum
15093	primulaeflorum
15095	eritimum
15096	trichostomum var. radinum
15097	irroratum
15102	delavayi
15103	scabrifolium
15120	diacritum
15123	traillianum
15124	beesianum
15126	primulaeflorum
15127	primulaeflorum
15128	adenophorum
15129	tatsienense aff.
15130	araliaeforme
15132	diacritum
15137	trichostomum var. radinum
15154	diacritum
15155	primulaeflorum
15159	tapetiforme
15164	adenophorum

FORREST NO.	
15165	euanthum
15166	primulaeflorum
15168	fictolacteum
15169	primulaeflorum
15171	adenophorum
15202	brevistylum
15203	mollicomum
15204	tatsienense
15206	racemosum
15210	drumonium
15216	uvarifolium
15218	cuneatum
15219	desquamatum aff.
15222	oreotrephes
15243	adenogynum
15245	primulaeflorum
15248	sp.
15249	polycladum aff.
15251	hippophaeoides
15257	sp. 2–3 ft. Bright rose
15259	trichostomum var. ledoides
15262	trichostomum var. ledoides
15263	tatsienense
15264	hippophaeoides
15265	hippophaeoides
15266	racemosum
15267	intricatum
15268	drumonium
15269	intricatum
15270	rupicola
15271	primulaeflorum
15278	fulvum
15293	eclecteum
15305	traillianum
15354	agglutinatum aff.
15356	tapetiforme. In cult. hippophaeoides
15367	rupicola
15370	drumonium
15386	drumonium
15391	rupicola
15392	complexum. Very pale purple, almost white
15399	primulaeflorum
15400	drumonium
15412	wardii
15414	dasycladum

FORREST

15415	agglutinatum aff.
15417	puralbum
15418	oreotrephes aff.
15427	cuneatum
15444	uvarifolium
15446	tatsienense
15448	ravum
15449	trichostomum var. radinum
15450	hippophaeoides
15452	trichostomum var. radinum
15459	hippophaeoides
15462	racemosum
15464	cuneatum
15465	oreotrephes aff.
15466	primulaeflorum
15467	drumonium
15468	diacritum
15487	brachyanthum
15497	balfourianum
15500	sp.
15504	scabrifolium
11515	sp.
15519	sp. 6–9 ft.
15520	cyanocarpum
15521	haematodes
15542	sp. 10–18 ft.
15545	sp.
15570	cyanocarpum var. eriphyllum
15575	dimitrum
15578	yunnanense
15579	jucundum
15581	rigidum
15582	sp. 10 ft. Creamy-yellow, flushed rose, marked crimson. In cult. at Tower Court, irroratum
15588	cyanocarpum
15589	sulfureum
15594	sulfureum
15606	sp.
15609	bureavii
15612	fastigiatum aff.
15613	fastigiatum aff.
15614	fastigiatum
15615	fastigiatum
15645	idoneum

15651	schistocalyx
15658	lophogynum
15659	sinogrande
15660	fulvum
15663	euchaites
15665	diphrocalyx
15667	supranubium aff.
15673	leptothrium
15688	zaleucum
15701	heliolepis vel aff.
15706	araiophyllum
15719	delavayi
15732	araiophyllum
15733	leptothrium
15734	laxiflorum
15736	leptothrium
15745	pennivenium
15756	s. Stamineum. 6–12 ft. White
15761	desquamatum
15764	basilicum
15766	cerochitum
15767	meddianum
15770	sulfureum
15774	megacalyx
15776	trichocladum vel aff.
15777	fulvum
15778	habrotrichum. White
15779	euchaites
15782	sulfureum
15791	diaprepes
15808	callimorphum
15815	griersonianum
15816	diaprepes
15887	crassum
15898	arizelum
15899	valentinianum
15908	campylogynum
15917	facetum
15932	apodectum
15933	heliolepis
15954	hardingii
15967	coryphaeum
15968	flavorufum var.
15969	balfourianum
15975	peramoenum
15977	fictolacteum
15998	nematocalyx aff.
16000	araiophyllum

FORREST NO.

16002	basilicum
16006	habrotrichum
16032	pachypodum
16084	stenaulum aff.
16128	hippophaeoides
16249	hypophaeum
16250	hemitrichotum
16252	chryseum
16257	scintillans
16277	litangense
16282	tapetiforme
16284	litangense
16287	orthocladum
16288	telmateium
16289	drumonium
16291	oreotrephes
16292	impeditum
16295	primulaeflorum var. cephalanthoides
16296	telmateium
16299	s. Lapponicum. 1½–2 ft. Rose-purple
16300	s. Lapponicum. 1–2 ins.
16301	eudoxum. 2–3 ft. Rose
16302	schizopeplum
16305	s. Lapponicum. 9–16 ins. Pale rose-purple
16306	primulaeflorum
16307	s. Lapponicum. 9–12 ins. Lavender-purple
16308	primulaeflorum
16311	trichostomum var. radinum
16312	primulaeflorum
16313	diacritum aff.
16314	globigerum
16315	adenophorum
16316	balfourianum var. aganniphoides
16318	selense
16319	agglutinatum
16320	mimetes
16321	wardii
16351	protistum
16352	leptopeplum
16353	adroserum
16354	eritimum
16355	leptothrium
16356	primulaeflorum

FORREST NO.

16360	augustinii var. chasmanthum
16361	coriaceum
16362	yunnanense
16363	cephalanthum
16364	coriaceum
16367	gymnanthum
16375	beesianum
16377	sphaeroblastum
16378	admirabile
16379	roxieanum
16380	traillianum aff.
16428	globigerum
16436	primulaeflorum
16439	agglutinatum
16449	chameunum
16450	edgarianum
16451	aganniphum var.
16455	adenophorum
16459	agglutinatum
16464	agglutinatum aff.
16464a	agglutinatum
16467	aiolopeplum
16469	globigerum
16472	glaucopeplum
16473	adenophorum
16474	beesianum
16477	roxieanum
16488	schizopeplum
16489	agglutinatum
16493	wardii
16508	roxieanum
16509	lampropeplum
16511	wardii
16531	uvarifolium
16533	floccigerum
16543	oreotrephes
16555	glischrum
16576	brevistylum
16577	s. Lapponicum. 4–6 ins. Purple-blue, throat white
16579	chryseum
16580	s. Lapponicum. 2 ft. Purplish-rose
16581	esetulosum
16583	achroanthum
16584	oreotrephes aff.

16591	eritimum aff.
16595	primulaeflorum var. cephalanthoides
16597	desquamatum
16598	tapetiforme aff.
16604	proteoides
16606	roxieanum
16609	proteoides
16616	roxieanum
16617	rupicola
16631	irroratum
16632	delavayi
16637	roxieanum
16643	adenophorum
16652	clementinae
· 16655	fictolacteum
16656	dryophyllum
16667	globigerum
16668	bathyphyllum
16673	dryophyllum
16677	aganniphum
16679	selense
16680	flavorufum
16681	chryseum
16683	beesianum
16684	selense
16687	gymnocarpum
16688	eritimum
16691	chaetomallum
16692	augustinii var. chasmanthum
16693	beesianum
16695	porphyrophyllum
16699	beesianum
16702	pothinum
16711	eudoxum
16713	heptamerum
16721	fulvum
16724	beesianum
16726	schizopeplum
16727	melleum
16728	himertum
16729	iodes
16734	dictyotum
16735	beesianum
16736	haemaleum
16739	saluenense
16742	dumosulum aff.
16743	beesianum

16745	iodes
16746	beesianum
16749	wardii
16750	s. Selense. 4–6 ft. Pure white, or very faintly flushed rose
16751	mesopolium
16752	iodes
16753	flavorufum
16754	agglutinatum aff.
16755	dictyotum
16760	schizopeplum
16764	flavorufum
16765	proteoides
16770	aganniphum
16771	flavorufum
16778	flavorufum
16779	iodes
16780	iodes
16790	yunnanense
16806	balfourianum aff.
16811	balfourianum
16816	hormophorum
16836	traillianum
17100	agglutinatum aff.
17110	sphaeroblastum
17165	trichostomum var. ledoides
17205	fictolacteum
17220	ciliicalyx
17227	dendricola
17330	chaetomallum
17333	phaeochrysum
17357	sphaeroblastum
17406	sinogrande
17407	beesianum
17447	iodes
17456	augustinii var. chasmanthum
17461	lukiangense
17463	lukiangense
17464	desquamatum
17466	flavorufum
17473	dryophyllum
17476	augustinii var. chasmanthum
17483	desquamatum
17495	gymnogynum
17501	lophogynum

FORREST NO.		FORREST NO.	
17539	ciliicalyx	18022	trichocladum
17551	diaprepes	18028	arizelum
17559	roseatum	18030	campylogynum
17560	apodectum	18036	meddianum
17572	crassum forma	18041	platyphyllum
17586	diaprepes	18042	zaleucum
17588	oleifolium	18044	callimorphum
17596	valentinianum	18045	arizelum
17610	facetum	18049	griersonianum
17616	facetum	18052	basilicum
17622	heliolepis	18054	sidereum
17626	euchaites	18069	habrotrichum
17636	fulvum	18108	basilicum
17637	schistocalyx	18153	apodectum
17650	basilicum	18167	apodectum
17651	callimorphum	18168	gymnogynum
17665	supranubium	18171	facetum
17678	basilicum	18173	crassum
17681	fulvum	18210	crassum aff.
17696	griersonianum	18273	facetum
17703	meddianum	18310	fulvum
17708	peramoenum	18329	genestierianum
17735	desquamatum	18349	s. Trichocladum. 2–2½ ft.
17738	supranubium	18355	pachypodum
17750	valentinianum	18393	protistum
17819	stenaulum	18394	protistum
17824	genestierianum	18395	kyawi
17827	heptamerum	18458	giganteum
17828	leptothrium	18475	stenaulum
17829	tanastylum	18548	protistum
17832	stenaulum	18686	melleum
17835	tanastylum	18900	oleifolium
17836	araiophyllum	18901	eclecteum
17851	agetum	18902	diaprepes
17852	facetum	18903	augustinii var. chasman-
17853	mallotum		thum
17854	fulvum	18904	yunnanense
17900	supranubium	18905	saluenense
17918	microphyton	18906	augustinii var. chasman-
17920	desquamatum		thum
17927	basilicum	18907	brevistylum
17928	kyawi	18908	s. Stamineum. 18–20 ft.
17930	peramoenum	18909	semilunatum
17937	zaleucum	18912	iodes
17943	gymnogynum	18914	coryphaeum
17950	euchaites	18917	chaetomallum
17963	valentinianum	18918	keleticum
17996	euchaites	18920	flavorufum
18000	yunnanense	18933	desquamatum

FORREST

FORREST NO.

18934 haemaleum
18937 mesopolium
18938 citriniflorum
18943 eclecteum var. brachy-
       andrum
19006 proteoides
19007 araliaeforme
19008 s.s. Sanguineum
19009 s.s. Sanguineum

FORREST NO.

19010 beesianum
19011 beesianum
19014 pholidotum
19015 rubiginosum
19019 selense
19154 proteoides
19165 proteoides
19169 cloiophorum
19193 araliaeforme

1921–22 EXPEDITION
N.W. Yunnan

19404 racemosum
19437 chameunum
19440 russatum
19450 scintillans
19458 russatum
19460 leptothrium
19467 litiense
19468 eritimum
19479 saluenense
19492 cephalanthum
19512 wardii
19515 forrestii var. repens
19540 martinianum
19541 brachyanthum var.
       hypolepidotum
19544 oreotrephes
19552 beesianum
19554 ceraceum
19555 fictolacteum
19562 roxieanum
19567 iodes
19569 roseotinctum
19570 megeratum
19574 triplonaevium
19597 stictophyllum
19607 chryseum
19674 tapetiforme
19695 desquamatum
19701 yunnanense
19704 tritifolium
19713 aganniphum
19714 agglutinatum
19716 aganniphum
19733 agglutinatum

19743 wardii
19744 aganniphum
19758 aganniphum
19769 floccigerum
19772 lukiangense
19773 aganniphum
19781 lukiangense
19783 agglutinatum
19793 dryophyllum
19798 dryophyllum
19814 augustinii var. chasman-
       thum
19819 ceraceum
19822 agglutinatum
19825 augustinii var. chasman-
       thum
19827 taliense
19828 aganniphum forma
19844 monanthum
19866 In cult. at R.B.G.
       chryseum
19869 stenaulum
19872 brachyanthum var. hypo-
       lepidotum
19911 chaetomallum
19912 rubrolineatum
19913 saluenense forma
19915 keleticum
19917 genestierianum
19919 radicans
19926 s. Selense. 5 ft.
19930 trichocladum
19952 eclecteum
19954 selense

19955	chaetomallum
19956	monanthum
19958	mesaeum
19959	chaetomallum
19960	glaphyrum
19977	pocophorum
19978	chaetomallum
19982	didymoides
19983	pocophorum
19993	In cult. chryseum
19994	aff. saluenense
20003	sperabiloides
20005	heliolepis
20008	ceraceum
20015	chaetomallum
20019	pocophorum
20020	fulvum
20021	xanthostephanum
20023	telopeum
20025	chaetomallum
20026	chaetomallum
20027	forrestii
20028	hemidartum
20062	cephalanthum
20063	augustinii var. chasman-thum
20064	augustinii var. chasman-thum
20067	oleifolium
20071	temenium ?
20073	vaccinioides
20075	fulvum
20078	catacosmum
20085	eritimum
20090	citriniflorum
20094	megacalyx
20095	desquamatum or rubi-ginosum
20106	protistum
20118	crassum
20120	arizelum
20176	yunnanense
20185	yunnanense
20196	primulaeflorum
20208	tapetiforme
20213	phaeochrysum
20215	chaetomallum
20218	citriniflorum ?

20220	didymum
20230	tephropeplum
20235	radicans
20239	didymum
20246	martinianum
20253	sanguineum ?
20255	keleticum
20262	habrotrichum
20286	flavorufum
20291	araliaeforme
20297	bainbridgeanum
20299	chaetomallum
20302	eclecteum var. brachy-andrum
20305	floccigerum aff.
20306	arizelum
20318	dryophyllum
20321	martinianum aff. In cult. floccigerum
20322	coryanum
20323	s.s. Haematodes. 3–4 ft.
20330	dryophyllum
20332	megeratum
20333	chaetomallum
20338	esetulosum
20347	phaeochrysum
20365	arizelum
20381	arizelum
20387	sinogrande
20388	sinonuttallii
20415	adenophorum
20416	sphaeroblastum
20418	dryophyllum
20419	mimetes
20425	roxieanum
20426	roxieanum
20428	mimetes var. simulans
20429	primulaeflorum
20430	yunnanense
20432	chryseum
20434	yunnanense
20440	sphaeroblastum
20442	dryophyllum
20444	adenophorum
20445	sphaeroblastum
20446	sphaeroblastum
20447	sphaeroblastum
20450	intricatum
20451	beesianum

21006	tatsienense
21009	sphaeroblastum
21010	sphaeroblastum
21011	aff. dryophyllum
21012	dryophyllum
21013	eclecteum
21017	litiense
21018	dryophyllum
21019	dryophyllum
21020	agglutinatum
21021	agglutinatum
21022	roxieanum
21027	rubiginosum
21030	cuneatum
21031	blepharocalyx
21036	leptothrium
21039	sphaeroblastum
21040	sphaeroblastum
21045	agglutinatum
21047	dryophyllum
21048	phaeochrysum
21049	roxieanum
21051	globigerum
21052	dryophyllum
21055	balfourianum var. aganniphoides
21056	balfourianum var. aganniphoides
21239	telmateium
21241	orthocladum
21248	hippophaeoides
21250	telmateium
21252	racemosum
21253	trichostomum var. radinum
21265	prostratum
21270	tatsienense
21274	orthocladum
21282	aff. tapetiforme
21287	dryophyllum
21288	orthocladum
21289	aff. diacritum. In cult. orthocladum
21292	elegantulum
21297	tapetiforme. In cult. at Headfort glomerulatum
21299	trichostomum var. radinum
21301	stictophyllum

21304	dasypetalum
21306	racemosum
21321	racemosum
21323	irroratum
21339	hemitrichotum
21344	intricatum
21348	rubiginosum
21351	racemosum
21358	yunnanense
21375	cuneatum
21377	telmateium
21390	beesianum
21400	dryophyllum
21405	sphaeroblastum
21408	roxieanum
21409	adenophorum
21410	adenophorum
21442	tatsienense
21462	hippophaeoides
21463	xanthostephanum
21470	augustinii var. chasmanthum
21475	irroratum
21476	hippophaeoides
21478	lukiangense
21483	scintillans
21487	scintillans
21488	racemosum
21490	russatum
21492	impeditum
21506	russatum
21507	russatum
21528	impeditum
21529	russatum
21531	floccigerum var. appropinquans
21532	fastigiatum
21533	rigidum
21539	fictolacteum
21546	roxieanum
21547	stictophyllum
21549	racemosum
21551	litiense
21559	scintillans
21560	racemosum
21563	dasycladum
21464	bullatum
21577	aff. idoneum
21581	fastigiatum

21582 crassum
21586 beesianum
21588 adenophorum
21680 sinonuttallii
21681 floccigerum
21682 lukiangense
21683 adroserum
21685 lukiangense
21686 eritimum
21687 eclecteum var. brachyandrum
21688 bainbridgeanum
21689 selense var. pagophilum
21690 ciliicalyx
21691 stenaulum aff.
21692 genestierianum
21693 coryanum
21694 eurysiphon
21695 martinianum
21696 megacalyx
21697 bainbridgeanum
21698 leptothrium
21699 trichocladum
21700 eritimum
21701 megeratum
21702 floccigerum
21703 floccigerum
21704 floccigerum
21705 sinogrande var.
boreale
21706 tephropeplum
21707 xanthostephanum
21708 eurysiphon forma
21709 hemidartum
21710 chaetomallum
21711 pocophorum
21712 pocophorum
21713 pocophorum. In cult. at
Headfort and Edin-
burgh hemidartum
21714 bullatum
21716 oleifolium
21718 forrestii var. repens
21720 pocophorum
21721 pocophorum
21723 chamae-thomsonii
21724 forrestii

21725 chaetomallum var.
xanthanthum
21727 catacosmum
21728 chaetomallum var.
hemigymnum
21729 chaetomallum var.
xanthanthum
21730 chaetomallum var.
xanthanthum
21731 chaetomallum var.
xanthanthum
21732 haemaleum
21733 glaphyrum
21734 pothinum
21735 mesaeum
21736 chaetomallum var.
hemigymnum
21737 mesopolium
21738 eudoxum
21739 cloiophorum
21740 mesaeum
21741 jucundum
21743 selense var. pagophilum
21744 eudoxum
21745 chaetomallum var.
xanthanthum
21746 didymoides
21747 roseotinctum
21748 roseotinctum
21750 didymum
21751 citriniflorum
21752 citriniflorum
21753 chaetomallum aff.
21754 horaeum
21755 telopeum
21756 keleticum
21757 keleticum
21758 chaetomallum var.
21759 chaetomallum
21760 saluenense
21761 bainbridgeanum
21762 bainbridgeanum
21763 stewartianum
21764 mesopolium
21765 didymoides
21766 bainbridgeanum
21767 eudoxum
21768 chamae-thomsonii var.
chamaethauma

21769	eclecteum aff.
21770	eclecteum var. bellatulum
21771	fictolacteum
21772	saluenense
21773	gymnogynum
21774	lukiangense
21775	martinianum var.
21776	chloranthum
21777	floccigerum var.
21778	xanthostephanum
21779	floccigerum
21780	floccigerum
21781	eurysiphon forma
21782	himertum
21783	roseotinctum
21784	s.s. Sanguineum 4–5 ft. Creamy-yellow
21785	chaetomallum var. xanthanthum
21786	forrestii
21787	eurysiphon forma
21809	pothinum
21810	fulvum
21811	micromeres
21812	glischrum
21813	glischrum
21814	fulvum
21815	fulvum
21816	uvarifolium
21817	uvarifolium
21818	coriaceum
21819	haemaleum
21821	bainbridgeanum. In cult. myiagrum
21822	oreotrephes aff.
21823	haemaleum
21824	sperabiloides
21825	monanthum
21826	chaetomallum var.
21827	eudoxum
21828	pocophorum
21829	bainbridgeanum
21830	coelicum
21831	chaetomallum
21832	bainbridgeanum
21833	bainbridgeanum
21834	bainbridgeanum
21835	oreotrephes
21836	telopeum

21837	chaetomallum var. hemigymnum
21837a	chaetomallum aff.
21838	eclecteum
21839	eclecteum var. bellatulum
21840	eclecteum var.
21841	stewartianum
21842	eclecteum var. brachyandrum
21843	coriaceum
21844	glaphyrum
21845	mesopolium
21846	chaetomallum var.
21848	chaetomallum var. xanthanthum
21849	chaetomallum var. xanthanthum
21850	horaeum
21851	horaeum
21852	aureolum
21853	chaetomallum var.
21854	aureolum
21855	horaeum
21856	roseotinctum
21857	chaetomallum
21858	chaetomallum
21860	aureolum
21861	arizelum
21862	arizelum
21863	arizelum
21864	arizelum
21865	arizelum
21866	arizelum
21867	arizelum
21868	arizelum
21869	arizelum
21870	semnoides
21871	arizelum
21872	chaetomallum
21873	chaetomallum
21874	selense var. probum aff.
21875	telopeum
21876	selense var. pagophilum
21877	vestitum
21878	selense var. probum
21879	selense var. probum aff.
21880	crinigerum
21881	eclecteum var. brachyandrum

FORREST

21882 eclecteum var. bellatu-
    lum
21884 eclecteum var. brachy-
    andrum
21885 stewartianum
21886 eclecteum
21887 eclecteum
21888 stewartianum
21889 stewartianum
21891 stewartianum
21892 erythrocalyx
21893 bainbridgeanum forma
21894 bainbridgeanum
21895 bainbridgeanum
21896 fulvum
21897 fulvum
21898 fulvum
21899 coriaceum
21900 chamae-thomsonii
21901 glaphyrum
21902 glaphyrum
21903 glaphyrum
21904 glaphyrum
21905 sanguineum var. Pale
    yellow
21906 chaetomallum var.
21907 haemaleum
21908 chaetomallum var.
    hemigymnum
21909 sanguineum var.
21910 s.s. Haematodes. 4 ft.
    Deep rose
21911 chaetomallum var.
21912 chaetomallum var.
21914 gilvum
21915 mesaeum
21916 chamae-thomsonii var.
    chamaethauma
21917 erythrocalyx
21918 stewartianum
21919 stewartianum
21923 cephalanthum

21932 russatum
21934 traillianum
21936 crassum
21944 bathyphyllum
21948 cuneatum
21954 litiense
21959 racemosum
21965 racemosum
21969 delavayi
21972 diacritum
21974 diacritum
21975 russatum
21977 lukiangense
21981 eritimum
21987 russatum
21988 orthocladum
21990 russatum
21995 russatum
22014 roxieanum
22019 erythrocalyx
22020 fictolacteum
22092 hemitrichotum
22108 scintillans
22187 roxieanum
22197 ravum. In cult. at Head-
    fort fimbriatum
22202 clementinae
22203 cuneatum
22295 russatum
22299 scintillans
22300 campylogynum
22320 trichostomum var.
    ledoides. In cult.
    primulaeflorum
22723 brachyanthum var.
    hypolepidotum
22853 eclecteum
22922 forrestii var. repens
22924 forrestii
22938 eurysiphon
22939 martinianum
22941 hemidartum

1924–25 EXPEDITION
N. Yunnan, Salween-Nmaikha and Salween-Mekong divide

FORREST NO.

24009	delavayi
24022	leptothrium
24060	tanastylum
24070	tanastylum
24071	leptothrium
24088	s. Azalea. 3–5 ft. Lilac-rose with crimson markings
24091	euchaites
24099	leptothrium
24101	zaleucum
24104	meddianum
24107	diphrocalyx
24110	fulvum
24113	apodectum
24116	griersonianum
24117	laxiflorum
24131	sulfureum
24138	valentinianum
24139	basilicum
24140	sinogrande
24144	vaccinioides
24149	pennivenium
24154	shweliense
24160	trichocladum
24193	arizelum
24201	facetum
24219	meddianum
24220	euchaites
24225	basilicum
24228	oleifolium
24229	sulfureum
24235	sulfureum
24283	ciliicalyx
24284	leptothrium
24305	apodectum
24308	supranubium
24312	tanastylum
24314	fulvum
24315	habrotrichum
24321	campylogynum
24331	apodectum
24347	valentinianum
24350	callimorphum
24496	crassum
24528	stewartianum

FORREST NO.

24529	trichocladum
24530	stewartianum
24532	scyphocalyx
24535	desquamatum
24542	kyawi
24544	scyphocalyx
24546	scyphocalyx
24562	zaleucum
24563	sidereum
24570	campylogynum var. myrtilloides
24571	cephalanthum
24572	calostrotum
24574	s. Lapponicum. 4–8 ins. Deep plum-purple
24575	mekongense. 3–4 ft. Deep greenish-orange
24577	s. Heliolepis. 8–14 ft. Rose
24587	campylogynum var. myrtilloides
24592	facetum
24598	stewartianum
24600	heptamerum
24603	scyphocalyx
24616	herpesticum
24618	yunnanense
24620	herpesticum
24633	lepidostylum
24660	hylaeum
24680	agapetum
24683	scyphocalyx
24688	megacalyx
24712	apodectum
24728	apodectum
24729	megacalyx
24730	crassum
24739	facetum
24740	arizelum
24742	sidereum
24747	crassum aff.
24748	facetum aff.
24774	taronense
24775	protistum
24831	genestierianum
25011	calostrotum

25020	fulvum
25064	preptum
25065	scyphocalyx
25067	mallotum
25076	fulvum
25090	sidereum
25100	basilicum
25340	sulfureum
25446	ciliicalyx. In cult. chrysodoron
25447	sperabile var. weihsiense
25448	leptothrium
25449	desquamatum
25458	leptothrium
25474	floccigerum
25477	s. Azalea. molle at Exbury
25481	sperabile var. weihsiense
25483	fulvum
25494	wardii
25496	russatum
25498	scintillans. In cult. dasycladum
25500	russatum
25503	calostrotum
25505	roxieanum
25506	calostrotum
25507	consanguineum
25508	chameunum
25509	chloranthum
25512	fictolacteum
25513	beesianum
25514	roxieanum
25515	roxieanum
25516	beesianum
25518	sanguineum
25520	glaucopeplum var.
25521	cloiophorum
25524	forrestii var. repens
25526	hippophaeoides
25529	achroanthum
25532	achroanthum
25534	wardii
25535	dasycladum
25542	calostrotum
25543	sanguineum
25553	russatum
25555	scintillans aff.
25560	chameunum
25563	aperantum var.

25564	horaeum
25565	chaetomallum var. xanthanthum
25569	sperabile var. weihsiense
25570	charitopes
25572	tephropeplum
25574	crassum
25575	brachyanthum var. hypolepidotum
25576	zaleucum aff.
25577	septentrionale
25578	chaetomallum var.
25579	herpesticum
25580	dumicola
25581	charitopes
25583	lacteum var.
25584	kyawi
25585	crinigerum var. euadenium
25586	crassum
25588	micromeres
25589	lacteum var.
25593	s.s. Selense. 6–8 ft. Creamy-white with a faint blotch. In cult. caloxanthum
25597	chaetomallum var.
25601	chaetomallum
25602	chaetomallum
25603	eclecteum
25604	eclecteum var. brachyandrum
25605	chaetomallum var. hemigymnum
25606	s. Triflorum. 3 ft. White flushed rose
25607	chaetomallum var. glaucescens
25608	arizelum
25609	s. Triflorum. 3 ft. Shaded from pale rose to rose-crimson at base
25610	glischrum
25611	s. Triflorum. White base flushed purplish-rose
25612	micromeres
25614	martinianum. In cult. at Headfort temenium

25615	stewartianum
25616	glischrum
25617	monanthum
25618	stewartianum
25619	crinigerum var. euadenium
25620	stewartianum
25622	coriaceum
25624	sinonuttallii
25625	coelicum
25627	arizelum
25629	crassum
25630	coriaceum
25631	sulfureum
25633	crinigerum var. euadenium
25634	crinigerum var. euadenium
25636	s.s. Selense. 4 ft. Pure white
25638	s. Azalea. 3 ft. White flushed rose
25639	s. Falconeri. 10–20 ft. Clear yellow with a very slight crimson blotch
25640	floccigerum
25641	crinigerum
25642	stewartianum
25643	ciliicalyx
25644	tephropeplum
25645	rude
25646	stewartianum
25647	coelicum
25679	sinogrande
25683	calostrotum
25684	giganteum
25688	vaccinioides
25697	flavorufum
25701	proteoides
25705	clementinae
25707	diacritum
25714	tephropeplum
25716	coryphaeum
25717	coryphaeum
25718	roxieanum
25719	fictolacteum
25725	glischrum
25737	dasycladum

25738	globigerum
25739	bathyphyllum
25740	traillianum
25742	clementinae
25744	fulvum
25749	roxieanum
25818	crinigerum var. euadenium
25831	floccigerum
25840	chaetomallum var. xanthanthum
25849	s. Stamineum
25865	taggianum
25872	coriaceum
25901	citriniflorum
25907	achroanthum
25914	augustinii var. rubrum
25915	triplonaevium
25944	fulvum
25958	fulvum
25959	arizelum
25981	hippophaeoides
25984	heptamerum. In cult. at Muncaster irroratum
25987	roxieanum
26022	s. Stamineum
26023	tanastylum
26024	simsii
26025	s. Azalea
26027	simsii var.
26040	tanastylum
26043	basilicum
26044	s. Trichocladum
26045	eriogynum
26046	euchaites
26047	stenaulum
26048	griersonianum
26065	oleifolium
26066	peramoenum
26068	crassum
26071	eriogynum
26078	pennivenium
26091	megacalyx
26092	sinogrande
26093	ciliicalyx
26109	crassum
26110	ciliicalyx
26111	vaccinioides
26113	sulfureum

FORREST NO.	
26120	crassum
26122	ciliicalyx
26145	ciliicalyx
26157	delavayi
26240 ?	leptothrium
26316	protistum
26418	stenaulum
26419	genestierianum
26421	araiophyllum
26422	sulfureum
26423	bullatum
26424	tanastylum
26425	glischroides var. arachnoideum. 4 ft.
26426	glischroides
26427	tanastylum
26428	glischroides
26429	protistum
26430	heptamerum
26431	tephropeplum
26432	heptamerum
26433	heptamerum
26434	sperabile
26435	sperabile
26436	heptamerum
26437	tanastylum
26438	araiophyllum
26439	tephropeplum
26440	taggianum
26441	taronense
26442	sperabile
26443	heptamerum
26444	ciliicalyx
26445	araiophyllum
26446	sperabile
26447	sulfureum
26448	glischroides
26449	euchaites
26450	s. Azalea. 6–7 ft. Dark purple-crimson
26452	heptamerum
26453	sperabile
26454	heptamerum
26455	glischroides
26456	sinogrande
26457	tephropeplum
26458	sidereum
26459	dendricola. In cult. at Headfort taronense

FORREST NO.	
26460	s. Azalea. 4 ft. Pale rose
26461	ciliicalyx
26462	taronense
26463	yunnanense
26464	ciliicalyx
26465	sperabile
26466	delavayi
26472	ciliicalyx
26473	brachyanthum var. hypolepidotum
26474	s. Triflorum. 10–15 ft. Pale rose
26475	delavayi
26476	meddianum var. atrokermesinum
26477	pennivenium
26478	sperabile var. weihsiense
26480	heptamerum
26481	araiophyllum
26482	desquamatum
26483	araiophyllum
26484	tanastylum
26486	yunnanense
26487	euchaites
26488	desquamatum
26489	tanastylum
26490	araiophyllum
26491	araiophyllum
26492	araiophyllum
26494	araiophyllum
26495	meddianum var. atrokermesinum
26499	meddianum var. atrokermesinum
26507	leptothrium
26528	araiophyllum
26596	yunnanense
26597	leptothrium
26615	ciliicalyx
26618	bullatum
26629	habrotrichum
26632	habrotrichum
26633	sidereum
26636	micromeres
26791	sidereum
26792	araiophyllum
26797	araiophyllum
26798	caesium
26921	stewartianum

FORREST NO.		FORREST NO.	
26922	basilicum	27050	herpesticum
26923	crassum	27051	herpesticum
26924	scyphocalyx forma	27052	herpesticum
26925	aperantum	27054	scyphocalyx
26926	aperantum	27057	scyphocalyx
26927	scyphocalyx	27059	scyphocalyx
26928	oporinum	27061	herpesticum
26929	stewartianum	27063	herpesticum
26930	aperantum	27065	calostrotum
26931	aperantum	27067	arizelum
26932	stewartianum	27069	facetum
26933	aperantum	27071	herpesticum
26934	aperantum	27073	aperantum
26935	arizelum	27075	aperantum
26936	aperantum	27077	aperantum
26937	aperantum	27079	aperantum
26938	aperantum	27081	aperantum
26961	heliolepis	27083	aperantum
26962	stewartianum	27085	glischrum
26963	herpesticum	27087	vaccinioides
26964	aperantum	27089	herpesticum
26964a	aperantum	27093	herpesticum
26965	herpesticum	27095	herpesticum
26966	herpesticum	27097	herpesticum
26974	herpesticum	27099	herpesticum
26977	herpesticum	27101	megacalyx
26978	scyphocalyx	27103	zaleucum
26980	stewartianum	27105	facetum
26981	stewartianum	27108	arizelum
26984	stewartianum	27109	ciliicalyx
26985	caloxanthum	27110	crassum
26986	stewartianum	27111	aperantum
26987	achroanthum	27113	herpesticum
26988	campylogynum var. myrtilloides	27115	scyphocalyx
		27116	herpesticum
26991	campylogynum var. myrtilloides	27117	trichocladum
		27118	campylogynum var. myrtilloides
26992	stewartianum		
26993	stewartianum	27119	achroanthum
27002	aperantum	27121	calostrotum
27003	herpesticum	27122	cephalanthum
27011	scyphocalyx	27123	caloxanthum
27012	herpesticum	27125	caloxanthum
27013	stewartianum	27126	kyawi
27018	scyphocalyx	27128	kyawi
27019	scyphocalyx	27129	stewartianum
27020	aperantum	27131	stewartianum
27022	aperantum	27132	scyphocalyx
27025	aperantum	27133	stewartianum

27134	scyphocalyx		27706	laxiflorum aff.
27135	stewartianum		27713	laxiflorum aff. In cult.
27136	stewartianum			facetum
27137	scyphocalyx		27714	tanastylum
27138	stewartianum		27715	valentinianum
27140	scyphocalyx		27717	delavayi
27142	myiagrum		27718	delavayi
27143	stewartianum		27724	crassum
27144	stewartianum		27725	ciliicalyx
27250	kyawi		27727	diaprepes
27343	habrotrichum		27731	supranubium aff.
27355	giganteum		27737	taronense
27357	campylogynum var.		27744	araiophyllum
	myrtilloides		27745	yunnanense
27358	euchaites		27746	araiophyllum
27359	apodectum		27757	tanastylum
27389	callimorphum		27758	genestierianum
27413	basilicum		27759	ciliicalyx
27415	hardingii		27766	araiophyllum
27416	laxiflorum		27768	delavayi
27685	dendricola		27769	bullatum
27687	taronense		27771	araiophyllum
27697	delavayi		27775	araiophyllum
27701	peramoenum		27776	crassum
27703	laxiflorum aff.		27792	arizelum
27705	laxiflorum aff.		27794	arizelum

1930–31 EXPEDITION

N. Yunnan and S.W. Szechwan

28236	desquamatum		28311	crassum
28237	flavorufum		28312	crassum
28241	platyphyllum		28315	decorum forma
28248	lacteum		28319	crassum
28250	trichocladum		28323	adenogynum
28254	campylogynum. In cult.		28326	s. Triflorum
	at R.B.G. russatum		28342	lepidotum
28266	brachyanthum		28343	s. Lapponicum
28283	dichroanthum?		28344	s. Lapponicum
28290	dichroanthum		28347	s. Maddenii
28295	racemosum		28348	dichroanthum?
28297	rigidum		28351	haematodes
28301	neriiflorum forma		28353	flavorufum
28302	cephalanthum		28355	globigerum forma
28304	irroratum forma		28357	flavorufum
28305	bullatum		29130	globigerum

FORREST NO.		FORREST NO.	
29131	s. Lacteum	29322	wardii
29132	globigerum	29323	rigidum
29242	litiense	29325	dryophyllum
29243	dryophyllum	29326	sphaeroblastum
29244	adenogynum	29327	dryophyllum
29245	sphaeroblastum	29328	sphaeroblastum
29246	sphaeroblastum	29329	sphaeroblastum
29247	beesianum	29331	siderophyllum
29248	hemitrichotum	29333	sphaeroblastum
29249	chryseum	29341	balfourianum
29250	trichostomum var. radinum	29545	euchaites
		29559	ciliicalyx
29251	s. Lapponicum	29588	habrotrichum
29252	phaeochrysum	29647	myiagrum
29253	dryophyllum	29655	tephropeplum
29254	dryophyllum	29663	stewartianum
29256	adenophorum	29666	saluenense
29257	roxieanum	29685	stewartianum
29258	sphaeroblastum	29687	yunnanense
29259	glomerulatum	29762	griersonianum
29260	glomerulatum	29763	facetum
29262	sphaeroblastum	29785	arizelum
29263	balfourianum var. aganniphoides	29809	megacalyx
		29894	achroanthum
29264	balfourianum var. aganniphoides	29926	facetum
		29929	kyawi
29266	s. Lapponicum	29937	s. Campylogynum
29267	primulaeflorum var. cephalanthoides	29938	aperantum
		30375	facetum
29268	glomerulatum	30392	griersonianum
29269	telmateium	30393	bullatum
29271	trichostomum var. radinum	30394	scyphocalyx
		30395	s. Lapponicum
29273	hemitrichotum	30526	beesianum
29278	balfourianum var. aganniphoides	30527	s. Trichocladum
		30528	basilicum
29280	balfourianum var. aganniphoides	30531	traillianum
		3053	beesianum
29281	mimetes var. simulans	30533	stewartianum
29282	balfourianum var. aganniphoides	30534	aperantum
		30535	haematodes
29283	primulaeflorum	30536	aperantum
29305	litiense	30539	chaetomallum
29312	adenophorum	30540	saluenense forma
29313	adenophorum	30543	prostratum
29314	adenophorum	30880	pronum
29317	roxieanum	30883	s. Campylogynum
29320	sphaeroblastum	30887	decorum
29321	sphaeroblastum	30888	adenophorum

FORREST

————

Farrer Rhododendrons

1914–15 EXPEDITION
Kansu

FARRER NO.

| 63 | reginaldii (geog. form of oreodoxa) |

FARRER NO.

| 79 | invictum |
| 119 | violaceum |

1919 EXPEDITION
Upper Burma

801	stenaulum
811	araiophyllum
812	tanastylum
813	sulfureum
814	heptamerum
815	mallotum
842	bullatum
848	supranubium
863	arizelum
872	sidereum
873	basilicum
874	fulvum
875	desquamatum
876	oulotrichum
877	phoenicodum
878	heliolepis
887	glischrum
888	sperabile

891	zaleucum
918	megacalyx
926	stewartianum
937	caloxanthum
959	sinogrande
979	decorum
980	zaleucum
1022	facetum
1024	scyphocalyx
1044	crassum
1045	calostrotum
1046	campylogynum var. myrtilloides
1046a	campylogynum var. myrtilloides
1047	achroanthum
1065	heliolepis
1444	kyawi

Kingdon-Ward Rhododendrons

1913 EXPEDITION

N. Yunnan, and Tibet Frontiers

K.W. NO.
260 davidsonianum
406 melinanthum
529 wardii

K.W. NO.
768 aganniphum
793 campylogynum

1919 EXPEDITION

N.E. Upper Burma

3038 bullatum
3039 s. Triflorum. 10–15 ft.
  Pinkish-purple
3040 euchaites
3042 glischrum. In cult. probably habrotrichum
3061 sidereum
3095 megeratum
3096 stewartianum
3097 trichocladum
3101 arizelum
3155 hylaeum and/or gymnogynum
3172 campylogynum var.
  myrtilloides
3248 crassum
3267 euchroum. In cult. herpesticum

3299 s. Triflorum. 8 ft. Bright
  purple
3300 stewartianum
3301 aperantum
3302 brachyanthum var. hypolepidotum
3303 campylogynum var.
  myrtilloides
3304 achroanthum
3305 lithophilum
3365 cephalanthum
3390 keleticum
3391 campylogynum
3392 herpesticum
3408 callimorphum
3721 callimorphum. In cult.
  caloxanthum ?

1921 EXPEDITION

N.E. Yunnan, Yunnan-Szechwan Borders

3776 pachypodum
3784 delavayi
3805 decorum
3948 delavayi
3952 racemosum
3952a mollicomum. In cult.
  pubescens
3953 pubescens
3998 trichostomum var.
  radinum

4023 chryseum
4050 hemitrichotum
4102 telmateium
4160 primulaeflorum
4170 wardii
4177 balfourianum var. aganniphoides
4184 intricatum
4185 sphaeroblastum
4207 roxieanum

K.W. NO.			K.W. NO.	
4211	beesianum		4583	lepidotum. In cult. race-mosum ?
4268	telmateium		4733	telmateium
4308	desquamatum		4843	phaeochrysum
4309	oreotrephes		4860	traillianum
4322	yunnanense		4974	yunnanense
4410	puralbum. In cult. also wardii		4994	hemitrichotum
4456	lysolepis		4995	uvarifolium
4458	wardii aff.		5001	scabrifolium
4465	trichostomum		5002	decorum. In cult. irroratum
4486	ravum. On limestone			
4487	decorum		5004	scabrifolium
4509	fictolacteum		5005	irroratum

1922 EXPEDITION

Yunnan-Szechwan-Tibet and N.E. Burma

5384	primulaeflorum		5440	seinghkuense
5385	ravum		5445	facetum or agapetum
5405	vernicosum		5446	xanthostephanum
5409	agglutinatum		5447	taronense
5414	selense aff.		5448	crassum
5415	heptamerum		5449	taronense
5416	sanguineum		5457	s. Thomsonii. 6–12 ft.
5417	forrestii var. repens		5458	Tree of 12–25 ft.
5418	sinogrande		5458a	Mixed seed of alpines
5421	oleifolium		5466	sinonuttallii
5425	stenaulum		5469	agapetum
5427	crinigerum		5480	neriiflorum
5428	rubiginosum		5481	brachyanthum var. hypolepidotum
5430	keleticum			
5431	chaetomallum		5482	nitens
5432	sanguineum. In cult. didymum		5483	phaedropum
			5484	pocophorum
5433	sanguineum ?		5485	sidereum
5434	martinianum		5487	dichroanthum ?
5435	temenium		5489	melinanthum
5436	saluenense		5490	s. Fortunei ? or s. Irroratum. 3–5 ft.
5437	brachyanthum var. hypolepidotum			
			5508	indicum forma
5438	arizelum		5533	agapetum
5438a	arizelum		5545	vaccinioides
5438b	s.s. Heliolepis		5602	oreotrephes
5439	bullatum			

1924–25 EXPEDITION

Tibet and Bhutan

K.W. NO.

5656 vellereum
5659 hirtipes
5660 uvarifolium
5687 ⎰ triflorum var.
5687a ⎱ mahogani
5700 kongboense
5718 calvescens. In cult. at Borde Hill melinanthum, Tower Court telopeum
5729 paludosum
5732 eclecteum var. brachyandrum aff. At Exbury wardii ?
5733 laudandum
5734 fragariflorum
5735 s. Lapponicum. 1–3 ft. Purple
5736 wardii
5756 s. Thomsonii, Seed mixed. In cult. at R.B.G. wardii
5759 agglutinatum
5777 paludosum
5778 paludosum
5790 oreotrephes
5792 paludosum
5828 calostrotum
5829 viridescens
5830 cerasinum. Brilliant scarlet, five coal-black glands at base
5842 campylogynum
5843 tsangpoense var. curvistylum
5844 tsangpoense
5844a tsangpoense
5845 chamae-thomsonii var. chamaethauma
5846 forrestii var. repens
5847 chamae-thomsonii var. chamaethauma
5848 laudandum var. temoense
5849 cephalanthum aff.
5850 kongboense

K.W. NO.

5851 mekongense
5853 campylocarpum
5856 pumilum
5861 s. Sanguineum. 2 ft.
5862 paludosum. In cult. at Exbury, pumilum
5863 doshongense
5874 concatenans
5875 parmulatum
5876 uniflorum
5877 arizelum
5878 temenium
5879 ⎰ eudoxum aff. Seed probably mixed together
5880 ⎱ with 5875
5911 sp.
5940 lepidotum
5953 sp.
5971 roxieanum aff. In cult. at Muncaster, near calvescens
5994 lepidotum
6020 kongboense
6021 kongboense
6026 xanthocodon
6069 virgatum. Also lepidotum in cult.
6079 sp.
6215 campanulatum var.
6223 hirtipes
6229 campylocarpum
6250 megeratum. In cult. at Exbury, baileyi
6251 micromeres
6256 glischrum
6257 ⎰ keysii var. unicolor.
6257a ⎱ Contains also a good Trichocladum (melinanthum aff.)
6258 lanigerum
6261 sinogrande
6261a sinogrande
6263 triflorum var. mahogani
6273 leucaspis
6275 s. Triflorum. 15–20 ft.

K.W. NO.

6276	maddenii. In cult. brachysiphon	
6278	auritum	
6279	oleifolium	
6281	glischrum	
6283	vaccinioides	
6284	ramsdenianum	
6285	venator	
6286	megacalyx	
6291	leucaspis	
6301	pemakoense	
6303	tephropeplum	
6304	s. Edgeworthii. 8–12 ft.	
6307	sp. 10–15 ft.	
6310	headfortianum	

K.W. NO.

6311	coryanum var.
6313	flavantherum
6325	scopulorum
6330	s. Ovatum. 12–18 ins.
6333	nuttallii var.
6335	s. Ovatum. 10–15 ft.
6354	scopulorum
6401	hylaeum
6403	arboreum
6409	s. Triflorum. 5–10 ft.
6411	s. Lepidotum
6413	polyandrum
6414	s. Stamineum. 13–35 ft.
6415	rhabdotum

1926 EXPEDITION

Burma and Assam

6735	insculptum
6736	maddenii
6751	xanthostephanum
6753	sidereum. In cult. sino-grande
6782	sinogrande
6792	sidereum
6793	seinghkuense. In cult. bullatum and seinghkuense
6794	tephropeplum
6795	martinianum
6805	beanianum
6806	trichocladum
6807	bullatum
6809	taggianum
6818	arizelum
6819	megeratum
6829	beanianum
6831	consanguineum
6832	forrestii var. repens
6833	hylaeum
6834	tephropeplum
6848	micromeres
6854	euchaites
6855	exasperatum
6856	vesiculiferum

6868	telopeum
6869	eclecteum var.
6884	imperator
6900	eclecteum var.
6903	calostrotum
6914	cephalanthum
6921	eclecteum
6923	cerasinum. Creamy-white with broad cherry-red band round the summit or cherry-red all through
6924	tsangpoense var. pruniflorum
6930	campylocarpum
6935	forrestii var. repens. Bright pink or pinkish-purple
6936	eclecteum var.
6945	sanguineum var.
6953	beesianum
6954	dryophyllum
6955	sanguineum
6960	luridum, Ward MS. 1 ft. Violet
6961	pumilum
6962	myiagrum

K.W. NO.

6967 cephalanthum var. crebre-florum

6984 calostrotum var. calciphilum

6991 horaeum

7012 saluenense

7023 anthopogon

7038 brachyanthum var. hypolepidotum

7046 brachyanthum var. hypolepidotum

7048 luridum, Ward MS. 1–2 ft. Dark purple-magenta

7058 paludosum

7061 calostrotum. Dwarf form

7062 calostrotum. Late flowering form

7084 s. Lapponicum

7090 s.s. Sanguineum

7108 brevistylum

7121 triflorum

7122 uvarifolium

7123 crinigerum

7124 sperabile

7125 s. Thomsonii. 40–60 ft.

K.W. NO.

7136 manipurense

7137 bullatum

7138 virgatum

7139 megacalyx

7140 arboreum

7171 leucaspis

7184 recurvoides

7187 s. Anthopogon. 1 ft.

7188 tsangpoense var. pruniflorum

7189 dasycladum

7190 setiferum

7196 s. Souliei. Snow white, basal purple flash

7229 lepidotum

7259 s. Maddenii. 10–15 ft.

7426 tanastylum

7427 protistum

7428 nuttallii

7455 chrysolepis

7523 calostrotum var. calciphilum

7606 s. Maddenii

7612 martinianum

7625 tanastylum

7630 notatum

7642 sinogrande

1927–28 EXPEDITION

Assam and Mishmi Hills

7701 formosum

7717 inaequale. Small bush

7723 manipurense

7724 macabeanum

7725 elliottii

7731 bauhiniiflorum. Pale purplish-pink

7732 johnstoneanum

7968 arboreum

7969 stenaulum ?

8016 dendricola

8044 tanastylum

8054 griffithianum

8052 bullatum

8069 protistum aff.

8081 vaccinioides

8101 xanthostephanum

8112 euchaites

8113 mishmiense

8122 = 8112 euchaites

8130 sinogrande

8163 arizelum

8164 crinigerum

8165 tephropeplum

8203 eclecteum aff.

8205 megacalyx. 9,000 ft. Possibly hardier than the type

K.W. NO.

8206	bullatum
8208	cinnabarinum var. roylei. Flame coloured
8221	kasoense
8225	megeratum
8227	concinnoides
8229	calostrotum
8238	hookeri. Purple
8239	cinnabarinum var. roylei. Flame coloured tawny-orange, salmon
8250	exasperatum
8251	lanigerum
8254	beanianum
8255	smithii
8256	campylocarpum
8257	tsangpoense var. pruniflorum
8258	cerasinum
8259	trichocladum
8260	patulum

K.W. NO.

8288	lanatum
8289	pocophorum
8293	sanguineum
8294	stewartianum forma
8300	fulvum
8326	micromeres
8337	cephalanthum var. crebreflorum
8341	forrestii var. repens
8362	s.s. Sanguineum
8400	manipurense
8415	tsangpoense var. pruniflorum
8431	s. Barbatum
8521	phaedropum. 1 ft.
8522	kasoense
8545	manipurense
8546	headfortianum
8591	virgatum
8592	mishmiense

1931 EXPEDITION

N.E. Upper Burma and Tibetan Frontier

9130	s. Maddenii. White
9170	formosanum
9195	s. Irroratum. Probably crimson
9200	magnificum
9210	vaccinioides
9220	taggianum
9221 (=9371)	chrysodoron
9236	tanastylum
9250	xanthostephanum
9252	s. Maddenii
9254 (=9543)	seinghkuense
9258	vesiculiferum
9260	arizelum
9261	megacalyx
9263	s. Neriiflorum
9273	manipurense ?
9274	nuttallii
9275	stenaulum
9293	s. Neriiflorum
9301	magnificum
9321 (=9506)	neriiflorum

9322	hylaeum
9360	s. Maddenii
9361	formosum
9371	chrysodoron
9382	neriiflorum
9383 (=9492)	campylogynum
9385	sinogrande ?
9394	calostrotum
9397	arizelum
9399	vaccinioides
9400	xanthostephanum
9402 (=9220)	taggianum
9403 (=9361)	formosum
9405 (=9210)	insculptum
9413	martinianum
9414	campylogynum
9415 (=9490)	genestierianum
9416	tephropeplum
9440	vaccinioides
9466	sinonuttallii
9478	kasoense
9479	uvarifolium

K.W. NO.

9483	neriiflorum
9485	vesiculiferum
9490	genestierianum
9492	s. Thomsonii. Dark cerise
9500	selense
9503	crinigerum
9504	bullatum
9505	oreotrephes
9506	neriiflorum
9509	oreotrephes
9517	calostrotum var. calciphilum
9519	trichocladum
9529	oleifolium
9543	seinghkuense
9544	arizelum
9561	(=9483) neriiflorum
9565	tephropeplum
9567	xanthostephanum
9569	megeratum
9584	manipurense
9591	cephalanthum var. crebreflorum
9601	beesianum
9608	chaetomallum
9609	chryseum
9620	trichocladum
9621	selense
9629	forrestii var. repens
9633	saluenense
9634	eclecteum
9635	forrestii var. repens f. Pinkish-carmine
9636	chryseum forma. Crushed strawberry, salmon-pink, apricot
9637	chaetomallum
9641	cephalanthum

K.W. NO.

9665	sp. or hybrid? Probably scarlet
9704	brachyanthum var. hypolepidotum
9710	chryseum
9717	calostrotum var. calciphilum
9726	vesiculiferum
9735	tsangpoense var. pruniflorum
9790	campylogynum
9795	praestans
9800	lepidotum
9810	campylogynum
9815	campylogynum
9816	forrestii var. repens. Sulphur coloured
9909	chryseum
10005	s. Lapponicum. Pale purple
10012	s. Lacteum
10020	heliolepis
10121	s. Campylogynum
10129	micromeres
10134	s.s. Haematodes. 15–20 ft.
10136	rubrantherum
10139	s. glaucophyllum
10140	campylogynum
10141	vaccinioides
10142	boothii
10159	eclecteum
10160	s. Thomsonii
10161	s.s. Souliei
10175	s. Maddenii, taronense? White with yellow flame
10180	dendricola
10231	simsii

1933 EXPEDITION

Assam and Upper Burma

10351	virgatum
10379	bullatum
10401b	tephropeplum?

10490	trichocladum
10496	sanguineum
10497	beesianum

K.W. NO.		K.W. NO.	
10498	fulvum	10929	bullatum
10498a	uvarifolium?	10950	tanastylum
10500	tsangpoense var. pruniflorum?	10950a	tanastylum
		10951	s. Thomsonii
10521	s. Lapponicum. Violet to lavender	10952	vesiculiferum
		10959	s. Barbatum? 15–20 ft.
10530	s. Thomsonii. s.s. Selense. Buds carmine. Primrose, sometimes flushed	10969	s. Anthopogon. Probably pink
		10970	s.s. Selense
		10971	roylei var.? triflorum?
10531	s. Lapponicum. Purple	11002	s. Neriiflorum. Crimson or scarlet
10532	calostrotum		
10533	s. Lapponicum. Deep purple	11004	s. Heliolepis
		11011	cerasinum?
10541	s. Anthopogon. Height 1–2 ft. Pink	11012	s. Anthopogon
		11016	s. Lapponicum
10542	s. Anthopogon (cephalanthum var. crebreflorum?) Delicately pink	11029	xanthostephanum
		11035	s. Neriiflorum? (sp. nov.?) Crimson and spotted
10579	dryophyllum?		
10582	s. Saluenense. Bright purple	11040	beanianum var. compactium
		11043	cerasinum?
10595	s. Lapponicum. Purple	11050	s.s. Sanguineum
10700	s. Taliense	11052	kasoense. Yellow
10830	s. Thomsonii. 10–15 ft.	11055	s. Maddenii
10832	beesianum	11057	dendricola? Probably white
10841	lepidotum		
10842	s. Anthopogon	11060	s. Grande. Apparently purple
10870	campylogynum		
10928	manipurense		

1935 EXPEDITION

Tibet, Assam-Himalaya Frontier Tract

11175	macabeanum	11640	hodgsonii. Cherry red
11378	pankimense	11915	trichocladum var. longipilosum
11464	megeratum. Cream		
11532	manipurense	11964	circinnatum
11565	glaucophyllum	12404	lanatum var.? Delicate pink
11568	concatenans		
11569	anthopogon	12414	boothii
11586	phaeochrysum	12438	sp. nov.?
11587	fulgens	12585	formosum?
11588	wightii	12588	bauhiniiflorum? Purple?
11605	argipeplum	12589	maddenii?
11612	wallichii		

8

1937 EXPEDITION

N.E. Upper Burma and Tibet

K.W. NO.

13006	tephropeplum
13017	martinianum
13020	s. Grande
13130	s. Maddenii. Probably yellow
13150	chaetomallum
13151	oreotrephes
13165	s. Neriiflorum
13180	s.s. Sanguineum
13190	s. Saluenense
13194	s.s. Haematodes ?
13195	s. Maddenii. Bright butter yellow
13210	s. Campylogynum
13225	forrestii var. repens

K.W. NO.

13230	s. Maddenii. Pale yellow
13324	chaetomallum var. ?
13327	s. Barbatum
13355	s.s. Haematodes
13361	tsangpoense var. pruniflorum ?
13365	s. Lapponicum
13367	calostrotum
13369	s. Grande. Same shade of crimson
13370	s. Lapponicum
13371	saluenense
13399	campylogynum ?
13405	s. Anthopogon
13416	s.s. Sanguineum

Kingdon-Ward Rhododendrons Collected Since 1938

1938–39 EXPEDITION
Vernay-Cutting North Burma

K.W. NO.

00005	simsii (also 00071, 00499)
00051	kyawi
00052	dendricola (also 00087, 00180, 00280, 00281, 00440)
00061	oreotrephes
00062	microphyton (also 00461)
00100	decorum
00135	stenaulum (also 00250, 00435)
00152	dendricola
00203	protistum
00213	magnificum
00227	megeratum
00228	eclecteum
00233	oreotrephes
00234	neriiflorum (also 00286)
00236	arizelum

K.W. NO.

00245	campylogynum var. myrtilloides
00251	chrysodoron (also 00354, 00395, 00404)
00252	callimorphum (?)
00293	bullatum (also 00346)
00312	euchaites (also 00445, 00448)
00347	(?) kasoense
00372	cf. bullatum
00396	delavayi
00400	manipurense
00404	habrotrichum
00409	habrotrichum
00412	vaccinioides
00413	(?) leptothrium
00416	tanastylum (also 00438)
00424	genestierianum
00460	leptothrium

1946 EXPEDITION
Khasi & Jaintia Hills, Assam

16029	sp.		16060	sp.

1948 EXPEDITION
East Manipur, Assam

17044	arboreum		17405	triflorum
17200	sp.		17407	macabeanum
17215	johnstoneanum		17436	Ciliicalyx Subseries
17216	arboreum		17700	manipurense
17217	manipurense		17818	manipurense
17261	vaccinioides			

1949 EXPEDITIONS
Mishmi Hills, Assam

K.W. NO.

18540	stenaulum (flowers white)	18541	Ciliicalyx Subseries

Khasi Hills, Assam

18753	formosum	18811	Ciliicalyx Subseries

Naga Hills, Assam

18829	vaccinioides	19083	elliottii
18985	johnstoneanum	19101	bauhiniiflorum (or
19082	macabeanum		triflorum ?)

1950 EXPEDITION
Lohit Valley, Assam/Tibet Frontier

19244	oleifolium	19452	sp. Thomsonii Series
19245	arboreum	19453	sperabile
19259	walongense	19573	rubrolineatum
19325	oleifolium	19588	sanguineum (?)
19398	vaccinioides	19589	Neriiflorum Series
19404	manipurense	19590	anthopogon
19405	sperabile	19591	imperator (?)
19406	sidereum	19606	intricatum
19431	sp. Thomsonii Series	19620	tsangpoense var. pruni
19432	megacalyx		florum
19433	bullatum	19657	manipurense
19447	crinigerum	20260	Barbatum Series
19448	triflorum	20280	Ciliicalyx Subseries
19449	sinogrande	20285	cerasinum (affin.)
19450	calostrotum	20305-A	johnstoneanum
19451	uvarifolium		

222

1953 EXPEDITION

The Triangle, North Burma

K.W. NO.

20601	dendricola
20629	Ciliicalyx Subseries
20651	dendricola
20679	stenaulum
20680	tanastylum
20681	ciliicalyx
20682	genestierianum
20693	vaccinioides
20696	euchaites
20702	crassum
20836	megacalyx
20837	zaleucum
20838	sidereum
20839	bullatum
20840	bullatum
20843	euchaites
20844	tephropeplum
20845	glaucophyllum var. luteiflorum
20876	cf. protistum
20877	sinogrande
20878	chrysodoron
20910	vaccinioides
20919	ciliicalyx
20922	arizelum
20923	apodectum
20924	chaetomallum
20925	chaetomallum var. hemigymnum
20926	orestrephes
20927	caloxanthum
20928	campylogynum
20929	cephalanthum var. crebre-florum
20934	trichocladum
20981	ciliicalyx
21000	apodectum

K.W. NO.

21001	Boothii Series
21003	oreotrephes (affin.)
21005	crassum
21006	eclecteum
21007	micromeres
21021	oreotrephes
21040	glaucophyllum var. luteiflorum
21073	forrestii var. repens
21074	Forrestii Subseries
21075	pocophorum
21077	chaetomallum
21078	cephalanthum var. crebre-florum
21079	trichocladum
21086	euchaites
21111	sinogrande
21130	campylogynum
21481	campylogynum
21512	supranubium
21494	vaccinioides
21498	Grande Series (same as 21602)
21525	stenaulum
21547	martinianum
21556	glaucophyllum var. luteiflorum (flowers bright yellow)
21557	martinianum
21559	megeratum
21601	Grande Series
21602	Grande Series (same as 21498)
21679	Boothii Series (?), Ciliicalyx Series (?)
22036	simsii

Rock Rhododendrons

1923–24 EXPEDITION
S.E. Tibet and N.W. Yunnan

ROCK NO.

59029	cephalanthum
59030	haemaleum
59031	sanguineum
59032	beesianum
59033	sanguineum
59034	cloiophorum
59035	sanguineum var. and/or didymum
59036	haemaleum
59037	gilvum
59038	roseotinctum
59039	consanguineum
59040	haemaleum
59041	melleum
59042	rhodanthum
59043	beesianum
59044	temenium
59045	eclecteum var. bellatulum
59046	haemaleum
59047	martinianum
59048	praestans
59049	chryseum (?)
59050	dasycladum
59051	beesianum
59052	brachyanthum var. hypolepidotum
59053	brachyanthum var. hypolepidotum
59054	wardii
59055	sanguineum
59056	sanguineum
59057	floccigerum
59058	crinigerum
59059	selense
59060	selense var. pagophilum
59061	forrestii var. repens
59062	crinigerum

ROCK NO.

59063	crinigerum
59064	roxieanum
59065	crinigerum
59066	crinigerum
59067	crinigerum
59068	crinigerum
59069	chaetomallum
59070	chaetomallum
59071	Triflorum Series. 3–4 ft. Rich lavender
59072	beesianum
59073	beesianum
59074	chaetomallum
59075	beesianum
59076	brachyanthum var. hypolepidotum
59077	crinigerum
59078	forrestii var. repens
59079	coryphaeum
59080	forrestii var. repens
59081	floccigerum
59082	saluenense
59083	sanguineum
59084	chamae-thomsonii var. chamaethauma
59085	praestans
59086	Triflorum Series
59087	gymnanthum
59088	fulvum
59089	beesianum
59090	sanguineum
59091	fulvum
59092	sanguineum
59093	selense var. pagophilum
59094	eclecteum var. bellatulum
59095	selense
59096	sanguineum

ROCK NO.		ROCK NO.	
59097	eclecteum var. bellatulum	59137	beesianum
59098	eclecteum var. bellatulum	59138	selense
59099	eclecteum	59139	beesianum
59100	fulvum	59140	phaeochrysum
59101	eclecteum	59141	dryophyllum
59102	eclecteum var. bellatulum	59142	dryophyllum
59103	chamae-thomsonii var. chamaethauma	59143	dryophyllum
		59144	Roxieanum Subseries
59104	fictolacteum	59145	Roxieanum Subseries, at Exbury. 5 ft. Pink, spotted purple
59105	uvarifolium		
59106	haemaleum		
59107	eclecteum var. bellatulum	59146	Taliense Series. 4–5 ft. Purple
59108	eclecteum var. bellatulum		
59109	eclecteum	59147	aganniphum and/or dryophyllum
59110	eclecteum var. bellatulum		
59111	eclecteum var. bellatulum	59148	chryseum
59112	eclecteum var. brachyandrum	59149	erythrocalyx
		59150	oreotrephes
59113	eclecteum var. bellatulum	59152	Lapponicum Series. 1 ft. Bluish-purple
59114	selense		
59115	selense	59153	Triflorum Series. 4–5 ft. Lavender-blue
59116	selense var. probum		
59117	selense	59154	flavorufum
59118	beesianum	59155	adenogynum and/or flavorufum
59119	coriaceum		
59120	Heliolepis Series	59156	litiense
59121	floccigerum	59157	gymnanthum
59122	forrestii	59158	gymnanthum
59123	proteoides	59159	oreotrephes
59124	selense var. pagophilum	59160	crinigerum
59125	eudoxum	59161	flavorufum
59126	eclecteum	59162	roxieanum
59127	chaetomallum	59163	Roxieanum Subseries. 4 ft. White
59128	haemaleum		
59129	crinigerum and/or iodes	59164	wardii
59130	roxieanum	59165	chryseum
59131	sp. 5–6 ft. Deep red	59166	aureolum
59132	schizopeplum	59167	aureolum
59133	cephalanthum	59168	Sanguineum Subseries. 1–2 ft. Reddish-purple
59134	drumonium		
59135	dryophyllum. In cult. at Muncaster globigerum	59169	melleum
		59170	pocophorum
59136	Lapponicum Series. 2–3 ft. Deep blue	59171	chaetomallum
		59172	arizelum

59173	micromeres
59174	chamae-thomsonii
59175	chaetomallum
59176	sanguineoides
59177	mixed seed
59178	hemidartum
59179	eclecteum var. brachy-andrum
59180	chaetomallum
59181	pocophorum
59182	radicans
59183	crinigerum
59184	bainbridgeanum
59185	crinigerum
59186	crinigerum
59187	bainbridgeanum
59188	crinigerum
59189	chryseum
59190	pocophorum
59191	genestierianum
59192	martinianum
59193	arizelum
59194	saluenense
59195	roxieanum
59196	trichostomum var. radinum
59197	dasycladum
59198	dasycladum
59199	rubiginosum
59200	tanastylum
59201	irroratum and/or lukiangense
59202	bullatum
59203	yunnanense
59204	Triflorum Subseries. In cult. brevistylum
59205	roxieanum
59206	cuneatum
59207	rigidum
59208	dasycladum
59209	russatum
59210	russatum
59211	russatum
59212	irroratum

59213	roxieanum
59214	impeditum
59215	telmateium
59216	campylogynum
59217	pronum
59218	roxieanum
59219	xanthostephanum
59220	irroratum
59221	roxieanum
59222	roxieanum
59223	traillianum
59224	traillianum
59225	Lapponicum Series
59226	molle
59227	wardii aff.
59228	dryophyllum
59229	phaeochrysum
59230	agglutinatum
59231	schizopeplum
59232	dryophyllum
59233	dryophyllum
59234	sinogrande
59235	fulvum
59236	gymnogynum
59237	wardii
59238	sp. 10–12 ft.
59239	eritimum
59240	lepidotum
59241	hippophaeoides
59242	eritimum
59243	cuneatum
59244	hylothreptum forma
59245	uvarifolium
59246	uvarifolium
59247	irroratum
59248	eritimum. In cult. bureavii
59249	eritimum. In cult. bureavii
59250	fictolacteum
59251	heptamerum
59252	eritimum
59253	cuneatum
59254	cuneatum

59255	sp.
59256	traillianum
59257	trichostomum var. radinum
59258	racemosum
59259	telmateium
59260	traillianum
59261	sp.
59262	telmateium
59263	impeditum
59435	araliaeforme (?)
59436	traillianum
59437	brunneifolium
59438	chaetomallum
59439	roxieanum
59440	fictolacteum
59441	cloiophorum
59442	triplonaevium
59443	cephalanthum
59444	sanguineum
59445	selense
59446	selense var. pagophilum
59447	fulvum
59448	brunneifolium
59449	dictyotum
59450	cloiophorum
59451	dryophyllum
59452	augustinii var. chasmanthum
59453	haemaleum
59454	eclecteum
59455	roseotinctum
59456	haemaleum
59457	albertsenianum
59458	mesopolium
59459	fulvastrum
59460	pothinum
59461	martinianum
59462	praestans
59463	crinigerum
59464	crinigerum
59465	Trichocladum Series. 3 ft. Deep yellow
59466	crinigerum

59467	crinigerum
59468	crinigerum
59469	crinigerum
59470	crinigerum
59471	crinigerum
59472	crinigerum
59473	forrestii var. repens
59474	floccigerum
59475	proteoides
59476	oreotrephes
59477	beesianum
59478	chameunum
59479	megeratum
59480	coryphaeum
59481	praestans
59482	saluenense
59483	sanguineum
59484	saluenense
59485	cephalanthum
59486	roxieanum
59487	haemaleum
59488	eclecteum var. bellatulum
59489	forrestii
59490	eclecteum
59491	chamae-thomsonii
59492	eclecteum var. bellatulum
59493	sanguineum
59494	eclecteum bar. bellatulum
59495	fulvum
59496	haemaleum
59497	fulvum
59498	haemaleum
59499	eclecteum
59500	cloiophorum
59501	eclecteum var. bellatulum
59502	selense
59503	eclecteum
59504	selense
59505	panteumorphum
59506	desquamatum
59507	uvarifolium
59508	oulotrichum
59509	russatum
59510	dryophyllum

59511	dryophyllum
59512	calvescens
59513	Lapponicum Series. 1 ft. Deep indigo shading to lighter blue
59514	globigerum
59515	globigerum
59516	dryophyllum
59517	dryophyllum
59518	dryophyllum
59519	dryophyllum
59520	dryophyllum
59521	russotinctum
59522	tritifolium
59523	wardii
59524	roxieanum
59525	gymnanthum
59526	wardii
59527	Taliense Series. 6 ft. Pale pink, spotted purple
59528	flavorufum
59529	flavorufum
59530	wardii
59531	flavorufum
59532	pocophorum
59533	chaetomallum
59534	arizelum
59535	campylogynum
59536	hemidartum
59537	crassum
59538	fulvum
59539	chaetomallum
59540	brachyanthum var. hypolepidotum
59541	coryanum
59542	chaetomallum
59543	catacosmum
59544	arizelum var. rubicosum
59545	dasycladum
59546	cloiophorum
59547	Stamineum Series. 18–20 ft. Red.
59548	chaetomallum
59549	cloiophorum

59550	arizelum var. rubicosum
59551	selense
59552	chaetomallum
59553	sanguineum aff.
59554	dasycladum
59555	didymum
59556	gymnogynum
59557	megacalyx
59558	fictolacteum
59559	fulvum
59560	chaetomallum
59561	sinonuttallii
59562	beesianum
59563	fictolacteum
59564	russatum
59565	fictolacteum
59566	traillianum
59567	wardii and/or roxieanum
59568	Triflorum Series. 5 ft. Pink
59569	Lapponicum Series. 1–2 ft. Deep blue-purple
59570	roxieanum
59571	roxieanum
59572	roxieanum
59573	clementinae
59574	eritimum. In cult. at Exbury pallescens
59575	roxieanum
59576	oreotrephes
59577	racemosum
59578	racemosum
59579	Irroratum Series. 6 ft. Pure white, spotted purple
59580	triflorum. 4 ft. White
59581	irroratum
59582	irroratum
59583	bullatum
59584	delavayi
59585	Triflorum Series. 4 ft. White, spotted purple
59586	agastum. In cult. delavayi forma. 8 ft.
59587	russatum
59588	fictolacteum

ROCK NO.

59589	roxieanum
59590	roxieanum
59591	oreotrephes
59592	xanthostephanum
59593	oreotrephes
59594	roxieanum
59595	roxieanum
59596	leptothrium
59597	russatum
59598	scintillans
59599	vernicosum forma
59600	dryophyllum
59601	vernicosum forma
59602	dryophyllum
59603	beesianum
59604	schizopeplum
59605	beesianum
59606	dryophyllum
59607	schizopeplum
59608	schizopeplum
59609	schizopeplum
59610	schizopeplum
59611	eritimum
59612	beesianum
59613	sp. 20 ft.
59614	irroratum

ROCK NO.

59615	hippophaeoides
59616	hippophaeoides
59617	adenogynum
59618	traillianum
59619	traillianum
59620	irroratum
59621	beesianum
59622	litiense
59623	uvarifolium
59624	fictolacteum
59625	vernicosum
59626	Triflorum Series. 3 ft. Purple-lavender
59627	Triflorum Series. 6 ft. Red
59628	fictolacteum
59629	brevistylum
59630	traillianum
59631	cephalanthum
59632	traillianum
59633	traillianum
59634	primulaeflorum
59635	traillianum
59636	adenophorum
59637	sp. 4 ft. White
59638	racemosum

1925–26 EXPEDITION

N.W. Kansu

13278	przewalskii
13279	anthopogonoides
13302	przewalskii
13303	thymifolium
13596	capitatum
13597	anthopogonoides
13598	thymifolium
13599	rufum
13600	capitatum
13601	rufum
13605	capitatum

13610	anthopogonoides
13611	capitatum
13612	przewalskii
13613	rufum
13622	capitatum
13628	rufum
13629	przewalskii
13630	rufum
13634	capitatum
13635	capitatum
13636	anthopogonoides

13640	rufum
13643	rufum
13645	rufum
13647	rufum
13649	rufum
13650	rufum
13674	capitatum
13675	rufum
13676	przewalskii
13677	przewalskii
13678	rufum
13679	przewalskii
13680	rufum
13681	przewalskii
13682	rufum

13683	rufum
13684	rufum
13685	przewalskii
13686	przewalskii
13688	capitatum
13691	rufum
13692	rufum
13693	rufum
13694	przewalskii
13695	przewalskii
13696	rufum
13697	rufum
14928	rufum
15004	micranthum
15014	rufum

1929 EXPEDITION

N.W. Yunnan

03749	Irroratum Series. 8–10 ft.
03750	balfourianum var. agan-niphoides
03751	schizopeplum aff.
03752	balfourianum var. aggani-phoides
03756	adenogynum
03757	intricatum
03758	Lacteum Series. 10 ft.
03760	balfourianum var. agan-niphoides
03761	balfourianum var. agan-niphoides
03763	roxieanum
03764	globigerum
03788	vernicosum aff.
03789	beesianum
03790	dryophyllum
03791	dryophyllum
03792	roxieanum
03794	adenogynum
03799	dryophyllum
03800	rex
03828	globigerum

03829	chryseum aff.
03830	dryophyllum
03831	balfourianum var. agan-niphoides
03832	Irroratum Series, Parishii Subseries. 25 ft.
03833	globigerum
03834	globigerum aff.
03835	sphaeroblastum
03837	Barbatum Series. 6–8 ft.
03838	intricatum
03839	litangense
03840	Barbatum Series. 10–12 ft.
03844	Lapponicum Series. 2 ft Dark blue
03845	adenogynum
03847	sinogrande
03848	wardii
03849	wardii
03850	stewartianum
03852	arizelum
03853	arizelum
03854	basilicum

03855	fulvum
03857	megeratum
03861	aperantum
03862	panteumorphum
03863	aperantum
03864	chaetomallum aff.
03865	chaetomallum aff.
03866	chaetomallum aff.
03868	chaetomallum aff.
03874	achroanthum
03875	roxieanum aff.
03876	achroanthum
03881	panteumorphum
03883	stewartianum
03884	stewartianum
03885	stewartianum
03886	stewartianum
03887	aperantum aff.
03890	chaetomallum
03891	panteumorphum
03892	rubiginosum
03893	coriaceum
03894	glischrum
03895	glischrum
03896	trichocladum. Pink
03897	chaetomallum
03898	basilicum
03899	basilicum
03902	sulfureum
03903	basilicum
03904	basilicum
03908	crinigerum
03910	crassum
03912	chaetomallum aff.
03913	coriaceum
03914	tephropeplum
03915	xanthostephanum
03916	Triflorum Series. 6–8 ft. White
03917	Triflorum Series. 10 ft. White
03919	tephropeplum
03920	eclecteum
03921	eclecteum

03923	Triflorum Series. 6 ft. Pink
03926	martinianum
03929	sp. 2–4 ft. White
03935	basilicum
03926	crassum
03937	roxieanum
03939	dictyotum
03940	dictyotum
03941	traillianum
03942	beesianum
03943	dictyotum
03945	beesianum
03946	dictyotum
03947	clementinae
03948	fictolacteum
03949	clementinae
03950	glischrum
03951	chameunum
03954	calostrotum
03955	calostrotum
03956	wardii
03959	Lapponicum Series. 1–2 ft. Blue
03960	fictolacteum
03961	Lapponicum Series. 2–3 ft. Pale blue
03963	cuneatum
03964	sanguineum aff.
03965	sanguineum aff.
03966	floccigerum
03967	floccigerum
03968	floccigerum
03969	floccigerum
03970	floccigerum
03972	leptothrium
03974	leptothrium
03977	ciliicalyx aff.
03983	dryopyllum
03984	wardii
03985	sphaeroblastum
03987	rubiginosum
03988	sphaeroblastum
03989	racemosum

ROCK NO.

03990	dryophyllum
03991	sphaeroblastum
03993	beesianum
04007	heliolepis
04012	sp. 10 ft. Pale pink
04020	sp. 8–10 ft. White

ROCK NO.

04021	sp. 3–4 ft. Pink
04022	sp. 2–3 ft. Blue
04023	s.p 6–12 ft. Pink
04084	sp. 15 ft. Pink
04085	sp. 4–6 ft. White, tinged pink

1932 EXPEDITION
N.W. Yunnan

21993	mesaeum
21994	sperabiloides
21995	bainbridgeanum
21997	saluenense
21999	bainbridgeanum
22000	crinigerum
22001	pocophorum
22002	pocophorum
22003	eclecteum var. brachyandrum
22004	fulvum
22005	eclecteum var. brachyandrum
22006	chaetomallum
22007	stewartianum
22013	genestierianum
22014	xanthostephanum
22019	bullatum
22021	fictolacteum
22023	arizelum
22024	arizelum var. rubicosum
22025	arizelum
22028	selense
22029	selense
22030	dasycladum
22031	bainbridgeanum
22032	dasycladum
22033	selense
22034	mesaeum
22037	fictolacteum
22038	fictolacteum
22039	fictolacteum
22040	beesianum
22041	beesianum
22042	uvarifolium
22045	oleifolium
22050	chamae-thomsonii
22056	monanthum
22058	chaetomallum
22059	chaetomallum
22063	chryseum
22064	cloiophorum
22065	chaetomallum
22066	citriniflorum
22067	chaetomallum
22069	forrestii var. repens
22070	pothinum
22090	mekongense
22091	fictolacteum
22092	fulvum
22094	arizelum
22095	eritimum
22096	uvarifolium
22097	fulvum
22100	eclecteum
22102	dasycladum
22106	arizelum var. rubicosum
22108	arizelum
22110	arizelum var. rubicosum
22111	fulvum
22112	crinigerum
22117	fictolacteum
22119	martinianum
22121	floccigerum
22122	sperabiloides
22123	martinianum

23307	schizopeplum
23308	beesianum
23310	ramosissimum
23314	wardii
23316	scintillans
23317	diacritum
23318	schizopeplum
23319	dryophyllum
23321	phaeochrysum
23322	primulaeflorum
23324	agglutinatum
23325	adenogynum
23326	fargesii. Large white
23328	aganniphum
23330	chameunum
23331	aganniphum
23332	yunnanense
23333	aganniphum
23338	schizopeplum
23348	sp. 6–10 ins. Large purplish-red
23350	dryophyllum
23360	chryseum
23369	dryophyllum
23371	aganniphum
23394	dryophyllum
23398	chryseum
23400	primulaeflorum
23401	aganniphum
23405	aganniphum
23406	dryophyllum
23407	Fortunei Series. 3–5 ft.
23408	caloxanthum
23452	beesianum
23453	fictolacteum
23467	achroanthum
23477	augustinii var. chasmanthum
23480	crinigerum
23481	Thomsonii Series
23482	martinianum
23483	megeratum
23485	crinigerum
23487	fulvum

23488	fulvum
23489	crinigerum
23490	crinigerum
23491	oreotrephes
23492	selense var. pagophilum
23494	Thomsonii Subseries
23495	floccigerum
23496	coryphaeum
23497	fulvum
23498	chamae-thomsonii var. chamaethauma
23505	fulvum
23506	floccigerum
23508	fulvum
23509	eclecteum
23510	eclecteum var. brachyandrum
23511	eclecteum
23512	eclecteum var. brachyandrum
23513	trichocladum
23514	desquamatum
23515	Thomsonii Series
23516	eclecteum
23517	uvarifolium
23518	beesianum
23520	coryphaeum
23521	beesianum
23524	sanguineum
23526	Roxieanum Subseries 5–6 ft.
23527	beesianum
23528	beesianum
23529	sanguineum
23530	beesianum
23540	chryseum
23542	proteoides
23545	saluenense
23546	chameunum
23548	saluenense
23553	brachyanthum var. hypolepidotum
23555	brachyanthum var. hypolepidotum

24317	phaeochrysum
24319	diacritum
24320	spilanthum
24321	trichostomum var. radinum
24322	cookeianum
24325	sphaeroblastum
24336	telmateium
24339	wardii. White
24343	sphaeroblastum
24350	clementinae
24359	phaeochrysum
24360	wardii
24361	telmateium
24363	agglutinatum
24365	agglutinatum
24366	agglutinatum
24368	wardii
24369	litangense
24381	balfourianum var. aganniphoides
24382	balfourianum var. aganniphoides
24383	balfourianum var. aganniphoides
24384	aff. impeditum. Pink
24385	stictophyllum
24395	agglutinatum
24403	dryophyllum
24404	oreotrephes
24406	balfourianum var. aganniphoides
24410	phaeochrysum
24413	przewalskii
24414	agglutinatum
24418	dryophyllum
24421	oreotrephes
24432	yunnanense
24433	decorum
24434	vernicosum
24439	trichostomum var. radinum
24440	cookeianum
24445	dryophyllum

24446	blepharocalyx
24457	dryophyllum
24458	Fortunei Series. 6–8 ft. White to pinkish
24459	dryophyllum
24460	impeditum
24461	dryophyllum
24464	Lapponicum Series. 2 ft.
24471	cookeianum
24481	sphaeroblastum
24487	wardii
24489	primulaeflorum var. cephalanthoides
24495	wardii
24501	pronum
24503	roxieanum
24512	agglutinatum
24524	agglutinatum
24531	hemitrichotum
24540	primulaeflorum
24541	hemitrichotum
24544	trichostomum var. radinum
24569	coriaceum
24573	fictolacteum
24582	beesianum
24583	beesianum
24591	yunnanense
24592	yunnanense
24599	desquamatum
24602	yunnanense
24604	uvarifolium
25233	indicum forma
25234	scabrifolium
25235	scottianum aff.
25236	scottianum aff.
25237	spinuliferum
25238	scottianum
25239	microphyton forma
25240	scottianum
25246	adenophorum
25247	desquamatum
25251	uvarifolium
25252	traillianum

25258	russatum
25259	traillianum
25260	dasycladum
25272	preptum aff. Rich pink
25277	russatum
25278	lepidotum
25301	traillianum
25302	achroanthum
25303	prostratum
25305	adenophorum
25306	fictolacteum
25308	adenogynum
25313	sphaeroblastum
25314	phaeochrysum
25326	rubiginosum
25327	yunnanense
25328	traillianum
25329	desquamatum
25331	vernicosum
25334	lepidotum
25340	eritimum
25345	beesianum
25349	adenophorum
25350	primulaeflorum
25352	uvarifolium
25368	traillianum
25370	websterianum
25372	rubiginosum
25373	vernicosum
25375	adenophorum
25376	primulaeflorum
25377	drumonium
25381	yunnanense
25384	traillianum
25386	irroratum
25387	adenogynum
25388	basilicum
25389	basilicum
25390	roxieanum
25391	litiense
25393	basilicum
25394	basilicum
25395	irroratum
25396	fictolacteum

25398	dasycladum
25400	irroratum
25401	clementinae
25402	hippophaeoides
25405	Roxieanum Subseries. 5–6 ft.
25406	Roxieanum Subseries. 3 ft.
25407	Roxieanum Subseries. 10–12 ft.
25414	fictolacteum
25417	fastigiatum
25418	fictolacteum
25419	uvarifolium
25421	uvarifolium
25422	roxieanum
25423	roxieanum
25424	fictolacteum
25425	fulvum
25426	fulvum
25428	dasycladum
25429	oreotrephes
25430	clementinae
25431	fulvum
25432	clementinae
25435	bureavii
25436	bureavii
25437	balfourianum var. aganniphoides
25438	desquamatum
25439	bureavii
25440	cephalanthum
25441	fictolacteum
25442	bureavii
25443	scabrifolium
25444	fictolacteum
25445	heptamerum
25446	heliolepis
25447	fictolacteum
25448	fictolacteum
25451	irroratum
25452	Roxieanum Subseries. 6–8 ft.
25453	bullatum

ROCK

25454	bullatum
25455	Roxieanum Subseries.
	4–5 ft.
25458	pronum
25459	campylogynum
25462	roxieanum
25463	roxieanum
25464	roxieanum
25465	xanthostephanum
25466	fictolacteum

25467	litiense
25468	fulvum
25470	agglutinatum
25472	sphaeroblastum
25474	dryophyllum
25476	cookeianum
25478	sphaeroblastum
25480	sphaeroblastum
25482	phaeochrysum

LUDLOW & SHERRIFF RHODODENDRONS

* — herbarium material at the British Museum destroyed by bombing

s — seed number only—no herbarium material.

T — type no. of new species.

1933 EXPEDITION
Bhutan

L.&S. NO.		L.&S. NO.	
7	cinnabarinum	49	wightii
* 8	cinnabarinum	88	setosum
9	campylocarpum	123	lepidotum
15	triflorum	173	triflorum
18	thomsonii	175	lepidotum
19	wallichii	176	lepidotum
20	wallichii	* 184	keysii
* 21	hodgsonii	* 190	camelliiflorum
22	wallichii	218	maddenii
* 25	arboreum	* 253	camelliiflorum
31	thomsonii		

1934 EXPEDITION
Bhutan and South Tibet

569	maddenii	* 619	campanulatum
570	maddenii	* 622	campanulatum
582	dalhousiae	* 624	campanulatum
583	rhabdotum	* 634	lepidotum
* 586	arboreum	* 638	anthopogon
* 588	keysii	* 647	cinnabarinum
* 589	camelliiflorum	* 661	hypenanthum
590	micromeres	* 716	lepidotum
595	thomsonii	811	aganniphum
* 605	campanulatum	* 976	lindleyi
606	wightii	1081	Campanulatum Series
* 613	hodgsonii	1082	campanulatum
* 616	campanulatum	1083	tsariense

L.&S. NO.		L.&S. NO.	
1084	Campanulatum Series	★ 1105	arboreum
1085	campanulatum	★ 1115	arboreum
★ 1091	anthopogon		

1936 EXPEDITION

Bhutan and South East Tibet

★ 1134	grande	1297	fulgens
1141	maddenii	1302	wallichii
1142	maddenii	1303	tsariense
★ 1143	arboreum	1304	argipeplum
1148	grande	1305	arboreum
★ 1181	camelliiflorum	1306	wallichii
★ 1182	arboreum	1307	arboreum
★ 1183	camelliiflorum	1308	arboreum
1184	kingianum	1309	pendulum
1185	arboreum	1342	vellereum
1186	grande	1346	virgatum
1193	Irroratum Series	1352	neriiflorum
★ 1204	Maddenii Series	1353	triflorum
★ 1205	lindleyi	1354	cinnabarinum
1206	kendrickii	1355	glaucophyllum
1208	grande	1356	ciliatum
★ 1209	camelliiflorum ?	1357	fulvum
1227	kendrickii	1358	arizelum
1235	grande	1359	populare
1251	edgeworthii	T 1360	dekatanum
1252	epapillatum	1361	megeratum
1257	neriiflorum	1362	probably pumilum
1258	grande	1364	tsariense
1260	epapillatum	T 1365	amandum
1261	arboreum	1366	virgatum
1262	triflorum	1380	arizelum
1266	lindleyi	1381	fulvum
1269	lindleyi	1383	fulvum
1276	arboreum	1384	fulvum
1279	virgatum	1385	hodgsonii
1280	kendrickii	T 1386	pudorosum
1281	arboreum	1387	erosum
1282	argipeplum	1389	lanatum var. luciferum
1283	thomsonii	T 1390	sherriffii
1285	baileyi	T 1391	populare
1296	wallichii	1392	vellereum

L.&S. NO.			L.&S. NO.	
	1397	vellereum		1728	thomsonii var. pallidum

L.&S. NO.		L.&S. NO.	
1397	vellereum	1728	thomsonii var. pallidum
T 1541	erosum	T 1730	thomsonii var. pallidum
1542	fulvum	1741	pumilum
1549	vellereum	1751	micromeres
1555	vellereum	1756	anthopogon
1557	lanatum var. luciferum	1757	concatenans
1558	lanatum var. luciferum	1760	aganniphum
1559	vellereum	1761	agglutinatum
T 1564	dignabile	T 1762	lanatum var. luciferum
1565	anthopogon	1770	agglutinatum
1566	dignabile	1771	calostrotum
1567	aff. aganniphum	1772	fragariflorum
1568	Taliense Series	1773	pumilum
1575	cinnabarinum	1776	lopsangianum
1583	primulaeflorum var. cephalanthoides	1779	paludosum
		1788	paludosum
1598	paludosum	1796	primulaeflorum
1606	anthopogon	1855	lepidotum
1607	dignabile	1860	vellereum
1608	lanatum var. luciferum	1863	triflorum var. mahogani
1610	lanatum var. luciferum	1870	lepidotum
1612	pudorosum	1873	cerasinum
1619	dignabile	1881	tsangpoense
1624	pumilum	1882	campylogynum
1627	miniatum	1883	forrestii var. repens
1628	campylocarpum	1889	pumilum
1629	erosum	1890	mekongense
1634	pumilum	1893	campylocarpum
T 1636	tsariense	1894	cinnabarinum
1647	tsangpoense var. pruniflorum	T 1895	ludlowii
		1896	mekongense
1649	calostrotum	1904	keysii
1651	lopsangianum	2085	wardii
1653	anthopogon	2108	micromeres
1656	caloxanthum	2109	trichocladum
1666	megeratum	T 2160	laudandum
1675	triflorum	2210	tsariense
1676	neriiflorum	2225	lepidotum
1677	neriiflorum	2244	lepidotum
1702	lindleyi	2300	paludosum
T 1710	miniatum	2332	crassum
1715	lindleyi	T 2334	igneum
T 1718	lopsangianum	2335	trichocladum
1720	phaedropum	2338	crassum

L.&S. NO.		L.&S. NO.	
2378	pumilum	2825	arboreum
2447	lepidotum	2826	thomsonii
2505	megeratum	2827	Campanulatum Series
2552	pumilum	2828	anthopogon
2622	bulu	2833	maddenii
2627	vellereum	2835	griffithianum
2643	cinnabarinum	2836	edgeworthii
2652	pumilum	2837	rhabdotum
2653	forrestii var. repens	2843	rhabdotum
2654	campylogynum	2845	camelliiflorum
2727	cinnabarinum	2846	fulgens
2736	lopsangianum	2847	thomsonii
2738	vellereum	2848	Thomsonii Series
2739	ciliatum	2849	camelliiflorum
2743	sp.	2850	camelliiflorum
2744	lindleyi	2851	Campanulatum Series
2745	edgeworthii	2852	camelliiflorum
2748	kendrickii	2853	camelliiflorum
2751	sherriffii	2855	camelliiflorum
2752	pudorosum	2856	glaucophyllum var.
2753	arizelum		tubiforme
2754	fulvum	2857	micromeres
2755	erosum	2858	tsariense
2757	ciliatum	2859	Lacteum Series
2758	trichocladum	2860	Campanulatum Series
2759	megeratum	2891	cf. dalhousiae
2760	camelliiflorum	2892	maddenii
2761	megeratum	2893	arboreum
2762	pumilum	2894	tsariense
2764	brachyanthum	2895	wallichii ?
2765	camelliiflorum	2896	baileyi
2766	tsariense	2898	pendulum
2767	sp.	2903	cf. campanulatum
2770	virgatum	2906	cf. campanulatum
2797	vellereum	2907	Campanulatum Series
2816	Taliense Series	2915	probably fulgens
2817	Taliense Series	2916	Lacteum Series
2818	lepidotum	2917	rhabdotum
2824	anthopogon ?		

1937 EXPEDITION

Bhutan

L.&S. NO.		L.&S. NO.	
2940	rhabdotum	3082	anthopogon
2944	rhabdotum	3087	campanulatum
2952	edgeworthii	3088	wightii
2960	arboreum	3089	lanatum
* 2977	grande	3090	fulgens
* 2980	lindleyi	3091	wightii
* 2983	falconeri	3095	glaucophyllum
2987	hodgsonii	3096	smithii
2988	smithii	3111	lepidotum
* 2989	eximium	* 3132	edgeworthii
* 2990	hodgsonii	3136	rhabdotum
* 2992	keysii	3147	maddenii
3017	arboreum	3164	polyandrum
3021	virgatum	3184	glaucophyllum
3025	phaedropum	3202	baileyi
* 3026	griffithianum	3216	pogonophyllum
3039	keysii	3217	anthopogon
* 3041	falconeri	3218	campanulatum
3042	thomsonii	3221	setosum
* 3047	hodgsonii	* 3239	fulgens
3048	campylocarpum	3243	campanulatum
3049	smithii	3244	campanulatum var.
3050	cinnabarinum		aeruginosum
* 3058	campylocarpum	3254	lepidotum
3061	triflorum	3267	camelliiflorum
3063	lanatum	3289	lepidotum
3066	thomsonii var.	3324	camelliiflorum
	candelabrum	3400	anthopogon
* 3074	lanatum	3428	pogonophyllum
3075	fulgens	* 3578	sp.
3081	campanulatum		

1938 EXPEDITION

South East Tibet (Ludlow, Sherriff & Taylor)

L. S. & T. NO.		L. S. & T. NO.	
3587	vellereum	3607	vellereum
s 3589	sp.	3609	vellereum
3600	vellereum	3613	thomsonii
3601	primulaeflorum var.	3617	sp.
	cephalanthoides	3618	clementinae

L.S.&T. NO.		L S.&T. NO.	
3619	Taliense Series	3752	charitopes
3620	lanatum var. luciferum	3753	lopsangianum
3623	vellereum	3761	concatenans
3624	hirtipes	3765	cerasinum
3628	vellereum	3766	lopsangianum
3629	kongboense	3768	lopsangianum
3631	hirtipes	3769	tsariense
3634	exasperatum	3777	dignabile
3635	lopsangianum	3778	charitopes
3641	sulfureum	3783	forrestii var. repens
3642	forrestii var. repens	3784	pumilum
3643	hodgsonii	3785	calostrotum
3644	sulfureum	T 3786	chaetomallum var.
3645	tsariense		chamaephytum
3646	hodgsonii	3792	pudorosum
3652	hookeri	3793	lanatum var. luciferum
3654	ciliatum	3795	triflorum var. mahogani
3655	hookeri	3797	hirtipes
3656	phaedropum	3801	cinnabarinum var. roylei
3657	megeratum	3802	kongboense
3663	grande	3805	paludosum
3664	tsangpoense	3829	dignabile
3665	lindleyi	3830	nivale
3666	xanthostephanum	3849	wardii
3667	lindleyi	3861	anthopogon
3670	rude	3878	clementinae
3674	arizelum	3900	laudandum
3676	hookeri	3902	agglutinatum
3677	ramsdenianum	3925	pumilum
3680	grande	3933	kongboense
3689	Maddenii Series	3938	lopsangianum
3692	lindleyi	3939	callimorphum
3702	neriiflorum	3940	lopsangianum
3706	rude	3941	ludlowii
3709	edgeworthii	3942	forrestii var. repens
3720	edgeworthii	3975	calostrotum
3726	xanthostephanum	3976	lanatum var. luciferum
3728	edgeworthii	3994	campylocarpum
3731	campylocarpum	3995	forrestii var. repens
3736	micromeres	3997	populare
3741	lindleyi	3999	nivale
3749	arizelum	4028	grande
3750	thomsonii var. pallidum	4029	arboreum
3751	charitopes	4031	arboreum

L.S.&T. NO.		L.S.&T. NO.	
5868	wardii	6582	xanthostephanum
5869	cerasinum	6583	kasoense
5883	xanthocodon	6586	wardii
6213	bulu	6587	cerasinum
6302	vellereum	6588	calostrotum
6342	pumilum	6590	mekongense
6349	cinnabarinum var.	6591	wardii
	purpurellum	6598	forrestii var. repens
6349a	cinnabarinum var. roylei	6599	wardii
6350	lepidotum	6600	ludlowii
6411	arboreum	6602	campylocarpum
6424	wallichii	6608	clementinae
6533	pumilum	6612	agglutinatum
6538	trichocladum	6626	neriiflorum
6548	wardii	6633	micromeres
6549	lanatum var. luciferum	6638	cf. miniatum
6556	pumilum	6645	vellereum
6560	concatenans	6648	smithii
6561	lopsangianum	6652	lanatum var. luciferum
6562	lindleyi	6656	baileyi
6563	neriiflorum	6657	tsariense
6565	keysii	6659	wallichii
6567	lopsangianum	6660	pendulum
6568	ciliatum	6661	tsariense
6569	rude	6676	crassum
6572	monanthum	6694	cf. dalhousiae
6573	manipurense	6754	maddenii
6576	cf. brachyanthum var.	6776	arboreum
	hypolepidotum	7012	crassum
6579	hookeri	7190	vellereum
6580	sulfureum	7200	clementinae
6581	edgeworthii	7291	lepidotum

1939 EXPEDITION
Kashmir

L. & S. NO.		L. & S. NO.	
7369	lepidotum	7385	campanulatum
7384	hypenanthum		

1940 EXPEDITION
Kashmir

7660	hypenanthum	8134	campanulatum
7736	lepidotum		

1942 EXPEDITION

Tibet

L.&S. NO.		L.&S. NO.	
8653	nivale	8824	nivale
8654	primulaeflorum var. cephalanthoides	8825	primulaeflorum var. cephalanthoides

---

1943 EXPEDITION

Tibet

9145	hypenanthum	9574	primulaeflorum var. cephalanthoides
9146	lepidotum		
9537	nivale	9575	nivale
9538	primulaeflorum var. cephalanthoides		

1944 EXPEDITION

Tibet

9979	nivale	10039	cinnabarinum (1942 collection)
9980	primulaeflorum var. cephalanthoides		

1946–47 EXPEDITION

South East Tibet (Ludlow, Sherriff & Elliot)

L. S. & E. NO.		L. S. & E. NO.	
12002	vellereum	12289	anthosphaerum
12010	triflorum	12290	anthosphaerum
12014	triflorum	12313	anthosphaerum
12019	Irroratum Series	12326	virgatum
12024	virgatum	12329	uvarifolium var. griseum
12045	Irroratum Series	12342	uvarifolium
12117	sinonuttallii	12348	auritum
12137	tanastylum	12354	scopulorum
12208	Irroratum Series	12370	scopulorum
12231	scopulorum	12372	uvarifolium
s 12239	sp.	12374	triflorum
12246	tanastylum	12375	uvarifolium
12248	Maddenii Series	12380	vellereum
12253	virgatum	12388	uvarifolium var. griseum
12264	scopulorum	12393	vellereum
12280	tanastylum	12395	triflorum var. mahogani

L.S.&E. NO.		L.S.&E. NO.	
12397	russatum	13129	didymum
12397a	russatum	13133	laudandum
12400	triflorum var. mahogani	13147	concatenans
12428	primulaeflorum var.	13151	haemaleum
	cephalanthoides	13152	hirtipes
12469	cinnabarinum var. roylei	13155	stewartianum forma
12470	wallichii	13163	oreotrephes
12484	campylocarpum	13166	laudandum var.
12485	triflorum		temoense
12490	baileyi	T 13177	pomense
12491	arboreum	13180	beesianum
12498	tsariense	13181a	campylogynum
12505	trichocladum	13181b	campylogynum
12510	tanastylum	13183	pumilum
12514	anthosphaerum	13205	cerasinum
12515	virgatum	13217	wardii
12525	pendulum	13251	vellereum
12526	campylocarpum	13269	kongboense
12535	glaucophyllum	13276	campylogynum
12536	keysii	13278	forrestii var. repens
12537	ciliatum	13283	brachyanthum
12548	maddenii	13316	bulu
12550	maddenii	13509	vellereum
12564	maddenii	13516	vellereum
12592	maddenii	13520	bulu
13035	sinonuttallii	13521	uvarifolium var.
13043	lanigerum		griseum
13044	glischrum	13524	vellereum
13045	tsangpoense var.	13526	hirtipes
	pruniflorum	13527	kongboense
13077	sinonuttallii	13534	kongboense
13108	cerasinum	13535	kongboense
13109	wardii	13546	triflorum var. mahogani
13110	oreotrephes	13549	leucaspis
13113	tsangpoense var.	13550	virgatum
	pruniflorum	13551	hirtipes
13118	oulotrichum	13554	uvarifolium
13120	uniflorum	13559	anthosphaerum
13123	calostrotum	13561	ramsdenianum
13124	cephalanthum	13567	uvarifolium
13125	nivale	13568	mollyanum
13126	haemaleum	13570	auritum
13127	forrestii var. repens	13584	venator
13128	hirtipes	13589	thomsonii

L.S.&E. NO.		L.S.&E. NO.	
13590	glischrum	13733	wardii
13591	lanigerum	13746	roxieanum
13592	uniflorum	13747	vellereum
13593	anthosphaerum	13753	agglutinatum
13594	anthosphaerum	13754	wardii
13595	exasperatum	13755	anthosphaerum
13596	ramsdenianum	13756	stewartianum
13598	populare	13760	dignabile
13603	megacalyx	13761	oreotrephes
13606	glischrum var.	13780	calostrotum
	adenosum	13781	puralbum
13609	fictolacteum	13782	hirtipes
13610	anthosphaerum	13783	forrestii var. repens
13611	anthosphaerum	13792	dignabile
13612	parmulatum	13793	dignabile
13613	oreotrephes	13794	dignabile
13614	oreotrephes	13795	agglutinatum
13618	mishmiense	13842	puralbum
13619	wardii	13843	dignabile
13620	ramsdenianum	13855	agglutinatum
13622	oreotrephes	13857	dignabile
13625	tephropeplum	13858	agglutinatum
13629	hirtipes	13872	alpicola
13633	kongboense	13909	vellereum
13634	hirtipes	13969	forrestii var. repens
13643	anthosphaerum	13974	calostrotum
13645	virgatum	13981	puralbum
13661	wardii	13982	hirtipes
13663	forrestii var. repens	13985	lepidotum
13664	wardii	14006	agglutinatum
13665	uvarifolium	14023	laudandum var.
13667	thomsonii var. pallidum		temoense
13668	wardii	14024	agglutinatum
13671	vellereum	14026	agglutinatum
13672	kongboense	14028	hirtipes
13675	hirtipes	14029	campylogynum
13698	primulaeflorum var.	14030	calostrotum
	cephalanthoides	14101	lepidotum
13699	primulaeflorum var.	14244	trichocladum
	cephalanthoides	14295	campylogynum
13701	nivale	14297	campylogynum var.
13703	dignabile		cremastum
13705	oreotrephes	14395	doshongense
13732	oreotrephes	15001	vellereum

L.S.&E. NO.		L.S.&E. NO.	
15263	hirtipes	15325	sp.
15272	hirtipes	15326	agglutinatum
15273	hirtipes	15327	agglutinatum
15277	mekongense	15328	agglutinatum
15279	cerasinum	15356	lepidotum
15280	cerasinum	15399	agglutinatum
15281	cerasinum	15400	forrestii var. repens
15284	pumilum	15443	agglutinatum
15285	forrestii var. repens	15462	agglutinatum
15286	cephalanthum var.	15466	agglutinatum
	nmaiense	15469	wardii
15287	chamae-thomsonii var.	15499	lepidotum
	chamaethauma	15535	agglutinatum
15288	agglutinatum	15650	nivale
15289	agglutinatum	15668	nivale
15290	agglutinatum	15669	rufescens
15291	parmulatum	15729	russatum
15292	forrestii var. repens	15751	kongboense
15295	chamae-thomsonii var.	15752	kongboense
	chamaethauma	15763	agglutinatum
15296	chamae-thomsonii var.	15764	wardii
	chamaethauma	15765	hirtipes
15297	chamae-thomsonii var.	15774	vellereum
	chamaethauma	15796	calostrotum
15306	telopeum forma	15797	vellereum
15307	dignabile	15817	uvarifolium var.
15308	dignabile		griseum
15309	agglutinatum	15819	oreotrephes
15321	oreotrephes	15828	fragariflorum
15324	agglutinatum	15831	vellereum

1948 EXPEDITION

Sikkim

L.&S. NO.		L.&S. NO.	
15835	ciliatum	15841	virgatum
15840	dalhousiae		

1949 EXPEDITION

Bhutan (Ludlow, Sherriff & Hicks)

L.S.&H. NO.		L.S.&H. NO.	
16007	arboreum	16351	aff. fulgens
16009	ramsdenianum	16366	campylocarpum
16019	ciliatum	16371	falconeri
16026	arboreum	16372	keysii
16027	cinnabarinum	16378	edgeworthii
16054	virgatum	16419	anthopogon
16062	triflorum	16442	baileyi
16068	griffithianum	16443	campanulatum
16090	wallichii	16448	thomsonii
16095	arboreum	16472	campanulatum
16096	epapillatum	16492	cinnabarinum
16099	anthopogon var.	16493	cinnabarinum var. roylei
	haemonium	16494	hodgsonii
16100	wightii	16495	campylocarpum
16101	aff. fulgens	16510	lepidotum
16103	epapillatum	16523	rhabdotum
16116	thomsonii	16524	maddenii
16117	pendulum	16532	vaccinioides
16120	hodgsonii	16578	lepidotum
16121	wallichii	16604	lepidotum
16123	kendrickii	16681	lepidotum
16126	cinnabarinum	16752	lepidotum
16128	wallichii	16851	campanulatum
16136	wallichii	16865	lepidotum
16137	hodgsonii	16927	camelliiflorum
16140	wallichii	17359	baileyi
16155	lanatum	17447	baileyi
16157	setosum	17448	wallichii
16160	campylocarpum	17449	campanulatum
16168	campylocarpum	17478	wallichii
16184	lindleyi	17498	ciliatum
16206	virgatum	17509	lepidotum
16246	cinnabarinum	17512	wallichii
16248	wallichii	17521	xanthocodon
16249	wightii	17525	barbatum
16250	campanulatum	17526	campanulatum
16294	nivale	17527	wallichii
16324	lanatum	17531	maddenii
16339	campanulatum	17543	setosum
16346	hodgsonii	17546	hirtipes
16349	campanulatum	17550	anthopogon

L.S.&H. NO.	
17552	lepidotum
18620	arboreum
18660	grande
18677	smithii
18682	smithii
18683	ciliatum
18687	virgatum
18697	thomsonii
18703	arboreum
18710	kendrickii
18719	falconeri
18720	griffithianum
18732	keysii
18736	grande
18739	lindleyi
18743	smithii
18771	pendulum
18776	griffithianum
18777	edgeworthii
18801	hodgsonii
18850	thomsonii
18877	rhabdotum
18881	triflorum
18882	arboreum
18884	hodgsonii
18887	glaucophyllum
18888	pendulum
18889	cinnabarinum
18890	lanatum
18890a	lanatum
18893	aff. fulgens
18898	wallichii
18899	wightii
18921	xanthocodon
18922	campylocarpum
18927	keysii
18930	hodgsonii
18945	campanulatum
18949	anthopogon
18956	setosum
18959	wightii
18960	nivale
18961	wallichii
18966	campanulatum

L.S.&H. NO.	
18998	lanatum
19023	hodgsonii
19039	campanulatum
19046	thomsonii
19049	baileyi
19071	campanulatum
19102	campanulatum
19124	baileyi
19140	lepidotum
19234	lepidotum
19277	camelliiflorum
19361	anthopogon
19481	keysii
19847	cf. tsariense
19848	Maddenii Series
19849	triflorum
19850	aff. fulgens
s 19869	sp.
20107	aff. fulgens
20182	hodgsonii
20184	fulgens
20186	aff. fulgens
20205	maddenii
20220	griffithianum
20232	arboreum
20239	phaedropum
20267	hodgsonii
20277	wightii
20286	campanulatum
20366	lepidotum
20488	camelliiflorum
20489	rhabdotum
20519	arboreum
20523	arboreum
20527	smithii
20535	lindleyi
20581	keysii
20582	phaedropum
20583	arboreum
20586	arboreum
20613	glaucophyllum **var.** tubiforme
20614	thomsonii
20615	triflorum

L.S.&H. NO.		L.S.&H. NO.	
20620	niveum	21170	anthopogon
20622	cinnabarinum	21184	pumilum
20623	glaucophyllum var	21257	rhabdotum
	tubiforme	21274	Campanulatum Series
20626	campylocarpum	21282	glaucophyllum
20627	pendulum	21283	cinnabarinum
20628	lanatum	21284	keysii
20640	fulgens	21285	thomsonii
20641	wightii	21286	thomsonii
20642	wightii	21287	epapillatum
20643	aff. fulgens	21289	micromeres
20648	lanatum	21290	phaedropum
20649	hodgsonii	21292	fragariflorum
20655	anthopogon	21293	cinnabarinum forma
20655a	anthopogon	21294	arboreum
20659	baileyi	21295	aff. fulgens
20665	fulgens	21296	hodgsonii
20672	wallichii	21297	baileyi
20686	pumilum	21298	campanulatum
20720	fragariflorum	21299	keysii
20825	micromeres	21475	baileyi
20900	lepidotum	21483	griffithianum

Professor Hu Expedition (Collector Mr. Yu) 1937

N. Yunnan and Szechwan, Atuntze, Wei-hsi-lung-Chungtien Plateau, Lichiang Range, Muli

HU NO.		HU NO.	
7859	schizopeplum	10681	setosum
7860	saluenense	10682	s. Lapponicum
7863	s. Lapponicum	10683	bathyphyllum
7867	s. Thomsonii/Selense	10684	traillianum
7868	s. Thomsonii	10685	beesianum
7869	uvarifolium	10686	schizopeplum
7870	s. Trichocladum	10687	s. Lapponicum
7871	dictyotum	10688	roxieanum
7872	aganniphum	10689	s. Lapponicum
7887	s. Lapponicum	10690	aganniphum
7896	heliolepis	10691	apodectum
7905	heliolepis	10692	recurvum
7922	s. Thomsonii/Selense	10698	yunnanense
7924	uvarifolium	10699	uvarifolium
7926	s. Trichocladum	10700	oreotrephes
7927	beesianum	10701	heliolepis
7933	desquamatum	10709	s. Thomsonii
7934	eritimum	10723	s. Fortunei
7949	s. Fortunei	10729	s. Thomsonii/Selense
7951	s. Fortunei	10755	agglutinatum
7962	s. Triflorum	10779	s. Lapponicum
7989	augustinii var. chasman-	10795	phaeochrysum
	thum	10851	s. Triflorum
7991	oreotrephes	10857	s. Taliense
7992	s. Thomsonii	10884	s. Fortunei
7994	diacritum	10925	racemosum
7995	s. Lapponicum	10937	eritimum
8000	s. Lacteum	10949	s. Heliolepis
8610	sanguineum	10952	dryophyllum
8611	saluenense	10953	traillianum
8624	chryseum	10958	s. Fortunei
8630	campylogynum	10961	desquamatum
8645	chameunum	10974	s. Thomsonii/Selense
8660	cephalanthum	10979	s.s. Taliense
10566	melinanthum	10983	s. Taliense
10596	beesianum	10984	primulaeflorum
10599	s. Fortunei	10993	racemosum
10609	s. Thomsonii/Selense	13680	racemosum
10678	roxieanum	13723	s. Thomsonii
10679	aganniphum	13729	aganniphum
10680	s. Thomsonii	13730	beesianum

HU NO.		HU NO.	
13731	aganniphum	14641	chamaezelum
13732	aganniphum	14647	primulaeflorum
13736	s. Lapponicum	14662	balfourianum
13755	s. Thomsonii/Souliei	14663	beesianum
13760	recurvum	14694	s. Fortunei
13762	aganniphum	14703	rubiginosum
13763	aganniphum	14720	s. Triflorum
13765	beesianum	14752	s. Thomsonii
13785	setosum	14753	s. Thomsonii
13806	agglutinatum	14754	s. Thomsonii
13809	s. Thomsonii/Souliei	14755	desquamatum
13845	hippophaeoides	14757	s. Thomsonii
13851	s. Thomsonii	14803	s. Lapponicum
13880	racemosum	14843	hemitrichotum
13881	s. Fortunei	14901	s. Fortunei
13886	rubiginosum	14904	traillianum
13893	racemosum	14917	s. Triflorum
13894	decorum	14935	s. Fortunei
13895	s. Fortunei	14945	roxieanum
13897	s. Fortunei	14947	beesianum
13901	s. Heliolepis	14950	clementinae
13909	fulvum	14952	uvarifolium
13910	s. Thomsonii/Selense	14953	fictolacteum
13911	uvarifolium	14955	adenogynum
13913	heliolepis	14957	desquamatum
13919	heliolepis	14987	eritimum
13920	beesianum	14990	rubiginosum
13924	aganniphum	15009	s. Irroratum
13925	aganniphum	15010	hippophaeoides
13926	beesianum	15011	racemosum
13927	adenogynum	15012	racemosum
13928	adenogynum	15013	rubiginosum
13931	beesianum	15014	yunnanense
13937	hippophaeoides	15027	cuneatum
13961	s. Fortunei	15089	dictyotum
13978	s. Thomsonii/Souliei	15104	vernicosum
13984	s. Lapponicum	15139	primulaeflorum
13986	heliolepis	15155	diacritum
13989	beesianum	15157	traillianum
13995	traillianum	15300	adenophorum
14405	racemosum	15362	lepidotum
14431	s. Fortunei	15629	primulaeflorum var.
14436	rubiginosum		cephalanthoides
14444	s. Lapponicum	15641	setosum
14636	agglutinatum	15656	s. Fortunei

N.W. Yunnan, Mekong-Salween and Salween-Kiukiang divides

HU NO.		HU NO.	
15812	microphyton	19754	calostrotum var. calci-
16063	irroratum forma		philum
16694	crassum	19779	campylogynum
17839	diaprepes	19792	chryseum
18226	bullatum	19803	cephalanthum
18288	decorum	19813	heliolepis
19005	decorum	20052	brachyanthum var.
19034	forrestii		hypolepidotum
19037	sanguineum	20066	calostrotum
19040	praestans	20247	sanguineum
19042	selense	20266	keleticum
19046	melinanthum	20291	desquamatum
19047	fulvum	20372	forrestii var. repens
19049	sanguineum	20595	seinghkuense
19058	saluenense	20606	chryseum
19065	chamaezelum	20607	saluenense
19073	desquamatum	20609	chaetomallum
19074	beesianum	20611	temenium
19088	chameunum	20614	forrestii
19306	haemaleum	20616	melinanthum
19310	sanguineum	20623	sanguineum
19314	keleticum	20700	crinigerum
19315	brachyanthum var.	20704	desquamatum
	hypolepidotum	20705	sanguineum
19339	horaeum	20706	keleticum
19340	campylogynum	20707	campylogynum
19341	forrestii var. repens	20714	sanguineum
19351	s.s. Sanguineum	20716	horaeum
19358	chryseum	20729	forrestii var. repens
19373	glaphyrum	20738	chaetomallum
19374	trichocladum	20744	arizelum
19423	sinonuttallii	20745	eritimum
19510	eritimum ?	20750	fulvum
19567	seinghkuense	20778	chryseum
19568	megacalyx	20780	selense
19583	genestierianum	20796	brachyanthum var.
19615	vaccinioides		hypolepidotum
19631	bullatum	20812	sanguineum
19642	lukiangense	20816	s. Thomsonii
19650	vesiculiferum	20817	cephalanthum
19676	desquamatum	20820	chryseum
19677	fulvum	20834	floccigerum
19709	neriiflorum	20840	s. Fortunei
19740	eclecteum	20844	eritimum
19741	s. Lapponicum	20849	xanthostephanum
19744	brachyanthum var.	20886	vaccinioides
	hypolepidotum	20897	floccigerum

HU

McLaren Rhododendrons

259

McLAREN

Nepal

1949 EXPEDITION
Polunin (Central Nepal)

135	lepidotum	427	barbatum
175	cowanianum	551	cowanianum
176	campanulatum	1009	barbatum
178	setosum	1041	lepidotum
207	anthopogon	1103	anthopogon
210	lepidotum	1202	campanulatum
352	nivale	1252	lepidotum
359	setosum	1352	cinnamomeum
409	lepidotum		

1950 EXPEDITION
Lowndes

950	anthopogon	1005	anthopogon
986	lepidotum	1174	lowndesii
1004	lepidotum	1392	lepidotum

1952 EXPEDITION
Polunin, Sykes and Williams (Western Nepal)

4	nivale	3670	arboreum
28	nivale	3853	arboreum
300	lepidotum	3854	arboreum
959	campanulatum	3875	barbatum
1065	lepidotum	4061	hypenanthum
1141	nivale	4071	campanulatum
1344	nivale	4113	campanulatum
1345	lowndesii	4141	barbatum
1872	arboreum	4142	campanulatum
2047	campanulatum	4548	lepidotum
2057	hypenanthum	4629	hypenanthum
2161	lepidotum	5943	campanulatum
2205	nivale	5944	campanulatum
2359	lepidotum	5945	campanulatum
3486	lowndesii	5947	campanulatum

1954 EXPEDITION

Stainton, Sykes & Williams (Central Nepal)

8	arboreum	2971	hypenanthum
224	arboreum	3047	cowanianum
231	barbatum	3353	lepidotum
235	campanulatum	4914	arboreum
730	lepidotum	4947	barbatum
769	lepidotum	4963	arboreum
776	cowanianum	5083	arboreum
822	hypenanthum	5096	campanulatum
845	campanulatum	5097	arboreum
928	campanulatum	5384	dalhousiae
930	cowanianum	5435	lepidotum
1020	lepidotum	5590	cowanianum
1090	lowndesii	5698	lepidotum
1128	lepidotum	5699	lowndesii
1167	lepidotum	5785	barbatum
1205	lepidotum	6096	hypenanthum
1316	hypenanthum	6190	lepidotum
1327	lepidotum	6359	lowndesii
1428	lowndesii	7913	hypenanthum
1473	lowndesii	7960	lepidotum
1530	lepidotum	8239	lowndesii
1681	lepidotum	8274	dalhousiae
1712	lepidotum	8293	campanulatum
1732	lowndesii	8294	barbatum
2601	campanulatum	9090	hypenanthum
2607	campanulatum	9097	cowanianum
2608	arboreum	9106	campanulatum
2609	campanulatum	9107	campanulatum
2614	arboreum	9362	arboreum
2914	lepidotum		

1956 EXPEDITION

Stainton

166	virgatum	240	fulgens
183	dalhousiae	241	wightii
184	arboreum	244	thomsonii
187	triflorum	245	wallichii
193	triflorum	263	anthopogon
195	glaucophyllum	270	anthopogon
226	campanulatum	271	setosum
227	hodgsonii	272	wightii
228	arboreum	273	campanulatum
230	cinnabarinum var. roylei	275	campylocarpum
239	anthopogon	276	hodgsonii

NOTES

NOTES

NOTES